BESSEL FUNCTIONS
WITH SOME PHYSICAL
APPLICATIONS

BESSEL FUNCTIONS WITH SOME PHYSICAL APPLICATIONS

C. J. TRANTER, C.B.E., M.A., D.Sc., F.I.M.A.

Bashforth Professor of Mathematical Physics,
Royal Military College of Science, Shrivenham

HART PUBLISHING COMPANY, INC.
NEW YORK CITY

FIRST AMERICAN PUBLICATION, 1969
PRINTED IN THE UNITED STATES OF AMERICA

EDITORS' FOREWORD

The object of the *Applied Mathematics Series* is to provide texts in the subject which will cover school and university requirements and extend to the post-graduate field. The texts will be convenient for use by pure and applied mathematicians and also by scientists and engineers wishing to acquire mathematical techniques to improve their knowledge of their own subjects. Applied mathematics is expanding at a great rate, and every year mathematical techniques are being applied in new fields of physical, biological, and economic sciences. The series will aim at keeping abreast of these developments. Wherever new applications of mathematics arise it is hoped to persuade a leader in the field to describe them briefly.

F. BOWMAN
IAN N. SNEDDON
F. M. ARSCOTT

PREFACE

The classic work on Bessel functions is G. N. Watson's monumental treatise. This great work was completed in 1922 and therefore lacks references to developments in the subject during the last forty-five years. Its high standard of rigour and great size also make it somewhat forbidding to the scientist who is only interested in applications to physical problems. I have consequently attempted in the present book to provide a short up-to-date account of Bessel functions which will be useful to the increasing number of scientists and engineers who encounter these functions in their work.

I have included those properties of Bessel functions which, in my view, are likely to be important in scientific and engineering applications but in so doing I am conscious that there may well be many others which should have found a place. Where generality in the parameters involved would have necessitated difficult and/or lengthy analysis, I have usually restricted the discussion to a limited range of values but I have indicated where fuller expositions can be found. Since much of the theory of dual integral equations is of recent development and is not at present readily available in book form, I have given it at some length in Chapter 6.

I wish to thank all those who gave advice when the book was in its first draft and I am particularly grateful to Professor F. M. Arscott of the University of Surrey for a very valuable list of suggestions for improvement.

Shrivenham C. J. TRANTER

CONTENTS

CHAPTER 1

THE SOLUTION OF BESSEL'S AND ASSOCIATED EQUATIONS

1.1 Introduction

The differential equation

$$z^2 \frac{d^2w}{dz^2} + z\frac{dw}{dz} + (z^2 - \nu^2)w = 0, \tag{1.1}$$

in which ν is a (possibly complex) constant, is known as *Bessel's equation* of order ν and the functions occurring in its solution are called *Bessel functions*. Such functions were used by Bessel when he was working on a problem of dynamical astronomy in the nineteenth century but they were, in fact, used by other workers much earlier. The present importance of the functions is chiefly due to the occurrence of equation (1.1) in many problems which arise in science and engineering.

1.2 The series solution of Bessel's equation

We seek a formal solution of the differential equation (1.1) in the form

$$\begin{aligned} w &= a_0 z^\alpha + a_1 z^{\alpha+1} + a_2 z^{\alpha+2} + \ldots + a_r z^{\alpha+r} + \ldots \\ &= \sum_{r=0}^{\infty} a_r z^{\alpha+r}, \end{aligned} \tag{1.2}$$

where the index α and the coefficients $a_r (r = 0, 1, 2, \ldots)$ are to be determined. Arranging equation (1.1) in the form

$$\left(z^2 \frac{d^2}{dz^2} + z\frac{d}{dz} - \nu^2\right) w + z^2 w = 0$$

and substituting from (1.2), we have

$$\sum_{r=0}^{\infty} \{(\alpha + r)(\alpha + r - 1) + (\alpha + r) - \nu^2\} a_r z^{\alpha+r} + \sum_{r=0}^{\infty} a_r z^{\alpha+r+2} = 0.$$

This can be written

$$\sum_{r=0}^{\infty} \{(\alpha + r)^2 - \nu^2\} a_r z^{\alpha+r} + \sum_{r=0}^{\infty} a_r z^{\alpha+r+2} = 0$$

and, by equating to zero the coefficients of all powers of z, we get

$$\left.\begin{aligned} &(\alpha^2 - \nu^2)a_0 = 0, \quad \{(\alpha+1)^2 - \nu^2\}a_1 = 0, \\ &\{(\alpha + r)^2 - \nu^2\}a_r + a_{r-2} = 0, \quad r \geqslant 2. \end{aligned}\right\} \tag{1.3}$$

If a_0 is not to be zero, the first of equations (1.3) gives $\alpha = \pm\nu$. First taking $\alpha = \nu$, the other equations in (1.3) become

$$(2\nu + 1)a_1 = 0, \quad r(2\nu + r)a_r + a_{r-2} = 0, \quad r \geqslant 2, \tag{1.4}$$

and these lead to definite values for all the coefficients a_r in terms of a_0 except when 2ν is a negative integer. Disregarding such values of ν for the moment, we find from equations (1.4) that $a_1 = a_3 = a_5 = \ldots = a_{2r-1} = \ldots = 0$ and that

$$a_{2r} = -\frac{a_{2r-2}}{2^2 r(\nu + r)}.$$

Hence,

$$a_2 = -\frac{a_0}{2^2(\nu + 1)}, \quad a_4 = -\frac{a_2}{2^2 . 2(\nu + 2)} = \frac{a_0}{2^4 . 2(\nu + 1)(\nu + 2)},$$

$$a_6 = -\frac{a_4}{2^2 . 3(\nu + 3)} = -\frac{a_0}{2^6 . 3!\,(\nu + 1)(\nu + 2)(\nu + 3)}, \ldots$$

and one solution of Bessel's equation is given by

$$w_1 = a_0 z^\nu \left\{1 - \frac{z^2}{2^2(\nu + 1)} + \frac{z^4}{2^4 . 2!\,(\nu + 1)(\nu + 2)} - \frac{z^6}{2^6 . 3!\,(\nu + 1)(\nu + 2)(\nu + 3)} + \ldots\right\}.$$

The constant a_0 is at our disposal* and we take it to be $1/\{2^\nu\Gamma(\nu + 1)\}$ where the gamma function $\Gamma(\nu + 1)$ has the properties $\Gamma(\nu + 1) = \nu\Gamma(\nu)$, $\Gamma(1) = 1$.

This procedure gives the standard solution

$$J_\nu(z) = \frac{(z/2)^\nu}{\Gamma(\nu + 1)}\left\{1 - \frac{(z/2)^2}{1!\,(\nu + 1)} + \frac{(z/2)^4}{2!\,(\nu + 1)(\nu + 2)} - \frac{(z/2)^6}{3!\,(\nu + 1)(\nu + 2)(\nu + 3)} + \ldots\right\}$$

$$= \sum_{r=0}^{\infty} \frac{(-1)^r (z/2)^{\nu+2r}}{r!\,\Gamma(\nu + r + 1)}, \tag{1.5}$$

and $J_\nu(z)$ is called the *Bessel function of the first kind of order ν and argument z*. With $\alpha = -\nu$ in equations (1.3) and excepting now cases in which 2ν is a positive integer, the solution

$$J_{-\nu}(z) = \sum_{r=0}^{\infty} \frac{(-1)^r (z/2)^{-\nu+2r}}{r!\,\Gamma(-\nu + r + 1)} \tag{1.6}$$

is found in the same way.

For the values of ν considered, the power series in (1.5), (1.6) converge for all values of z except $z = 0$. Term-by-term differentiation is therefore permissible and the analysis by which the series have been derived is consequently valid.

* This choice of a_0 is made so that, when ν is an integer n, $J_\nu(z)$ reduces to the coefficient of t^n in the expansion of $\exp\{\frac{1}{2}z(t - t^{-1})\}$, see §1.10.

1.3 The independence of the solutions $J_\nu(z)$ and $J_{-\nu}(z)$

Bessel's equation (1.1) is a second order linear differential equation and for the solutions $J_\nu(z)$, $J_{-\nu}(z)$ to be linearly independent (in the sense that one solution is not a constant multiple of the other) it is necessary that the Wronskian W of $J_\nu(z)$ and $J_{-\nu}(z)$ given by

$$W \equiv \begin{vmatrix} J_\nu(z) & J_{-\nu}(z) \\ J_\nu'(z) & J_{-\nu}'(z) \end{vmatrix}, \tag{1.7}$$

where dashes denote derivatives with respect to z, shall not vanish. Since $J_\nu(z)$, $J_{-\nu}(z)$ both satisfy equation (1.1),

$$z^2J_\nu''(z) + zJ_\nu'(z) + (z^2 - \nu^2)J_\nu(z) = 0,$$
$$z^2J_{-\nu}''(z) + zJ_{-\nu}'(z) + (z^2 - \nu^2)J_{-\nu}(z) = 0,$$

so that multiplication by $J_{-\nu}(z)$, $J_\nu(z)$ and subtraction gives

$$z\{J_\nu(z)J_{-\nu}''(z) - J_{-\nu}(z)J_\nu''(z)\} + J_\nu(z)J_{-\nu}'(z) - J_{-\nu}(z)J_\nu'(z) = 0.$$

This can be written

$$\frac{\mathrm{d}}{\mathrm{d}z}\,[z\{J_\nu(z)J_{-\nu}'(z) - J_{-\nu}(z)J_\nu'(z)\}] = 0,$$

that is, $\mathrm{d}(zW)/\mathrm{d}z = 0$ and it follows on integration that $W = C/z$ where C is constant to be evaluated.

To determine C, we have from (1.5) and (1.6),

$$J_\nu(z) = \frac{(z/2)^\nu}{\Gamma(\nu+1)}\{1 + O(z^2)\}, \quad J_\nu'(z) = \frac{(z/2)^{\nu-1}}{2\Gamma(\nu)}\{1 + O(z^2)\}$$

with similar expressions for $J_{-\nu}(z)$ and $J_{-\nu}'(z)$. From these and (1.7) we have

$$W = \frac{1}{z}\left\{\frac{1}{\Gamma(\nu+1)\Gamma(-\nu)} - \frac{1}{\Gamma(-\nu+1)\Gamma(\nu)}\right\} + O(z)$$
$$= -\frac{2\sin\nu\pi}{\pi z} + O(z),$$

using the formula $\Gamma(\nu)\Gamma(1-\nu) = \pi \operatorname{cosec} \nu\pi$. Comparing this result with $W = C/z$, it can be seen that the term $O(z)$ on the right must vanish and that $C = -(2/\pi)\sin\nu\pi$.

Since we are at present excluding integral values of 2ν, $\sin\nu\pi$ (and therefore the Wronskian) does not vanish. The functions $J_\nu(z)$, $J_{-\nu}(z)$ derived in §1.2 are therefore independent solutions of Bessel's equation and its *general* solution is

$$w = AJ_\nu(z) + BJ_{-\nu}(z) \tag{1.8}$$

where A and B are arbitrary constants.

1.4 The solution of Bessel's equation when 2ν is an odd integer

The cases excluded from the discussion of §1.2 were those in which 2ν was an integer. We shall now show that, when the integer is *odd*, the general result (1.8) still applies.

Let $2\nu = 2n + 1$ where n is any positive integer or zero. Then 2ν is not a negative integer and, as in §1.2, one solution of Bessel's equation is

$$J_{n+\frac{1}{2}}(z) = \sum_{r=0}^{\infty} \frac{(-1)^r (z/2)^{n+\frac{1}{2}+2r}}{r!\,\Gamma(n + r + \frac{3}{2})}. \tag{1.9}$$

A second solution was found in §1.2 by taking $\alpha = -\nu$ in equations (1.3). With $\alpha = -n - \frac{1}{2}$, these equations now show that, not only a_0, but also a_{2n+1} take arbitrary values. Finding the coefficients $a_2, a_4, \ldots, a_{2r}, \ldots$ and $a_{2n+3}, a_{2n+5}, \ldots, a_{2n+2r+1}, \ldots$ from equations (1.3) in terms respectively of a_0 and a_{2n+1}, the second solution can be written

$$BJ_{-n-\frac{1}{2}}(z) + AJ_{n+\frac{1}{2}}(z) \tag{1.10}$$

where $B = 2^{-n-\frac{1}{2}}\Gamma(\frac{1}{2} - n)a_0$, $A = 2^{n+\frac{1}{2}}\Gamma(\frac{3}{2} + n)a_{2n+1}$ and where $J_{-n-\frac{1}{2}}(z)$ is given by (1.6) with $\nu = n + \frac{1}{2}$. The analysis of §1.3, which gives the Wronskian of $J_{n+\frac{1}{2}}(z)$ and $J_{-n-\frac{1}{2}}(z)$ as $-(2/\pi z)\sin(n + \frac{1}{2})\pi \neq 0$, shows that $J_{n+\frac{1}{2}}(z)$ and $J_{-n-\frac{1}{2}}(z)$ are independent solutions of Bessel's equation. Hence (1.10) is, in fact, the *general* solution of the equation and this solution is simply (1.8) with $\nu = n + \frac{1}{2}$.

1.5 The solution of Bessel's equation when ν is an integer

There remains for consideration the case in which 2ν is an even integer $2n$ and, for such values of ν, we can show that $J_n(z)$, $J_{-n}(z)$ are no longer independent solutions of Bessel's equation. To do this, we use equation (1.6) and remember that $\Gamma(-n + r + 1)$ is infinite when $r = 0, 1, 2, \ldots, n - 1$. Thus

$$\begin{aligned} J_{-n}(z) &= \sum_{r=n}^{\infty} \frac{(-1)^r (z/2)^{-n+2r}}{\Gamma(r + 1)\Gamma(-n + r + 1)} \\ &= \sum_{s=} \frac{(-1)^{n+s}(z/2)^{n+2s}}{\Gamma(n + s + 1)\Gamma(s + 1)}, \quad (r = n + s) \\ &= (-1)^n J_n(z), \end{aligned} \tag{1.11}$$

and hence $J_{-n}(z)$ is merely a constant multiple of $J_n(z)$ when n is an integer (or zero).

When ν is an integer n (or zero), it is therefore necessary to construct a second solution of Bessel's equation which is *linearly independent* of $J_n(z)$; a linear combination of this second solution with $J_n(z)$ will then give the general solution of the equation for these values of ν. Such a solution is considered in §1.6.

1.6 Bessel functions of the second kind of integral order

If the function $Y_\nu(z)$ is defined by

$$Y_\nu(z) = \frac{(\cos \nu\pi)J_\nu(z) - J_{-\nu}(z)}{\sin \nu\pi}, \tag{1.12}$$

it is clear from §§1.2, 1.4 that as the terms on the right of (1.12) are a linear combination of $J_\nu(z)$ and $J_{-\nu}(z)$, the expression

$$w = AJ_\nu(z) + BY_\nu(z) \tag{1.13}$$

in which A, B are arbitrary constants, can be taken as the general solution of Bessel's equation whenever ν is not an integer n (or zero). Since $J_{-n}(z) = (-1)^n J_n(z)$, the expression on the right of (1.12) takes the form (0/0) when $\nu = n$ (or zero) but its limit as $\nu \to n$ does, in fact, exist and we now consider

$$Y_n(z) = \lim_{\nu\to n} Y_\nu(z). \tag{1.14}$$

From (1.12) and (1.14), using L'Hospital's rule for evaluating a limit,

$$\begin{aligned} Y_n(z) &= \lim_{\nu\to n}\left[\frac{(-\pi\sin\nu\pi)J_\nu + (\cos\nu\pi)(\partial J_\nu/\partial\nu) - (\partial J_{-\nu}/\partial\nu)}{\pi\cos\nu\pi}\right] \\ &= \frac{1}{\pi}\left[\frac{\partial J_\nu}{\partial\nu} - (-1)^n\frac{\partial J_{-\nu}}{\partial\nu}\right]_{\nu=n} \end{aligned} \tag{1.15}$$

where, for brevity, the argument of the Bessel functions has been omitted. Since $J_{\pm\nu}$ both satisfy Bessel's equation (1.1),

$$\left(z^2\frac{d^2}{dz^2} + z\frac{d}{dz} + z^2 - \nu^2\right)J_{\pm\nu} = 0$$

so that, interchanging the order of differentiation with respect to z and ν, we have

$$\left(z^2\frac{d^2}{dz^2} + z\frac{d}{dz} + z^2 - \nu^2\right)\frac{\partial J_{\pm\nu}}{\partial\nu} = 2\nu J_{\pm\nu}.$$

Hence (1.15) gives

$$\begin{aligned} \pi\left(z^2\frac{d^2}{dz^2} + z\frac{d}{dz} + z^2 - \nu^2\right)Y_n(z) &= [2\nu J_\nu - (-1)^n 2\nu J_{-\nu}]_{\nu=n} \\ &= 2n[J_n - (-1)^n J_{-n}] = 0, \end{aligned}$$

by (1.11), and we have shown formally that $Y_n(z)$ as defined by (1.12) and (1.14) satisfies Bessel's equation.

Formula (1.15) and the series (1.5), (1.6) for $J_\nu(z)$, $J_{-\nu}(z)$ can be used to find a series for $Y_n(z)$. We give the analysis for the special case of $n = 0$ for which (1.15) gives

$$\pi Y_0(z) = \left[\frac{\partial J_\nu}{\partial\nu} - \frac{\partial J_{-\nu}}{\partial\nu}\right]_{\nu=0} = 2\left[\frac{\partial J_\nu}{\partial\nu}\right]_{\nu=0},$$

and from (1.5),

$$\frac{\partial J_\nu}{\partial\nu} = \sum_{r=0}^{\infty}\frac{(-1)^r(z/2)^{\nu+2r}}{r!\Gamma(\nu+r+1)}\left\{\log_e(z/2) - \frac{\Gamma'(\nu+r+1)}{\Gamma(\nu+r+1)}\right\}.$$

Hence

$$\pi Y_0(z) = 2\sum_{r=0}^{\infty} \frac{(-1)^r (z/2)^{2r}}{r!r!}\left\{\log_e (z/2) - \frac{\Gamma'(r+1)}{\Gamma(r+1)}\right\}$$

and, since

$$\frac{\Gamma'(r+1)}{\Gamma(r+1)} = -\gamma + 1 + \frac{1}{2} + \frac{1}{3} + \ldots + \frac{1}{r}, \qquad \frac{\Gamma'(1)}{\Gamma(1)} = -\gamma,$$

where $\gamma = 0{\cdot}5772\ldots$ is Euler's constant, see Appendix (A.4), this can be written

$$\frac{\pi}{2} Y_0(z) = \left(\gamma + \log_e \frac{z}{2}\right) J_0(z) - \sum_{r=1}^{\infty} \frac{(-1)^r (z/2)^{2r}}{r!r!}\left(1 + \frac{1}{2} + \frac{1}{3} + \ldots + \frac{1}{r}\right). \tag{1.16}$$

The series for $Y_n(z)$ when $n = 1, 2, 3, \ldots$ can be found in a similar way but the evaluation of $[\partial J_{-\nu}/\partial \nu]_{\nu=n}$ is rather intricate. The details can be found in more comprehensive works* and only the final result will be given here. This is

$$\frac{\pi}{2} Y_n(z) = \left(\gamma + \log_e \frac{z}{2}\right) J_n(z) - \frac{1}{2}\sum_{r=0}^{n-1} \frac{(n-r-1)!(z/2)^{2r-n}}{r!}$$
$$- \frac{1}{2}\sum_{r=0}^{\infty} \frac{(-1)^r (z/2)^{n+2r}}{r!(n+r)!}\left(1 + \frac{1}{2} + \frac{1}{3} + \ldots + \frac{1}{r} + 1 + \frac{1}{2} + \frac{1}{3} + \ldots + \frac{1}{n+r}\right), \tag{1.17}$$

the term corresponding to $r = 0$ in the second series being

$$\frac{(z/2)^n}{n!}\left(1 + \frac{1}{2} + \frac{1}{3} + \ldots + \frac{1}{n}\right),$$

and for $n = 0$ this formula reduces to formula (1.16) if the first summation is omitted.

The function $Y_\nu(z)$ defined by equation (1.12) is called the *Bessel function of the second kind of order* ν *and argument* z. When ν is a positive integer (or zero), the function is defined by equations (1.12) and (1.14) and convergent power series representing the function are given by (1.17) [or (1.16)]. From (1.12) we see that the Wronskian of $J_\nu(z)$ and $Y_\nu(z)$ is $-$ cosec $\nu\pi$ times that of $J_\nu(z)$ and $J_{-\nu}(z)$ so that, using the result given in §1.3, we have

$$J_\nu(z) Y_\nu'(z) - Y_\nu(z) J_\nu'(z) = \frac{2}{\pi z}, \tag{1.18}$$

and considerations of continuity show that this result remains true when ν is an integer or zero. Hence the functions $J_\nu(z)$, $Y_\nu(z)$ are linearly independent solutions of Bessel's equation (1.1) for *all values* of ν and its general solution can always be taken to be

$$w = AJ_\nu(z) + BY_\nu(z) \tag{1.19}$$

* See, for example, G. N. Watson, *Theory of Bessel Functions* (Cambridge, 1944), §3.52.

where A and B are arbitrary constants. It is worth noticing that some authors use a different definition of $Y_\nu(z)$ and some use other notations for the second solution of Bessel's equation. The definition and notation adopted here is that now generally used in this country.

Example 1. *If n is a positive integer or zero, express* (i) $Y_{\pm(n+\frac{1}{2})}(z)$ *in terms of* $J_{\pm(n+\frac{1}{2})}(z)$ *and* (ii) $Y_{-n}(z)$ *in terms of* $Y_n(z)$.

(i) Writing $\nu = \pm(n+\frac{1}{2})\pi$ in equation (1.12), we find immediately that

$$Y_{n+\frac{1}{2}}(z) = (-1)^{n+1}J_{-n-\frac{1}{2}}(z), \quad Y_{-n-\frac{1}{2}}(z) = (-1)^n J_{n+\frac{1}{2}}(z). \tag{1.20}$$

(ii) Equation (1.12) gives

$$(\sin \nu\pi)J_\nu(z) + (\cos \nu\pi)Y_\nu(z) = \frac{J_\nu(z) - (\cos \nu\pi)J_{-\nu}(z)}{\sin \nu\pi}$$
$$= Y_{-\nu}(z),$$

so that, in the limit as ν approaches n,

$$Y_{-n}(z) = (-1)^n Y_n(z). \tag{1.21}$$

1.7 Bessel functions of orders zero and unity

In physical applications, the most important Bessel functions are probably those of orders zero and unity. It seems therefore worth while to set out equations (1.5) and (1.17) in these special cases and to describe the general behaviour of the functions for real positive values x of the argument z.

We have

$$J_0(x) = 1 - \frac{x^2}{2^2(1!)^2} + \frac{x^4}{2^4(2!)^2} - \frac{x^6}{2^6(3!)^2} + \ldots, \tag{1.22}$$

$$Y_0(x) = \frac{2}{\pi}\left(\gamma + \log_e \frac{x}{2}\right) J_0(x) - \frac{2}{\pi}\sum_{r=1}^{\infty} \frac{(-1)^r(x/2)^{2r}}{(r!)^2}\left(1 + \frac{1}{2} + \frac{1}{3} + \ldots + \frac{1}{r}\right), \tag{1.23}$$

$$J_1(x) = \frac{x}{2} - \frac{x^3}{2^3 1!2!} + \frac{x^5}{2^5 2!3!} - \ldots, \tag{1.24}$$

$$Y_1(x) = \frac{2}{\pi}\left(\gamma + \log_e \frac{x}{2}\right) J_1(x) - \frac{2}{\pi x}$$
$$- \frac{1}{\pi}\sum_{r=0}^{\infty} \frac{(-1)^r(x/2)^{2r+1}}{r!(r+1)!}\left\{2\left(1 + \frac{1}{2} + \ldots + \frac{1}{r}\right) + \frac{1}{r+1}\right\}, \tag{1.25}$$

the first term in the series on the right in (1.25) being $\frac{1}{2}x$. For small values of x, these series show that

$$J_0(x) \simeq 1, \; Y_0(x) \simeq \frac{2}{\pi}\left(\gamma + \log_e \frac{x}{2}\right), \quad J_1(x) \simeq \frac{x}{2}, \quad Y_1(x) \simeq -\frac{2}{\pi x}, \tag{1.26}$$

and hence, as x tends to zero, $J_0(x)$ tends to 1, $J_1(x)$ to 0, while both $Y_0(x)$ and $Y_1(x)$ tend to $-\infty$.

Tabulated values of $J_n(x)$ and $Y_n(x)$ for $n = 0, 1$ can be found in the British Association Mathematical Tables, Vol. 6, 1937, and those for integral values of n up to $n = 20$ in Vol. 10, 1952. The functions are oscillatory and the general shapes of their graphs are shown in Figs. 1 and 2. It should be noted that the

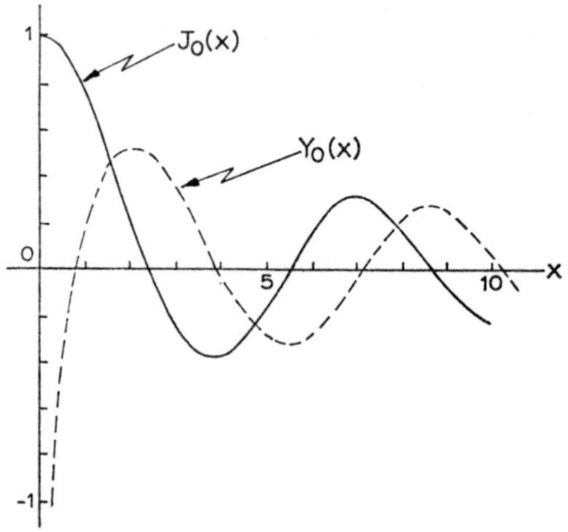

FIG. 1

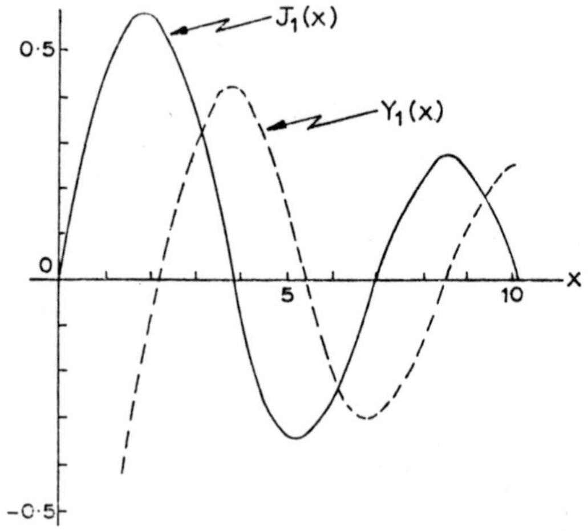

FIG. 2

functions vanish at an infinite sequence of values of x and that in this respect they behave similarly to the trigonometrical functions $\cos x$ and $\sin x$ which vanish respectively when $x = (r + \frac{1}{2})\pi$ and $x = r\pi$ $(r = 0, 1, 2, \ldots)$. In practical applications, the positive values of x for which the Bessel functions vanish are of considerable importance and these values are known as the positive *zeros* of the functions. Unlike those of the trigonometrical functions, the zeros of the Bessel functions are not equally spaced along the axis of x; they will be discussed further in Chapter 4 and a table of the first five zeros is given in §4.5. The behaviour of the Bessel functions when x is large will be considered in §3.7 but it is worth stating now that all the functions discussed in this section tend to zero as x tends to infinity.

1.8 Hankel functions

Although $J_\nu(x)$, $Y_\nu(x)$ are linearly independent solutions of Bessel's equation, it is sometimes convenient to take the fundamental solutions in a slightly different form. *Hankel functions*, often called Bessel functions of the *third kind*, are defined by

$$H_\nu^{(1)}(z) = J_\nu(z) + iY_\nu(z), \quad H_\nu^{(2)}(z) = J_\nu(z) - iY_\nu(z), \tag{1.27}$$

and these are independent solutions of Bessel's equation. In terms of these functions, the general solution of the equation (1.1) is

$$w = AH_\nu^{(1)}(z) + BH_\nu^{(2)}(z) \tag{1.28}$$

where A and B are again arbitrary constants.

The Hankel functions bear the same relation to the Bessel functions of the first and second kinds as the functions $\exp(\pm i\nu z)$ bear to $\cos \nu z$ and $\sin \nu z$ and they are convenient in mathematical analysis for similar reasons.

Example 2. *Find the value of the Wronskian of the Hankel functions.*

By the definition of the Wronskian [see (1.7)] and using equations (1.27), the required value is

$$\begin{aligned}[J_\nu(z) + iY_\nu(z)][J_\nu'(z) - iY_\nu'(z)] - [J_\nu(z) - iY_\nu(z)][J_\nu'(z) + iY_\nu'(z)] \\ = -2i[J_\nu(z)Y_\nu'(z) - Y_\nu(z)J_\nu'(z)] \\ = -\frac{4i}{\pi z},\end{aligned}$$

the result (1.18) being used in the last step.

1.9 Recurrence formulae

Equation (1.5) can be written in the form

$$z^{-\nu}J_\nu(z) = 2^{-\nu}\sum_{r=0}^{\infty}\frac{(-1)^r(z/2)^{2r}}{r!\Gamma(\nu+r+1)}$$

so that, dashes denoting derivatives with respect to z,

$$\begin{aligned}\frac{\nu}{z}J_\nu(z) - J_\nu'(z) &= -z^\nu\frac{\mathrm{d}}{\mathrm{d}z}\{z^{-\nu}J_\nu(z)\} \\ &= -z^\nu 2^{-\nu}\sum_{r=1}^{\infty}\frac{(-1)^r r(z/2)^{2r-1}}{r!\Gamma(\nu+r+1)} \\ &= \sum_{r=0}^{\infty}\frac{(-1)^r(z/2)^{\nu+1+2r}}{r!\Gamma(\nu+r+2)} = J_{\nu+1}(z).\end{aligned} \tag{1.29}$$

Similarly

$$z^\nu J_\nu(z) = 2^\nu \sum_{r=0}^{\infty} \frac{(-1)^r (z/2)^{2\nu+2r}}{r!\Gamma(\nu+r+1)},$$

giving

$$\begin{aligned}\frac{\nu}{z} J_\nu(z) + J_\nu'(z) &= z^{-\nu} \frac{\mathrm{d}}{\mathrm{d}z}\{z^\nu J_\nu(z)\} \\ &= z^{-\nu} 2^\nu \sum_{r=0}^{\infty} \frac{(-1)^r(\nu+r)(z/2)^{2\nu+2r-1}}{r!\Gamma(\nu+r+1)} \\ &= \sum_{r=0}^{\infty} \frac{(-1)^r (z/2)^{\nu-1+2r}}{r!\Gamma(\nu+r)} = J_{\nu-1}(z). \qquad (1.30)\end{aligned}$$

The equations given above relate Bessel functions whose orders differ by unity, and formulae relating three contiguous functions are easily obtained by addition and subtraction. Such relations are known as *recurrence formulae* and the four formulae are listed below for easy reference,

$$\left.\begin{aligned} J_{\nu+1}(z) &= \frac{\nu}{z} J_\nu(z) - J_\nu'(z), \\ J_{\nu-1}(z) &= \frac{\nu}{z} J_\nu(z) + J_\nu'(z), \\ J_{\nu-1}(z) + J_{\nu+1}(z) &= \frac{2\nu}{z} J_\nu(z), \\ J_{\nu-1}(z) - J_{\nu+1}(z) &= 2J_\nu'(z), \end{aligned}\right\} \qquad (1.31)$$

and the special case ($\nu = 0$) of the first of these, viz.

$$J_1(z) = -J_0'(z) \qquad (1.32)$$

is worth noting.

It follows from formulae (1.12) and (1.27) that the functions of the second kind $Y_\nu(z)$ and the Hankel functions $H_\nu^{(1)}(z)$, $H_\nu^{(2)}(z)$ satisfy the same recurrence formulae and considerations of continuity enable the validity of the formulae to be established when ν is an integer n. The details are left as an exercise for the reader.

The relation (1.30) can be written in the form

$$\left(\frac{\mathrm{d}}{z\,\mathrm{d}z}\right)\{z^\nu J_\nu(z)\} = z^{\nu-1} J_{\nu-1}(z),$$

so that, by repeated differentiations, when m is a positive integer

$$\left(\frac{\mathrm{d}}{z\,\mathrm{d}z}\right)^m \{z^\nu J_\nu(z)\} = z^{\nu-m} J_{\nu-m}(z). \qquad (1.33)$$

Equation (1.29) leads in the same way to

$$\left(\frac{\mathrm{d}}{z\,\mathrm{d}z}\right)^m \{z^{-\nu} J_\nu(z)\} = (-1)^m z^{-\nu-m} J_{\nu+m}(z), \qquad (1.34)$$

and these relations are often useful.

1.10 The Bessel coefficients

The partial differential equation

$$\frac{\partial^2 V}{\partial \rho^2} + \frac{1}{\rho}\frac{\partial V}{\partial \rho} + \frac{1}{\rho^2}\frac{\partial^2 V}{\partial \phi^2} + k^2 V = 0$$

is of importance in mathematical physics. It is easy to verify (by substitution and use of Bessel's equation) that the equation is satisfied by both $\exp(ik\rho \sin \phi)$ and $J_n(k\rho)e^{in\phi}$ and it is reasonable to expect that there is some connection between these two functions. Since $\exp(ik\rho \sin \phi)$ is a periodic function of ϕ, it will have a Fourier expansion of the form

$$\sum_{n=-\infty}^{\infty} c_n(k\rho)e^{in\phi}$$

where the coefficients c_n are functions of $k\rho$ and, because of the above mentioned connection, it is likely that $c_n(k\rho)$ will be connected with $J_n(k\rho)$. As is shown below (but for convenience we work with $k\rho = z$, $e^{i\phi} = t$), it turns out that $c_n(k\rho)$ is precisely $J_n(k\rho)$.

Provided that t is not zero, the functions $\exp(\frac{1}{2}zt)$ and $\exp(-\frac{1}{2}z/t)$ can be expanded in powers of t and the product of these expansions gives

$$\begin{aligned}\exp\{\tfrac{1}{2}z(t - t^{-1})\} &= \sum_{r=0}^{\infty} \frac{1}{r!}\left(\frac{zt}{2}\right)^r \sum_{s=0}^{\infty} \frac{1}{s!}\left(-\frac{z}{2t}\right)^s \\ &= \sum_{r=0}^{\infty}\sum_{s=0}^{\infty} \frac{(-1)^s}{r!s!}\left(\frac{z}{2}\right)^{r+s} t^{r-s},\end{aligned}$$

term-by-term multiplication of the series being valid because of the absolute convergence of the separate series. If n is a positive integer or zero, the coefficient of t^n in the series is found by taking $r = n + s$ and letting s vary from 0 to infinity; thus

$$\text{the coefficient of } t^n = \sum_{s=0}^{\infty} \frac{(-1)^s}{(n+s)!s!}\left(\frac{z}{2}\right)^{n+2s} = J_n(z),$$

by equation (1.5). The coefficient of t^{-n} is found by taking $r = -n + s$ and letting s vary from n to infinity. Hence

$$\text{the coefficient of } t^{-n} = \sum_{s=n}^{\infty} \frac{(-1)^s}{(-n+s)!s!}\left(\frac{z}{2}\right)^{-n+2s} = J_{-n}(z),$$

using equation (1.11). Hence

$$\exp\{\tfrac{1}{2}z(t - t^{-1})\} = \sum_{n=-\infty}^{\infty} t^n J_n(z) \qquad (1.35)$$

and, because of the form of this relation, the functions $J_n(z)$ where $n = 0, 1, 2, 3, \ldots$, are often called the *Bessel coefficients* while the exponential on the left of (1.35) is sometimes referred to as the *generating function* of the Bessel coefficients.

Two interesting results, originally due to Jacobi, are obtained by writing $t = e^{i\theta}$ in equation (1.35). Thus

$$\exp\{\tfrac{1}{2}z(e^{i\theta} - e^{-i\theta})\} = \sum_{n=-\infty}^{\infty} e^{ni\theta} J_n(z)$$

$$= J_0(z) + \sum_{n=1}^{\infty} \{e^{ni\theta} + (-1)^n e^{-ni\theta}\} J_n(z), \quad (1.36)$$

as $J_{-n}(z) = (-1)^n J_n(z)$. Since

$$e^{ni\theta} + (-1)^n e^{-ni\theta} = \begin{cases} 2\cos n\theta, & n \text{ even}, \\ 2i\sin n\theta, & n \text{ odd}, \end{cases}$$

and since the left-hand side of (1.36) is

$$\exp(iz\sin\theta) = \cos(z\sin\theta) + i\sin(z\sin\theta),$$

it follows by equating real and imaginary parts that

$$\left.\begin{aligned} \cos(z\sin\theta) &= J_0(z) + 2\sum_{n=1}^{\infty} J_{2n}(z)\cos 2n\theta, \\ \sin(z\sin\theta) &= 2\sum_{n=0}^{\infty} J_{2n+1}(z)\sin(2n+1)\theta. \end{aligned}\right\} \quad (1.37)$$

By replacing θ with $\frac{1}{2}\pi - \theta$, we find

$$\left.\begin{aligned} \cos(z\cos\theta) &= J_0(z) + 2\sum_{n=1}^{\infty} (-1)^n J_{2n}(z)\cos 2n\theta, \\ \sin(z\cos\theta) &= 2\sum_{n=0}^{\infty} (-1)^n J_{2n+1}(z)\cos(2n+1)\theta, \end{aligned}\right\}$$

and these relations have an application to the evaluation of definite integrals (see, for example, §3.2).

1.11 Bessel functions whose order is half an odd integer

When the order $\nu = \pm(n + \frac{1}{2})$ where $n = 0, 1, 2, 3, \ldots$, the Bessel functions so far considered can be expressed in finite terms by algebraic and trigonometrical functions of the argument z. Such Bessel functions arise in problems in connection with spherical waves and are often called *spherical Bessel functions*.

Since $r!\Gamma(r + \frac{3}{2}) = \Gamma(r+1)\Gamma(r + \frac{3}{2}) = \pi^{\frac{1}{2}} 2^{-2r-1}\Gamma(2r+2)$, equation (1.5) with $\nu = \frac{1}{2}$ gives

$$J_{\frac{1}{2}}(z) = \sum_{r=0}^{\infty} \frac{(-1)^r (z/2)^{2r+\frac{1}{2}}}{r!\Gamma(r + \frac{3}{2})}$$

$$= \left(\frac{2}{\pi z}\right)^{\frac{1}{2}} \sum_{r=0}^{\infty} \frac{(-1)^r z^{2r+1}}{(2r+1)!} = \left(\frac{2}{\pi z}\right)^{\frac{1}{2}} \sin z, \quad (1.38)$$

and (1.6) leads in the same way to

$$J_{-\frac{1}{2}}(z) = \left(\frac{2}{\pi z}\right)^{\frac{1}{2}} \cos z. \quad (1.39)$$

Setting $\nu = \frac{1}{2}$, $m = n$ in equation (1.34), we then have

$$(-1)^n z^{-(n+\frac{1}{2})} J_{n+\frac{1}{2}}(z) = \left(\frac{\mathrm{d}}{z\,\mathrm{d}z}\right)^n \{z^{-\frac{1}{2}} J_{\frac{1}{2}}(z)\},$$

giving, after substitution from (1.38)

$$J_{n+\frac{1}{2}}(z) = \left(\frac{2}{\pi}\right)^{\frac{1}{2}} z^{n+\frac{1}{2}} \left(-\frac{\mathrm{d}}{z\,\mathrm{d}z}\right)^n \left(\frac{\sin z}{z}\right). \tag{1.40}$$

Equations (1.33) and (1.39) lead in a similar way to

$$J_{-n-\frac{1}{2}}(z) = \left(\frac{2}{\pi}\right)^{\frac{1}{2}} z^{n+\frac{1}{2}} \left(\frac{\mathrm{d}}{z\,\mathrm{d}z}\right)^n \left(\frac{\cos z}{z}\right) \tag{1.41}$$

so that $J_{\pm(n+\frac{1}{2})}(z)$ are expressible in a finite number of terms involving sines, cosines and powers of z. For example, with $n = 1$ we have

$$J_{\frac{3}{2}}(z) = \left(\frac{2}{\pi z}\right)^{\frac{1}{2}} \left(\frac{\sin z}{z} - \cos z\right), \quad J_{-\frac{3}{2}}(z) = \left(\frac{2}{\pi z}\right)^{\frac{1}{2}} \left(-\frac{\cos z}{z} - \sin z\right). \tag{1.42}$$

The functions of the second kind and the Hankel functions of order $\pm(n + \frac{1}{2})$ can now be found from equations (1.20) and (1.27).

Example 3. *Show that*

$$H_{-\frac{1}{2}}^{(1)}(z) = \left(\frac{2}{\pi z}\right)^{\frac{1}{2}} e^{iz}, \quad H_{-\frac{1}{2}}^{(2)}(z) = \left(\frac{2}{\pi z}\right)^{\frac{1}{2}} e^{-iz}. \tag{1.43}$$

From (1.20) with $n = 0$ and (1.38)

$$Y_{-\frac{1}{2}}(z) = J_{\frac{1}{2}}(z) = \left(\frac{2}{\pi z}\right)^{\frac{1}{2}} \sin z.$$

Using this result, equation (1.27) with $\nu = -\frac{1}{2}$ and equation (1.39), we have

$$H_{-\frac{1}{2}}^{(1)}(z) = J_{-\frac{1}{2}}(z) + iY_{-\frac{1}{2}}(z) = \left(\frac{2}{\pi z}\right)^{\frac{1}{2}} \cos z + i\left(\frac{2}{\pi z}\right)^{\frac{1}{2}} \sin z = \left(\frac{2}{\pi z}\right)^{\frac{1}{2}} e^{iz},$$

$$H_{-\frac{1}{2}}^{(2)}(z) = J_{-\frac{1}{2}}(z) - iY_{-\frac{1}{2}}(z) = \left(\frac{2}{\pi z}\right)^{\frac{1}{2}} \cos z - i\left(\frac{2}{\pi z}\right)^{\frac{1}{2}} \sin z = \left(\frac{2}{\pi z}\right)^{\frac{1}{2}} e^{-iz}.$$

1.12 Bessel functions with argument $ze^{m\pi i}$

The functions $J_{\pm\nu}(z)$, except when $\nu = 0, 1, 2, \ldots$, are not single-valued, but have a branch point when $z = 0$. However $J_\nu(z)/z^\nu$ is single-valued and it is convenient to assume that, when the phase of z is unrestricted, $J_\nu(z)$ is to be defined in the same way as that in which z^ν is defined. Hence we take

$$J_\nu(ze^{m\pi i}) = e^{m\nu\pi i} J_\nu(z), \quad J_{-\nu}(ze^{m\pi i}) = e^{-m\nu\pi i} J_{-\nu}(z), \tag{1.44}$$

where $m = \pm 1, \pm 2, \pm 3, \ldots$ It follows from equation (1.12) that

$$\begin{aligned}(\sin \nu\pi) Y_\nu(ze^{m\pi i}) &= (\cos \nu\pi)J_\nu(ze^{m\pi i}) - J_{-\nu}(ze^{m\pi i}) \\ &= (e^{m\nu\pi i} \cos \nu\pi)J_\nu(z) - e^{-m\nu\pi i}J_{-\nu}(z) \\ &= e^{-m\nu\pi i}\{(\cos \nu\pi)J_\nu(z) - J_{-\nu}(z)\} + (e^{m\nu\pi i} - e^{-m\nu\pi i})(\cos \nu\pi)J_\nu(z),\end{aligned}$$

giving

$$Y_\nu(ze^{m\pi i}) = e^{-m\nu\pi i} Y_\nu(z) + 2i \sin m\nu\pi \cot \nu\pi \; J_\nu(z). \tag{1.45}$$

It is left as an example to be worked by the reader (Exercises 1, No. 10) to obtain corresponding formulae for the Hankel functions.

1.13 Some transformations of Bessel's equation

Many physical problems can be reduced to the solution of a differential equation which, by suitable transformations, can itself be reduced to Bessel's equation. We give below an example of a useful transformation of this type.

Writing $z = \beta t^\gamma$, where β and γ are constants, we have

$$\frac{dw}{dz} = \frac{dw}{dt}\bigg/\frac{dz}{dt} = \frac{1}{\beta\gamma t^{\gamma-1}}\frac{dw}{dt},$$

so that

$$z\frac{dw}{dz} = \frac{t}{\gamma}\frac{dw}{dt}.$$

Hence Bessel's equation (1.1), which can be written in the form

$$z\frac{d}{dz}\left(z\frac{dw}{dz}\right) + (z^2 - \nu^2)w = 0, \tag{1.46}$$

becomes

$$t\frac{d}{dt}\left(t\frac{dw}{dt}\right) + (\beta^2\gamma^2t^{2\gamma} - \nu^2\gamma^2)w = 0. \tag{1.47}$$

Now write $w = t^\alpha u$, where α is a constant. Then

$$t\frac{dw}{dt} = t^{\alpha+1}\frac{du}{dt} + \alpha t^\alpha u$$

and

$$t\frac{d}{dt}\left(t\frac{dw}{dt}\right) = t^{\alpha+2}\frac{d^2u}{dt^2} + (2\alpha + 1)t^{\alpha+1}\frac{du}{dt} + \alpha^2t^\alpha u.$$

Substitution in (1.47) gives, after division by t^α,

$$t^2\frac{d^2u}{dt^2} + (2\alpha + 1)t\frac{du}{dt} + (\beta^2\gamma^2t^{2\gamma} + \alpha^2 - \nu^2\gamma^2)u = 0. \tag{1.48}$$

The general solution of Bessel's equation (1.46) being $w = AJ_\nu(z) + BY_\nu(z)$, since $u = t^{-\alpha}w$ and $z = \beta t^\gamma$, we deduce that the general solution of equation (1.48) is

$$u = t^{-\alpha}\{AJ_\nu(\beta t^\gamma) + BY_\nu(\beta t^\gamma)\}. \tag{1.49}$$

Some particular examples of practical interest are:

(i) $\alpha = -\frac{1}{2}, \gamma = \frac{1}{2}, \nu = 1$

Equation (1.48) becomes

$$t\frac{d^2u}{dt^2} + \tfrac{1}{4}\beta^2 u = 0$$

with solution $u = t^{\frac{1}{2}}\{AJ_1(\beta t^{\frac{1}{2}}) + BY_1(\beta t^{\frac{1}{2}})\}$. This equation arises when the stability of a tapered strut is investigated.

(ii) $\alpha = \frac{1}{2}(m-1), \gamma = \frac{1}{2}, \nu = m - 1$

Equation (1.48) now reduces to

$$t\frac{d^2u}{dt^2} + m\frac{du}{dt} + \tfrac{1}{4}\beta^2 u = 0$$

and its general solution is $u = t^{-\frac{1}{2}(m-1)}\{AJ_{m-1}(\beta t^{\frac{1}{2}}) + BY_{m-1}(\beta t^{\frac{1}{2}})\}$. When m is an integer this equation appears in problems concerned with the vibrations of tapered beams.

(iii) $\alpha = -\frac{1}{2}, \beta = \frac{2}{3}i, \gamma = \frac{3}{2}, \nu = \frac{1}{3}$

For these values of α, β, γ, ν, equation (1.48) becomes

$$\frac{d^2u}{dt^2} = tu$$

and, since ν is not an integer, we can write the general solution of this equation as $u = t^{\frac{1}{2}}\{AJ_{\frac{1}{3}}(\frac{2}{3}it^{\frac{3}{2}}) + BJ_{-\frac{1}{3}}(\frac{2}{3}it^{\frac{3}{2}})\}$. This equation is known as *Airy's equation* and it was first encountered in a study of the intensity of light in the neighbourhood of a caustic. Two functions $Ai(t)$, $Bi(t)$, known as *Airy functions*, have been defined by taking

$$Ai(t) = \tfrac{1}{3}t^{\frac{1}{2}}\{e^{\frac{1}{6}\pi i}J_{-\frac{1}{3}}(\tfrac{2}{3}it^{\frac{3}{2}}) - e^{-\frac{1}{6}\pi i}J_{\frac{1}{3}}(\tfrac{2}{3}it^{\frac{3}{2}})\},$$
$$Bi(t) = (\tfrac{1}{3}t)^{\frac{1}{2}}\{e^{\frac{1}{6}\pi i}J_{-\frac{1}{3}}(\tfrac{2}{3}it^{\frac{3}{2}}) + e^{-\frac{1}{6}\pi i}J_{\frac{1}{3}}(\tfrac{2}{3}it^{\frac{3}{2}})\},$$

and tables of these functions can be found in the British Association Mathematical Tables, Part-Volume B, 1946.

Example 4. *Show that the general solution of the differential equation*

$$\frac{d^2w}{dt^2} + (e^{2t} - \nu^2)w = 0$$

is $w = AJ_\nu(e^t) + BY_\nu(e^t)$.

Writing $z = e^t$ so that $t = \log_e z$ and

$$z\frac{dw}{dz} = z\frac{dw}{dt}\cdot\frac{dt}{dz} = z\frac{dw}{dt}\cdot\frac{1}{z} = \frac{dw}{dt},$$

it follows that Bessel's equation, which can be written in the form

$$z\frac{d}{dz}\left(z\frac{dw}{dz}\right) + (z^2 - \nu^2)w = 0,$$

becomes

$$\frac{d^2w}{dt^2} + (e^{2t} - \nu^2)w = 0.$$

Since the general solution of Bessel's equation is $w = AJ_\nu(z) + BY_\nu(z)$ and since $z = e^t$, the required result immediately follows.

1.14 Modified Bessel functions

The differential equation

$$z^2\frac{d^2w}{dz^2} + z\frac{dw}{dz} - (z^2 + \nu^2)w = 0, \qquad (1.50)$$

which transforms into Bessel's equation (1.1) when z is replaced by iz, often occurs in physical problems. As in such problems it is more convenient to give the solution in real form, the fundamental solutions $J_\nu(iz)$ and $Y_\nu(iz)$, which (for general values of ν) are complex functions of z, are not really suitable for this purpose.

The function $e^{-\frac{1}{2}\nu\pi i}J_\nu(iz)$ is, however, a real function of z and it is clearly a solution of the differential equation (1.50).* This function is denoted by $I_\nu(z)$ so that

$$I_\nu(z) = \sum_{r=0}^{\infty}\frac{(z/2)^{\nu+2r}}{r!\Gamma(\nu + r + 1)} \qquad (1.51)$$

and it is known as the *modified Bessel function of the first kind*.

Starting from equations (1.50) and (1.51), the analysis of §1.3 is easily modified to show that the Wronskian of $I_\nu(z)$ and $I_{-\nu}(z)$ is equal to $-(2\sin\nu\pi)/(\pi z)$, so that these two functions are independent solutions of the differential equation (1.50) provided that ν is not an integer n (or zero). When $\nu = n$, since $\Gamma(-n + r + 1)$ is infinite for $r = 0, 1, 2, \ldots, n - 1$, equation (1.51) gives

$$\begin{aligned} I_{-n}(z) &= \sum_{r=n}^{\infty}\frac{(z/2)^{-n+2r}}{\Gamma(r + 1)\Gamma(-n + r + 1)} \\ &= \sum_{s=0}^{\infty}\frac{(z/2)^{n+2s}}{\Gamma(n + s + 1)\Gamma(s + 1)}, \quad (r = n + s) \\ &= I_n(z). \end{aligned} \qquad (1.52)$$

* When z is complex, it is convenient to define its phase with reference to the principal value of arg z rather than to that of arg iz. Hence

$$I_\nu(z) = \begin{cases} e^{-\frac{1}{2}\nu\pi i}J_\nu(ze^{\frac{1}{2}\pi i}) & \text{when } -\pi < \arg z \leq \frac{1}{2}\pi, \\ e^{\frac{3}{2}\nu\pi i}J_\nu(ze^{-\frac{3}{2}\pi i}) & \text{when } \frac{1}{2}\pi < \arg z \leq \pi. \end{cases}$$

Hence when ν is an integer n (or zero), it is necessary to construct a second solution of Bessel's modified equation (1.50) which is linearly independent of $I_n(z)$.

This is done by defining a function $K_\nu(z)$ by

$$\frac{2}{\pi} K_\nu(z) = \frac{I_{-\nu}(z) - I_\nu(z)}{\sin \nu\pi}; \tag{1.53}$$

since $K_\nu(z)$ is a linear combination of the solutions $I_\nu(z)$, $I_{-\nu}(z)$ of equation (1.50), the general solution of the equation can be taken as

$$w = AI_\nu(z) + BK_\nu(z), \tag{1.54}$$

where A and B are arbitrary constants, whenever ν is not an integer or zero. Since $I_{-n}(z) = I_n(z)$, the expression on the right of (1.53) takes the form (0/0) when $\nu = n$ but its limit as $\nu \to n$ exists and we now consider

$$K_n(z) = \lim_{\nu\to n} K_\nu(z). \tag{1.55}$$

From (1.55) and (1.53), L'Hospital's rule for evaluating a limit gives

$$\frac{2}{\pi} K_n(z) = \lim_{\nu\to n}\left[\frac{\dfrac{\partial I_{-\nu}}{\partial\nu} - \dfrac{\partial I_\nu}{\partial\nu}}{\pi\cos\nu\pi}\right],$$

so that

$$K_n(z) = \frac{(-1)^n}{2}\left[\frac{\partial I_{-\nu}}{\partial\nu} - \frac{\partial I_\nu}{\partial\nu}\right]_{\nu=n} \tag{1.56}$$

where, for brevity, the argument of the Bessel functions has again been omitted. Since $I_{\pm\nu}$ both satisfy equation (1.50),

$$\left(z^2\frac{d^2}{dz^2} + z\frac{d}{dz} - z^2 - \nu^2\right) I_{\pm\nu} = 0$$

so that

$$\left(z^2\frac{d^2}{dz^2} + z\frac{d}{dz} - z^2 - \nu^2\right)\frac{\partial I_{\pm\nu}}{\partial\nu} = 2\nu I_{\pm\nu}.$$

Hence (1.56) gives

$$\left(z^2\frac{d^2}{dz^2} + z\frac{d}{dz} - z^2 - \nu^2\right) K_n(z) = \frac{(-1)^n}{2}\,[2\nu I_{-\nu} - 2\nu I_\nu]_{\nu=n}$$
$$= 0$$

by (1.52), and $K_n(z)$ has therefore been shown (formally) to be a solution of the modified Bessel's equation (1.50).

Formulae (1.56) and (1.51) enable a series for $K_n(z)$ to be found. For the particular case of $n = 0$, (1.56) gives

$$2K_0(z) = \left[\frac{\partial I_{-\nu}}{\partial\nu} - \frac{\partial I_\nu}{\partial\nu}\right]_{\nu=0} = -2\left[\frac{\partial I_\nu}{\partial\nu}\right]_{\nu=0},$$

and, from (1.51)

$$\frac{\partial I_\nu}{\partial \nu} = \sum_{r=0}^{\infty} \frac{(z/2)^{\nu+2r}}{r!\Gamma(\nu+r+1)} \left\{ \log_e (z/2) - \frac{\Gamma'(\nu+r+1)}{\Gamma(\nu+r+1)} \right\}.$$

Combining these two formulae and using the expression for $\Gamma'(r+1)/\Gamma(r+1)$ given in §1.6, we have

$$K_0(z) = -\left(\gamma + \log_e \frac{z}{2}\right) I_0(z) + \sum_{r=1}^{\infty} \frac{(z/2)^{2r}}{r!r!} \left(1 + \frac{1}{2} + \frac{1}{3} + \ldots + \frac{1}{r}\right). \quad (1.57)$$

The series for $K_n(z)$ when $n = 1, 2, 3, \ldots$ can be found similarly but the evaluation of $[\partial I_{-\nu}/\partial \nu]_{\nu=n}$ is rather tedious and only the final result is given here. It is

$$K_n(z) = (-1)^{n+1}\left(\gamma + \log_e \frac{z}{2}\right) I_n(z) + \tfrac{1}{2} \sum_{r=0}^{n-1} \frac{(-1)^r (n-r-1)!(z/2)^{2r-n}}{r!}$$
$$+ \frac{(-1)^n}{2} \sum_{r=0}^{\infty} \frac{(z/2)^{n+2r}}{r!(n+r)!} \left(1 + \frac{1}{2} + \frac{1}{3} + \ldots + \frac{1}{r} + 1 + \frac{1}{2} + \frac{1}{3} + \ldots + \frac{1}{n+r}\right), \quad (1.58)$$

the term corresponding to $r = 0$ in the second series being

$$\frac{(z/2)^n}{n!}\left(1 + \frac{1}{2} + \frac{1}{3} + \ldots + \frac{1}{n}\right),$$

and for $n = 0$ this reduces to (1.57) if the first summation is omitted.

Using equations (1.53), (1.12) and the relation $I_\nu(z) = e^{-\frac{1}{2}\nu\pi i} J_\nu(iz)$, it is easy to show that

$$K_\nu(z) = \frac{\pi i}{2} e^{\frac{1}{2}\nu\pi i}\{J_\nu(iz) + iY_\nu(iz)\} = \frac{\pi i}{2} e^{\frac{1}{2}\nu\pi i} H_\nu^{(1)}(iz) \quad (1.59)$$

and the function $K_\nu(z)$ is often known as the *modified Bessel function of the third kind* or the *modified Hankel function*. When ν is a positive integer (or zero), the function is defined by equations (1.53) and (1.55) and convergent power series representing the function are given by (1.58) [or (1.57)]. From (1.53) we see that the Wronskian of $I_\nu(z)$ and $K_\nu(z)$ is $\frac{1}{2}\pi$ cosec $\nu\pi$ times that of $I_\nu(z)$ and $I_{-\nu}(z)$ and, since this is $-(2 \sin \nu\pi)/(\pi z)$, we have

$$I_\nu(z) K_\nu'(z) - K_\nu(z) I_\nu'(z) = -\frac{1}{z}, \quad (1.60)$$

and considerations of continuity show that this remains true when ν is an integer or zero. Hence the functions $I_\nu(z)$, $K_\nu(z)$ are independent solutions of the modified Bessel's equation (1.50) for *all values of* ν and its general solution can always be taken to be

$$w = AI_\nu(z) + BK_\nu(z) \quad (1.61)$$

where A and B are arbitrary constants.

Example 5. *Show that* $K_{\frac{1}{2}}(z) = \left(\frac{\pi}{2z}\right)^{\frac{1}{2}} e^{-z}$.

Since

$$r!\Gamma(r + \tfrac{3}{2}) = \Gamma(r + 1)\Gamma(r + \tfrac{3}{2}) = \pi^{\frac{1}{2}}2^{-2r-1}\Gamma(2r + 2)$$

and

$$r!\Gamma(r + \tfrac{1}{2}) = r\Gamma(r)\Gamma(r + \tfrac{1}{2}) = \pi^{\frac{1}{2}}r2^{-2r+1}\Gamma(2r) = \pi^{\frac{1}{2}}2^{-2r}\Gamma(2r + 1),$$

equation (1.51) gives

$$I_{\frac{1}{2}}(z) = \left(\frac{2}{\pi z}\right)^{\frac{1}{2}} \sum_{r=0}^{\infty} \frac{z^{2r+1}}{(2r + 1)!} = \left(\frac{1}{2\pi z}\right)^{\frac{1}{2}} (e^z - e^{-z}),$$

$$I_{-\frac{1}{2}}(z) = \left(\frac{2}{\pi z}\right)^{\frac{1}{2}} \sum_{r=0}^{\infty} \frac{z^{2r}}{(2r)!} = \left(\frac{1}{2\pi z}\right)^{\frac{1}{2}} (e^z + e^{-z}).$$

From (1.53) with $\nu = \frac{1}{2}$,

$$K_{\frac{1}{2}}(z) = \frac{\pi}{2}\{I_{-\frac{1}{2}}(z) - I_{\frac{1}{2}}(z)\} = \left(\frac{\pi}{2z}\right)^{\frac{1}{2}} e^{-z},$$

when we substitute for $I_{\frac{1}{2}}(z)$ and $I_{-\frac{1}{2}}(z)$.

1.15 Modified Bessel functions of orders zero and unity

The modified functions which occur most frequently in practical applications are those of orders zero and unity. As in §1.7, we set out equations (1.51) and (1.58) for these special cases and give a brief general description of the functions for real positive values x of the argument z.

We have

$$I_0(x) = 1 + \frac{x^2}{2^2(1!)^2} + \frac{x^4}{2^4(2!)^2} + \frac{x^6}{2^6(3!)^2} + \ldots, \tag{1.62}$$

$$K_0(x) = -\left(\gamma + \log_e \frac{x}{2}\right) I_0(x) + \sum_{r=1}^{\infty} \frac{(x/2)^{2r}}{r!r!}\left(1 + \frac{1}{2} + \frac{1}{3} + \ldots + \frac{1}{r}\right), \tag{1.63}$$

$$I_1(x) = \frac{x}{2} + \frac{x^3}{2^3 1!2!} + \frac{x^5}{2^5 2!3!} + \ldots, \tag{1.64}$$

$$K_1(x) = \left(\gamma + \log_e \frac{x}{2}\right) I_1(x) + \frac{1}{x}$$
$$- \frac{1}{2}\sum_{r=0}^{\infty} \frac{(x/2)^{2r+1}}{r!(r + 1)!}\left\{2\left(1 + \frac{1}{2} + \ldots + \frac{1}{r}\right) + \frac{1}{r + 1}\right\}, \tag{1.65}$$

the first term in the series on the right-hand side of (1.65) being $\frac{1}{2}x$. For small values of x, these series show that

$$I_0(x) \simeq 1, \quad K_0(x) \simeq -\gamma - \log_e \frac{x}{2}. \qquad I_1(x) \simeq \frac{x}{2}, \quad K_1(x) \simeq \frac{1}{x}. \tag{1.66}$$

Tabulated values of $I_n(x)$ and $K_n(x)$ for values of n up to $n = 20$ can be found in the British Association Mathematical Tables referred to in §1.7, and rough graphs for the functions of orders zero and unity are shown in Figs. 3 and 4. It is more convenient to plot $e^{-x}I_n(x)$ and $e^{x}K_n(x)$ than the functions

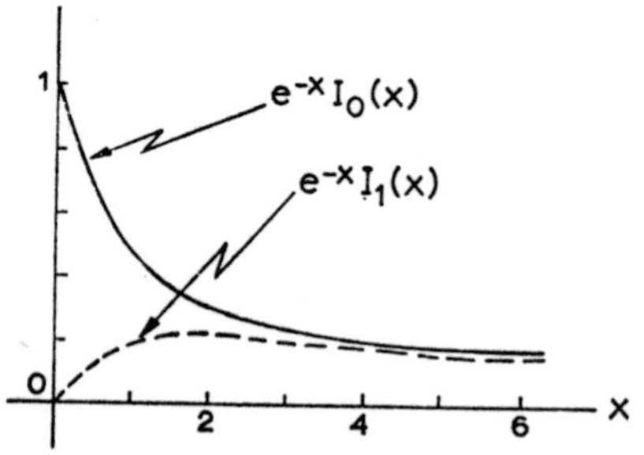

FIG. 3

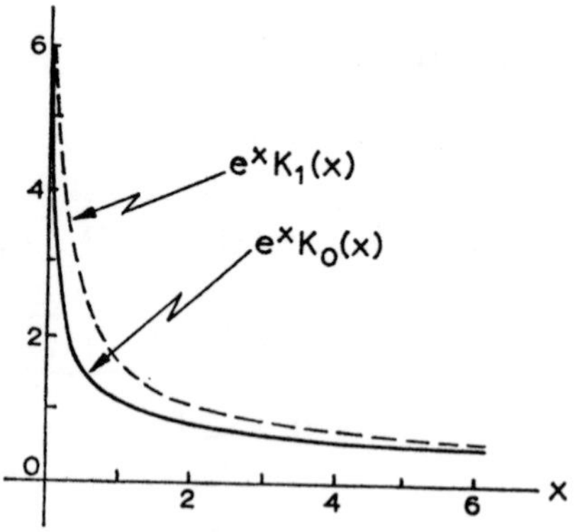

FIG. 4

themselves because of the way in which they behave for large values of x (see §§3.6, 3.7). The modified functions $I_\nu(x)$, $K_\nu(x)$ bear to the exponential functions $e^{\pm x}$ similar relations to those which the functions $J_\nu(x)$, $Y_\nu(x)$ bear to the trigonometrical functions, and the modified functions have no zeros for real values of x.

1.16 Recurrence formulae for the modified Bessel functions

Equation (1.51) can be written

$$z^{-\nu}I_\nu(z) = 2^{-\nu}\sum_{r=0}^{\infty}\frac{(z/2)^{2r}}{r!\Gamma(\nu+r+1)},$$

so that, dashes denoting derivatives with respect to z,

$$\begin{aligned}\frac{\nu}{z}I_\nu(z) - I_\nu'(z) &= -z^\nu\frac{\mathrm{d}}{\mathrm{d}z}\{z^{-\nu}I_\nu(z)\}\\ &= -z^\nu 2^{-\nu}\sum_{r=1}^{\infty}\frac{r(z/2)^{2r-1}}{r!\Gamma(\nu+r+1)}\\ &= -\sum_{r=0}^{\infty}\frac{(z/2)^{\nu+1+2r}}{r!\Gamma(\nu+r+2)} = -I_{\nu+1}(z).\end{aligned} \quad (1.67)$$

Similarly

$$z^\nu I_\nu(z) = 2^\nu\sum_{r=0}^{\infty}\frac{(z/2)^{2\nu+2r}}{r!\Gamma(\nu+r+1)},$$

giving

$$\frac{\nu}{z} I_\nu(z) + I_\nu'(z) = z^{-\nu} \frac{d}{dz} \{z^\nu I_\nu(z)\}$$
$$= z^{-\nu} 2^\nu \sum_{r=0}^{\infty} \frac{(\nu + r)(z/2)^{2\nu+2r-1}}{r!\Gamma(\nu + r + 1)}$$
$$= \sum_{r=0}^{\infty} \frac{(z/2)^{\nu-1+2r}}{r!\Gamma(\nu + r)} = I_{\nu-1}(z). \tag{1.68}$$

We have therefore established the recurrence formulae

$$\left.\begin{aligned} -I_{\nu+1}(z) &= \frac{\nu}{z} I_\nu(z) - I_\nu'(z), \\ I_{\nu-1}(z) &= \frac{\nu}{z} I_\nu(z) + I_\nu'(z), \\ I_{\nu-1}(z) - I_{\nu+1}(z) &= \frac{2\nu}{z} I_\nu(z), \\ I_{\nu-1}(z) + I_{\nu+1}(z) &= 2I_\nu'(z), \end{aligned}\right\} \tag{1.69}$$

the last two of these following from the first two by addition and subtraction. The special case ($\nu = 0$) of these, viz.,

$$I_1(z) = I_0'(z) \tag{1.70}$$

is worth noting as also are the differences in sign in comparison with the recurrence formulae (1.31) for the functions $J_\nu(z)$.

Writing $-\nu$ in place of ν in the second of equations (1.69),

$$I_{-(\nu+1)}(z) = -\frac{\nu}{z} I_{-\nu}(z) + I_{-\nu}'(z),$$

and adding the first of equations (1.69),

$$I_{-(\nu+1)}(z) - I_{\nu+1}(z) = -\frac{\nu}{z}\{I_{-\nu}(z) - I_\nu(z)\} + I_{-\nu}'(z) - I_\nu'(z).$$

Multiplying this relation by $(\pi/2)\operatorname{cosec}\nu\pi$, noting that $\operatorname{cosec}(\nu + 1)\pi = -\operatorname{cosec}\nu\pi$ and using equation (1.53), this gives

$$-K_{\nu+1}(z) = -\frac{\nu}{z} K_\nu(z) + K_\nu'(z).$$

This and the relations

$$\left.\begin{aligned} -K_{\nu-1}(z) &= \frac{\nu}{z} K_\nu(z) + K_\nu'(z), \\ K_{\nu-1}(z) - K_{\nu+1}(z) &= -\frac{2\nu}{z} K_\nu(z), \\ K_{\nu-1}(z) + K_{\nu+1}(z) &= -2K_\nu'(z), \end{aligned}\right\} \tag{1.71}$$

of which the first is obtained similarly and the other two follow by subtraction and addition, are the recurrence formulae for the function $K_\nu(z)$. The special case $\nu = 0$ of the first of these formulae,

$$K_1(z) = -K_0'(z), \tag{1.72}$$

and the result

$$K_{-\nu}(z) = K_\nu(z), \tag{1.73}$$

which can be easily obtained from equation (1.53), are worth noting.

Example 6. *Show that* $zI_1(z) = 4\sum_{r=1}^{\infty} rI_{2r}(z)$.

Writing $\nu = 2, 4, 6, \ldots$ in the third of the reduction formulae (1.69),

$$z\{I_1(z) - I_3(z)\} = 4I_2(z),$$
$$z\{I_3(z) - I_5(z)\} = 8I_4(z),$$
$$z\{I_5(z) - I_7(z)\} = 12I_6(z),$$
$$\cdots\cdots\cdots,$$

and the required result follows by addition.

1.17 Kelvin functions

The differential equation

$$x^2\frac{d^2w}{dx^2} + x\frac{dw}{dx} - ix^2w = 0 \tag{1.74}$$

arises in problems of electrical engineering. It can be derived from Bessel's modified equation (1.50) by writing $\nu = 0$, $z = xe^{\frac{1}{4}\pi i}$ and a formal solution of the equation is therefore

$$w = AI_0(xe^{\frac{1}{4}\pi i}) + BK_0(xe^{\frac{1}{4}\pi i}),$$

where A, B are arbitrary constants. The arguments of the modified Bessel functions being complex, Lord Kelvin found it convenient to introduce four functions defined by

$$ber\,(x) + i\,bei\,(x) = I_0(xe^{\frac{1}{4}\pi i}), \tag{1.75}$$

$$ker\,(x) + i\,kei\,(x) = K_0(xe^{\frac{1}{4}\pi i}), \tag{1.76}$$

and all these four new functions are real when x is real.

From the series for $I_0(z)$ given in (1.51) with $\nu = 0$, we have by writing $z = xe^{\frac{1}{4}\pi i}$ and equating real and imaginary parts

$$ber\,(x) = 1 - \frac{(x/2)^4}{(2!)^2} + \frac{(x/2)^8}{(4!)^2} - \ldots, \tag{1.77}$$

$$bei\,(x) = \frac{(x/2)^2}{(1!)^2} - \frac{(x/2)^6}{(3!)^2} + \frac{(x/2)^{10}}{(5!)^2} - \ldots. \tag{1.78}$$

Similar, but rather more complicated, formulae can be deduced from equation (1.57) for the functions *ker* (x) and *kei* (x), see Exercises 1, No. 19. Short tables giving numerical values of the four functions can be found, for instance, in *Bessel Functions for Engineers*, N. W. McLachlan, Oxford, 1934.

Generalization of these functions to ones derived from Bessel functions of general order and argument is clearly possible and the definitions usually adopted for this purpose are

$$\left.\begin{aligned} ber_\nu(z) \pm i\, bei_\nu(z) &= J_\nu(ze^{\pm\frac{3}{4}\pi i}),\\ her_\nu(z) \pm i\, hei_\nu(z) &= H_\nu^{(1)}(ze^{\pm\frac{3}{4}\pi i}),\\ ker_\nu(z) &= -\tfrac{1}{2}\pi\, hei_\nu(z),\\ kei_\nu(z) &= \tfrac{1}{2}\pi\, her_\nu(z). \end{aligned}\right\} \tag{1.79}$$

These more general functions are not, however, of great importance in physical applications and we shall not here develop formulae, such as recurrence relations, etc., which can be derived from these definitions.

Exercises 1

1. If n is a positive integer, show that as n tends to ∞ (x remaining finite) $2^n n!\, x^{-n} J_n(x)$ tends to unity.

2. Show that

$$H_\nu^{(1)}(z) = \frac{J_{-\nu}(z) - e^{-\nu\pi i}J_\nu(z)}{i \sin \nu\pi}, \quad H_\nu^{(2)}(z) = \frac{J_{-\nu}(z) - e^{\nu\pi i}J_\nu(z)}{-i \sin \nu\pi},$$

and deduce that $H_{-\nu}^{(1)}(z) = e^{\nu\pi i}H_\nu^{(1)}(z)$, $H_{-\nu}^{(2)}(z) = e^{-\nu\pi i}H_\nu^{(2)}(z)$.

3. Establish Lommel's formula

$$J_\nu(z)J_{1-\nu}(z) + J_{-\nu}(z)J_{\nu-1}(z) = \frac{2 \sin \nu\pi}{\pi z}.$$

4. Show that, n being an integer or zero,

$$\frac{d}{dz}\{J_n^2(z) + J_{n+1}^2(z)\} = \frac{2}{z}\{nJ_n^2(z) - (n+1)J_{n+1}^2(z)\}.$$

Deduce that

$$J_0^2(z) + 2\sum_{n=1}^{\infty} J_n^2(z) = 1.$$

5. Establish the recurrence formulae

$$Y_{\nu-1}(z) + Y_{\nu+1}(z) = \frac{2\nu}{z}\, Y_\nu(z),$$

$$Y_{\nu-1}(z) - Y_{\nu+1}(z) = 2\,Y_\nu'(z).$$

6. Use the generating function for the Bessel coefficients to show that

$$\exp(iz\cos\theta) = J_0(z) - 2\{J_2(z)\cos 2\theta - J_4(z)\cos 4\theta + \ldots\} + 2i\{J_1(z)\cos\theta - J_3(z)\cos 3\theta + \ldots\}.$$

The current in a rectifying valve is $a\exp(b\cos\omega t)$ where a and b are constants; prove that the mean value of the current over a period is $aJ_0(ib)$.

7. Use Jacobi's expansions of $\cos(z\sin\theta)$ and $\sin(z\sin\theta)$ to show that

$$1 = J_0(z) + 2\sum_{n=1}^{\infty} J_{2n}(z),$$

$$z = 2\sum_{n=0}^{\infty}(2n+1)J_{2n+1}(z).$$

8. Starting with the identity

$$[\exp\{\tfrac{1}{2}x(t - t^{-1})\}]^2 = \exp\{x(t - t^{-1})\}$$

and using formula (1.35), establish the formula

$$J_0(2x) = J_0^2(x) + 2\sum_{r=1}^{\infty}(-1)^r J_r^2(x).$$

9. Show that

$$\text{(i) } J_{\frac{1}{2}}(z)J_{-\frac{1}{2}}(z) = \frac{\sin 2z}{\pi z}, \quad \text{(ii) } J_{\frac{1}{2}}^2(z) + Y_{\frac{1}{2}}^2(z) = \frac{2}{\pi z},$$

$$\text{(iii) } J_{\frac{5}{2}}(z) = \left(\frac{2}{\pi z}\right)^{\frac{1}{2}}\left\{\left(\frac{3}{z^2} - 1\right)\sin z - \frac{3}{z}\cos z\right\}.$$

10. If m is an integer, show that

$$H_\nu^{(1)}(ze^{m\pi i}) = \frac{\sin(1-m)\nu\pi}{\sin\nu\pi}H_\nu^{(1)}(z) - e^{-\nu\pi i}\frac{\sin m\nu\pi}{\sin\nu\pi}H_\nu^{(2)}(z),$$

$$H_\nu^{(2)}(ze^{m\pi i}) = \frac{\sin(1+m)\nu\pi}{\sin\nu\pi}H_\nu^{(2)}(z) + e^{\nu\pi i}\frac{\sin m\nu\pi}{\sin\nu\pi}H_\nu^{(1)}(z).$$

11. Show that the general solution of the differential equation

$$\frac{d^2w}{dt^2} + \left(\frac{e^{2/t} - \nu^2}{t^4}\right)w = 0$$

is $w = t\{AJ_\nu(e^{1/t}) + BY_\nu(e^{1/t})\}$.

12. By changing the dependent variable from w to v where $w = v^{-1}(dv/dz)$, transform the equation

$$\frac{dw}{dz} + w^2 + z^m = 0$$

into a second order differential equation in v and z. By writing

$$v = uz^{\frac{1}{2}}, \quad t = \frac{2}{m+2}z^{1+\frac{1}{2}m},$$

show that the transformed equation can itself be transformed into Bessel's equation of order $(m+2)^{-1}$.

13. By means of the substitutions $y = x^{\frac{1}{2}}u$, $z = kx$, reduce the equation

$$\frac{d^2y}{dx^2} + \left(k^2 + \frac{1}{4x^2}\right) y = 0$$

to the form

$$\frac{d^2u}{dz^2} + \frac{1}{z}\frac{du}{dz} + u = 0.$$

If $x^{-\frac{1}{2}}y$ is finite when $x = 0$ and $(dy/dx) = a^{\frac{1}{2}}$ when $x = a$, show that the solution is

$$y = \frac{2ax^{\frac{1}{2}}J_0(kx)}{J_0(ka) - 2ka\, J_1(ka)}.$$

14. In a problem on the stability of a tapered strut, the displacement y satisfies the equation

$$\frac{d^2y}{dx^2} + \frac{k^2}{4x}y = 0,$$

where a suitable value of k has to be determined. Show that, by writing $y = x^{\frac{1}{2}}u$, $z = kx^{\frac{1}{2}}$, this equation can be reduced to the form

$$z^2\frac{d^2u}{dz^2} + z\frac{du}{dz} + (z^2 - 1)u = 0.$$

If $(dy/dx) = 0$ when $x = a$ and when $x = l$, show that the equation which determines k is $J_0(ka^{\frac{1}{2}})\,Y_0(kl^{\frac{1}{2}}) = J_0(kl^{\frac{1}{2}})\,Y_0(ka^{\frac{1}{2}})$.

15. Show that

$$I_\nu(z)K_{\nu+1}(z) + I_{\nu+1}(z)K_\nu(z) = \frac{1}{z},$$

and deduce that, when n is a positive integer,

$$K_n(z) = (-1)^n I_n(z)\left\{\frac{K_0(z)}{I_0(z)} + \frac{1}{z}\sum_{r=1}^{n}\frac{(-1)^r}{I_r(z)I_{r-1}(z)}\right\}.$$

16. If

$$S_n = (n!)^2\sum_{r=1}^{n}\frac{2}{r(n-r)!(n+r)!},$$

show that $S_n = \sum_{r=1}^{n} r^{-1}$ and deduce C. P. Singer's formula

$$K_0(z) = -\left(\gamma + \log_e\frac{z}{2}\right)I_0(z) + 2\sum_{s=1}^{\infty}s^{-1}I_{2s}(z).$$

17. When n is a positive integer or zero, show that

(i) $\frac{1}{2}zI_n'(z) = \frac{1}{2}nI_n(z) + (n+2)I_{n+2}(z) + (n+4)I_{n+4}(z) + \ldots,$

(ii) $\frac{1}{2}zK_n'(z) = \frac{1}{2}nK_n(z) + (n+2)K_{n+2}(z) + (n+4)K_{n+4}(z) + \ldots.$

18. Taking $I_\nu(ze^{m\pi i}) = e^{m\nu\pi i}I_\nu(z)$ where m is any integer, show that

$$K_\nu(ze^{m\pi i}) = e^{-m\nu\pi i}K_\nu(z) - \pi i\,\frac{\sin m\nu\pi}{\sin \nu\pi}\,I_\nu(z).$$

19. Show that

$$\begin{aligned} ker\,(x) &= (\log_e 2 - \gamma - \log_e x)\,ber\,(x) + \tfrac{1}{4}\pi\,bei\,(x) \\ &\quad - \frac{(x/2)^4}{(2!)^2}(1 + \tfrac{1}{2}) + \frac{(x/2)^8}{(4!)^2}(1 + \tfrac{1}{2} + \tfrac{1}{3} + \tfrac{1}{4}) - \ldots, \\ kei\,(x) &= (\log_e 2 - \gamma - \log_e x)\,bei\,(x) - \tfrac{1}{4}\pi\,ber\,(x) \\ &\quad + \frac{(x/2)^2}{(1!)^2} - \frac{(x/2)^6}{(3!)^2}(1 + \tfrac{1}{2} + \tfrac{1}{3}) + \ldots. \end{aligned}$$

20. Prove that

$$ber\,(x\sqrt{2}) = J_0(x)I_0(x) + 2\sum_{r=1}^{\infty}(-1)^r J_{2r}(x)I_{2r}(x).$$

(Start with the result of Exercises 1, No. 8.)

CHAPTER 2

SOME INDEFINITE INTEGRALS, EXPANSIONS AND ADDITION THEOREMS

2.1 Introduction

In this chapter we derive some formulae which can be obtained formally by operations of an elementary character. We start by giving some indefinite integrals and then obtain the expansions of powers of z and of $J_\nu(\lambda z)$ in series of Bessel functions of argument z. Next we derive the so-called multiplication theorem and obtain a useful series representing the product of two Bessel functions.

Finally we discuss the addition theorems. These are derived for Bessel functions of integral order and (in most cases) of real argument. The validity of the theorems when these restrictions are removed is touched upon but the reader is referred to more comprehensive works for the full details of the proofs in such circumstances.

2.2 Indefinite integrals

Some indefinite integrals involving $J_\nu(z)$ can be obtained immediately from formulae given in Chapter I. Thus, starting from the relations (1.30), (1.29), viz.

$$\frac{\mathrm{d}}{\mathrm{d}z}\{z^\nu J_\nu(z)\} = z^\nu J_{\nu-1}(z), \quad \frac{\mathrm{d}}{\mathrm{d}z}\{z^{-\nu} J_\nu(z)\} = -z^{-\nu} J_{\nu+1}(z), \tag{2.1}$$

it follows, by replacing ν with $\nu + 1$ and $\nu - 1$, that

$$\int z^{\nu+1} J_\nu(z)\,\mathrm{d}z = z^{\nu+1} J_{\nu+1}(z), \tag{2.2}$$

$$\int z^{-\nu+1} J_\nu(z)\,\mathrm{d}z = -z^{-\nu+1} J_{\nu-1}(z). \tag{2.3}$$

These two results enable a reduction formula for the integral $\int z^{\mu+1} J_\nu(z)\,\mathrm{d}z$ to be found as follows. We have, integrating by parts and using (2.2),

$$\begin{aligned}\int z^{\mu+1} J_\nu(z)\,\mathrm{d}z &= \int z^{\mu-\nu} z^{\nu+1} J_\nu(z)\,\mathrm{d}z \\ &= z^{\mu-\nu} z^{\nu+1} J_{\nu+1}(z) - (\mu - \nu)\int z^{\mu-\nu-1} z^{\nu+1} J_{\nu+1}(z)\,\mathrm{d}z \\ &= z^{\mu+1} J_{\nu+1}(z) - (\mu - \nu)\int z^{\mu} J_{\nu+1}(z)\,\mathrm{d}z. \end{aligned} \tag{2.4}$$

Integrating by parts and using (2.3) with ν replaced by $\nu + 1$,

$$\begin{aligned}\int z^{\mu} J_{\nu+1}(z)\,\mathrm{d}z &= \int z^{\mu+\nu} z^{-\nu} J_{\nu+1}(z)\,\mathrm{d}z \\ &= z^{\mu+\nu}\{-z^{-\nu} J_\nu(z)\} - (\mu + \nu)\int z^{\mu+\nu-1}\{-z^{-\nu} J_\nu(z)\}\,\mathrm{d}z \\ &= -z^{\mu} J_\nu(z) + (\mu + \nu)\int z^{\mu-1} J_\nu(z)\,\mathrm{d}z.\end{aligned}$$

Substitution in (2.4) then gives

$$\int z^{\mu+1}J_\nu(z)\,dz = z^{\mu+1}J_{\nu+1}(z) + (\mu-\nu)z^\mu J_\nu(z) - (\mu^2-\nu^2)\int z^{\mu-1}J_\nu(z)\,dz. \quad (2.5)$$

Example 1. *Show that*

$$\int_0^a z^3J_0(z)\,dz = 2a^2J_0(a) + a(a^2-4)J_1(a).$$

Writing $\mu = 2$, $\nu = 0$ in (2.5),

$$\begin{aligned}\int_0^a z^3J_0(z)\,dz &= \Big[z^3J_1(z) + 2z^2J_0(z)\Big]_0^a - 4\int_0^a zJ_0(z)\,dz\\ &= a^3J_1(a) + 2a^2J_0(a) - 4\Big[zJ_1(z)\Big]_0^a, \text{ using (2.2)},\\ &= 2a^2J_0(a) + a(a^2-4)J_1(a).\end{aligned}$$

Integrating the last of the reduction formulae (1.31), with $\nu - 1$ replaced by ν,

$$\int J_\nu(z)\,dz - \int J_{\nu+2}(z)\,dz = 2J_{\nu+1}(z).$$

Similarly

$$\int J_{\nu+2}(z)\,dz - \int J_{\nu+4}(z)\,dz = 2J_{\nu+3}(z),$$

and so on. By the addition of $m - 1$ relations of this type, we find

$$\int J_{\nu+2m}(z)\,dz = \int J_\nu(z)\,dz - 2\sum_{r=0}^{m-1} J_{\nu+2r+1}(z)\,dz, \quad (2.6)$$

where $m = 1, 2, 3, \ldots$. The relations (2.2), (2.3), (2.5) and (2.6) remain valid when $J_\nu(z)$ is replaced by $Y_\nu(z)$, $H_\nu^{(1)}(z)$ or $H_\nu^{(2)}(z)$ since the formulae from which they are derived are valid for such changes.

Using the relation (1.18)

$$\begin{aligned}\frac{2}{\pi z} &= J_\nu(z)Y_\nu'(z) - Y_\nu(z)J_\nu'(z)\\ &= J_\nu^2(z)\frac{d}{dz}\left\{\frac{Y_\nu(z)}{J_\nu(z)}\right\} = J_\nu(z)Y_\nu(z)\frac{d}{dz}\left\{\log_e\frac{Y_\nu(z)}{J_\nu(z)}\right\}\\ &= -Y_\nu^2(z)\frac{d}{dz}\left\{\frac{J_\nu(z)}{Y_\nu(z)}\right\},\end{aligned}$$

we find immediately that

$$\left.\begin{aligned}\int\frac{dz}{zJ_\nu^2(z)} &= \frac{\pi}{2}\frac{Y_\nu(z)}{J_\nu(z)},\\ \int\frac{dz}{zJ_\nu(z)Y_\nu(z)} &= \frac{\pi}{2}\log_e\frac{Y_\nu(z)}{J_\nu(z)},\\ \int\frac{dz}{zY_\nu^2(z)} &= -\frac{\pi}{2}\frac{J_\nu(z)}{Y_\nu(z)}.\end{aligned}\right\} \quad (2.7)$$

Another important integral is $\int zJ_\nu(\lambda z)J_\nu(\mu z)\,dz$ and this can be evaluated as follows. If $u = J_\nu(\lambda z)$, then u satisfies Bessel's equation (1.1) when u is written in place of w and λz in place of z. Hence

$$z^2\frac{d^2u}{dz^2} + z\frac{du}{dz} + (\lambda^2z^2 - \nu^2)u = 0$$

and $v = J_\nu(\mu z)$ similarly satisfies the equation

$$z^2\frac{d^2v}{dz^2} + z\frac{dv}{dz} + (\mu^2z^2 - \nu^2)v = 0.$$

Multiplying respectively by v/z, u/z and subtracting

$$(\lambda^2 - \mu^2)zuv = z\left(u\frac{d^2v}{dz^2} - v\frac{d^2u}{dz^2}\right) + \left(u\frac{dv}{dz} - v\frac{du}{dz}\right)$$
$$= \frac{d}{dz}\left\{z\left(u\frac{dv}{dz} - v\frac{du}{dz}\right)\right\}.$$

Substituting for u, v and integrating with respect to z,

$$(\lambda^2 - \mu^2)\int zJ_\nu(\lambda z)J_\nu(\mu z)\,dz = z\{\mu J_\nu(\lambda z)J_\nu'(\mu z) - \lambda J_\nu(\mu z)J_\nu'(\lambda z)\}$$
$$= z\{\lambda J_\nu(\mu z)J_{\nu+1}(\lambda z) - \mu J_\nu(\lambda z)J_{\nu+1}(\mu z)\}, \quad (2.8)$$

when use is made of equation (1.29). To evaluate the integral when $\mu = \lambda$ we have, using L'Hospital's rule for a limit,

$$\int zJ_\nu^2(\lambda z)\,dz = \lim_{\mu\to\lambda}\left\{\frac{z\mu J_\nu(\lambda z)J_\nu'(\mu z) - z\lambda J_\nu(\mu z)J_\nu'(\lambda z)}{\lambda^2 - \mu^2}\right\}$$
$$= \lim_{\mu\to\lambda}\left[-\frac{z}{2\mu}\frac{\partial}{\partial\mu}\{\mu J_\nu(\lambda z)J_\nu'(\mu z) - \lambda J_\nu(\mu z)J_\nu'(\lambda z)\}\right]$$
$$= -\frac{z}{2\lambda}\lim_{\mu\to\lambda}\{J_\nu(\lambda z)J_\nu'(\mu z) + \mu zJ_\nu(\lambda z)J_\nu''(\mu z) - \lambda zJ_\nu'(\mu z)J_\nu'(\lambda z)\}$$
$$= \frac{z^2}{2}\left[\{J_\nu'(\lambda z)\}^2 - J_\nu(\lambda z)J_\nu''(\lambda z) - \frac{1}{\lambda z}J_\nu(\lambda z)J_\nu'(\lambda z)\right].$$

Since $J_\nu(\lambda z)$ satisfies Bessel's equation,

$$J_\nu''(\lambda z) + \frac{1}{\lambda z}J_\nu'(\lambda z) + \left(1 - \frac{\nu^2}{\lambda^2z^2}\right)J_\nu(\lambda z) = 0$$

and, substituting for $J_\nu''(\lambda z)$, we find the formula reduces to

$$\int zJ_\nu^2(\lambda z)\,dz = \frac{z^2}{2}\left[\{J_\nu'(\lambda z)\}^2 + \left(1 - \frac{\nu^2}{\lambda^2z^2}\right)J_\nu^2(\lambda z)\right]. \quad (2.9)$$

Results similar to those given in this section can be found for integrals involving the modified Bessel functions. Their derivation follows the methods given here and the details are left to the reader (for examples, see Exercises 2, Nos. 1, 2, 5).

2.3 Two expansions in series of Bessel functions

In this section we derive the expansions of a power of z and of the Bessel function $J_\nu(\lambda z)$ as series of terms involving Bessel functions.

We first consider the series S given by

$$S = \sum_{r=0}^{\infty} \frac{(\mu + 2r)\Gamma(\mu + r)}{r!} (\tfrac{1}{2}z)^{-\mu} J_{\mu+2r}(z) \tag{2.10}$$

where μ is not a negative integer. Since

$$\frac{\mathrm{d}}{\mathrm{d}z} \{(\tfrac{1}{2}z)^{-\mu} J_{\mu+2r}(z)\} = (\tfrac{1}{2}z)^{-\mu} \left\{ -\frac{\mu}{z} J_{\mu+2r}(z) + J_{\mu+2r}'(z) \right\}$$

$$= \frac{(\tfrac{1}{2}z)^{-\mu}}{\mu + 2r} \{rJ_{\mu+2r-1}(z) - (\mu + r)J_{\mu+2r+1}(z)\},$$

when use is made of the last two of the reduction formulae (1.31), it follows that

$$\frac{\mathrm{d}S}{\mathrm{d}z} = (\tfrac{1}{2}z)^{-\mu} \left\{ \sum_{r=0}^{\infty} \frac{\Gamma(\mu + r)}{r!} rJ_{\mu+2r-1}(z) - \sum_{r=0}^{\infty} \frac{\Gamma(\mu + r + 1)}{(r + 1)!} (r + 1)J_{\mu+2r+1}(z) \right\}$$

$$= 0,$$

and hence that the value of S is independent of z. But as z tends to zero, all the terms in S except the first tend to zero. The value of the first term is

$$\mu\Gamma(\mu) \lim_{z\to 0} (\tfrac{1}{2}z)^{-\mu} J_\mu(z) = 1$$

and we have shown therefore that $S = 1$. Multiplication of (2.10) by $(\tfrac{1}{2}z)^\mu$ then gives the result

$$(\tfrac{1}{2}z)^\mu = \sum_{r=0}^{\infty} \frac{(\mu + 2r)\Gamma(\mu + r)}{r!} J_{\mu+2r}(z) \tag{2.11}$$

and this is the required expansion of z^μ valid for all values of μ except $-1, -2, -3, \ldots$. For the special case in which μ is zero or a positive integer, the result can be obtained by repeated differentiation of Jacobi's expansions for $\cos (z \sin \theta)$, $\sin (z \sin \theta)$ and then setting $\theta = 0$; see Exercises 1, No. 7, for $\mu = 0$ and 1.

The expansion of $J_\nu(\lambda z)$ can be obtained formally as follows. Using the series (1.5) for $J_\nu(\lambda z)$ and the result (2.11), we have

$$(\tfrac{1}{2}\lambda z)^{\mu-\nu} J_\nu(\lambda z) = \sum_{r=0}^{\infty} \frac{(-1)^r (\tfrac{1}{2}\lambda z)^{\mu+2r}}{r!\Gamma(\nu + r + 1)}$$

$$= \sum_{r=0}^{\infty} \frac{(-1)^r \lambda^{\mu+2r}}{r!\Gamma(\nu + r + 1)} \sum_{p=0}^{\infty} \frac{(\mu + 2r + 2p)\Gamma(\mu + 2r + p)}{p!} J_{\mu+2r+2p}(z).$$

Writing $p = s - r$ and changing the order of summations, this gives

$$(\tfrac{1}{2}\lambda z)^{\mu-\nu} J_\nu(\lambda z) = \lambda^\mu \sum_{s=0}^{\infty} \left\{ \sum_{r=0}^{s} \frac{(-1)^r \Gamma(\mu + r + s)\lambda^{2r}}{r!\Gamma(\nu + r + 1)(s - r)!} \right\} (\mu + 2s) J_{\mu+2s}(z).$$

Introducing the hypergeometric function

$$ {}_2F_1(a, b; c; x) = 1 + \frac{ab}{c}\cdot\frac{x}{1!} + \frac{a(a+1)b(b+1)}{c(c+1)}\cdot\frac{x^2}{2!} + \ldots, \tag{2.12} $$

this can be written in the form

$$ (\tfrac{1}{2}\lambda z)^{\mu-\nu}J_\nu(\lambda z) = \lambda^\mu \sum_{s=0}^{\infty} \frac{\Gamma(\mu+s)}{s!\,\Gamma(\nu+1)}\, {}_2F_1(\mu+s, -s; \nu+1; \lambda^2)(\mu+2s)J_{\mu+2s}(z), \tag{2.13} $$

and this expansion is valid when μ, ν and $\nu-\mu$ are not negative integers.

Example 2. *Show that*

$$ \tfrac{1}{2}z(1+z^2) = 1^3J_1(z) + 3^3J_3(z) + 5^3J_5(z) + \ldots. $$

From (2.11) with $\mu = 1$ and 3,

$$ \tfrac{1}{2}z = \sum_{r=0}^{\infty}(1+2r)J_{1+2r}(z), $$

$$ \tfrac{1}{8}z^3 = \sum_{r=0}^{\infty}\frac{(3+2r)\Gamma(r+3)}{r!}J_{3+2r}(z) = \sum_{r=0}^{\infty}(3+2r)(r+2)(r+1)J_{3+2r}(z). $$

These can be written

$$ \tfrac{1}{2}z = J_1(z) + \sum_{r=1}^{\infty}(1+2r)J_{1+2r}(z), $$

$$ \tfrac{1}{2}z^3 = 4\sum_{r=1}^{\infty}(1+2r)(r+1)rJ_{1+2r}(z), $$

so that by addition,

$$ \begin{aligned} \tfrac{1}{2}z(1+z^2) &= J_1(z) + \sum_{r=1}^{\infty}(1+2r)\{1+4(r+1)r\}J_{1+2r}(z) \\ &= J_1(z) + \sum_{r=1}^{\infty}(1+2r)^3J_{1+2r}(z). \end{aligned} $$

2.4 The multiplication theorem

The function $(z+h)^{-\frac{1}{2}\nu}J_\nu\{\sqrt{(z+h)}\}$ is an analytic function of $z+h$ and Taylor's theorem gives

$$ \begin{aligned} (z+h)^{-\frac{1}{2}\nu}J_\nu\{\sqrt{(z+h)}\} &= \sum_{r=0}^{\infty}\frac{h^r}{r!}\frac{d^r}{dz^r}\{z^{-\frac{1}{2}\nu}J_\nu(\sqrt{z})\} \\ &= \sum_{r=0}^{\infty}\frac{(-\frac{1}{2}h)^r}{r!}z^{-\frac{1}{2}(\nu+r)}J_{\nu+r}(\sqrt{z}), \end{aligned} \tag{2.14} $$

using equation (1.34) with z replaced by $\sqrt{z}$. This expansion is due to

E. C. J. Lommel and, taking $\nu = -\frac{1}{2}$, $z = x^2$, $h = -2xt$, use of the relation (1.39) leads to the interesting special case

$$\left(\frac{2}{\pi x}\right)^{\frac{1}{2}} \cos \sqrt{(x^2 - 2xt)} = \sum_{r=0}^{\infty} \frac{t^r}{r!} J_{r-\frac{1}{2}}(x). \tag{2.15}$$

If in equation (2.14) we replace z by z^2 and h by $(\lambda^2 - 1)z^2$, we find

$$\lambda^{-\nu} J_\nu(\lambda z) = \sum_{r=0}^{\infty} \frac{(-1)^r(\lambda^2 - 1)^r(\frac{1}{2}z)^r}{r!} J_{\nu+r}(z), \tag{2.16}$$

and this is often known as the *multiplication theorem* for $J_\nu(\lambda z)$. Two particular cases are of interest. When $\lambda = \sqrt{2}$, we have at once

$$J_\nu(z\sqrt{2}) = 2^{\frac{1}{2}\nu} \sum_{r=0}^{\infty} \frac{(-1)^r(\frac{1}{2}z)^r}{r!} J_{\nu+r}(z), \tag{2.17}$$

while, when λ tends to zero, (2.16) gives

$$\frac{(\frac{1}{2}z)^\nu}{\Gamma(\nu + 1)} = \sum_{r=0}^{\infty} \frac{(\frac{1}{2}z)^r}{r!} J_{\nu+r}(z). \tag{2.18}$$

2.5 A series representing the product of two Bessel functions

A useful series for the product $J_\mu(az)J_\nu(bz)$ can be obtained by multiplying the series for the Bessel functions to give

$$\begin{aligned} J_\mu(az)J_\nu(bz) &= \sum_{p=0}^{\infty} \frac{(-1)^p(\frac{1}{2}az)^{\mu+2p}}{p!\,\Gamma(\mu + p + 1)} \sum_{r=0}^{\infty} \frac{(-1)^r(\frac{1}{2}bz)^{\nu+2r}}{r!\,\Gamma(\nu + r + 1)} \\ &= \sum_{r=0}^{\infty} \frac{(-1)^r(\frac{1}{2}bz)^{\nu+2r}}{r!\,\Gamma(\nu + r + 1)} \sum_{s=r}^{\infty} \frac{(-1)^{s-r}(\frac{1}{2}az)^{\mu+2s-2r}}{(s - r)!\,\Gamma(\mu + s - r + 1)}, \end{aligned}$$

when we write $p = s - r$. Change of the order of the summations and a slight reduction then yields

$$\frac{J_\mu(az)J_\nu(bz)}{(\frac{1}{2}az)^\mu(\frac{1}{2}bz)^\nu} = \sum_{s=0}^{\infty} (-1)^s(\tfrac{1}{2}az)^{2s} \left\{ \sum_{r=0}^{s} \frac{(b/a)^{2r}}{r!\,\Gamma(\nu + r + 1)(s - r)!\,\Gamma(\mu + s - r + 1)} \right\},$$

and making use of the hypergeometric function introduced in §2.3, this can be written in the form

$$J_\mu(az)J_\nu(bz) = \frac{(\frac{1}{2}az)^\mu(\frac{1}{2}bz)^\nu}{\Gamma(\nu + 1)} \sum_{s=0}^{\infty} \frac{(-1)^s(\frac{1}{2}az)^{2s}\,{}_2F_1(-s, -\mu - s; \nu + 1; b^2/a^2)}{s!\,\Gamma(\mu + s + 1)}. \tag{2.19}$$

When $b = a$, the hypergeometric function in (2.19) reduces to

$${}_2F_1(-s, -\mu - s; \nu + 1; 1) = \frac{\Gamma(\nu + 1)\Gamma(\nu + \mu + 2s + 1)}{\Gamma(\nu + s + 1)\Gamma(\nu + \mu + s + 1)}.$$

Hence

$$J_\mu(z)J_\nu(z) = \sum_{s=0}^{\infty} \frac{(-1)^s\Gamma(\nu+\mu+2s+1)(\frac{1}{2}z)^{\mu+\nu+2s}}{s!\Gamma(\mu+s+1)\Gamma(\nu+s+1)\Gamma(\nu+\mu+s+1)}, \tag{2.20}$$

and, when $\mu = \nu$,

$$J_\nu^2(z) = \sum_{s=0}^{\infty} \frac{(-1)^s\Gamma(2\nu+2s+1)(\frac{1}{2}z)^{2\nu+2s}}{s!\Gamma^2(\nu+s+1)\Gamma(2\nu+s+1)}. \tag{2.21}$$

The result (2.19) and its special cases (2.20), (2.21) are useful in evaluating certain definite integrals which arise in acoustical problems concerned with vibrating discs.

Example 3. *Show that* $\displaystyle\int_0^{\pi/2} J_1^2(x\sin\theta)\operatorname{cosec}\theta\, d\theta = \frac{1}{2} - \frac{J_1(2x)}{2x}.$

Using (2.21) with $\nu = 1$, $z = x\sin\theta$, noting that when s is a positive integer $\Gamma(s+1) = s!$, and interchanging the order of integration and summation,

$$\int_0^{\pi/2} J_1^2(x\sin\theta)\operatorname{cosec}\theta\, d\theta = \sum_{s=0}^{\infty} \frac{(-1)^s(2s+2)!(\frac{1}{2}x)^{2+2s}}{s!\{(s+1)!\}^2(s+2)!}\int_0^{\pi/2} \sin^{2s+1}\theta\, d\theta.$$

Now

$$\int_0^{\pi/2} \sin^{2s+1}\theta\, d\theta = \frac{2s}{2s+1}\cdot\frac{2s-2}{2s-1}\cdots\frac{4}{5}\cdot\frac{2}{3} = \frac{2^{2s}(s!)^2}{(2s+1)!},$$

and substitution gives

$$\begin{aligned}\int_0^{\pi/2} J_1^2(x\sin\theta)\operatorname{cosec}\theta\, d\theta &= \frac{1}{2}\sum_{s=0}^{\infty}\frac{(-1)^s x^{2+2s}}{(s+1)!(s+2)!}\\ &= \frac{1}{2}\left\{1 - \sum_{r=0}^{\infty}\frac{(-1)^r x^{2r}}{r!(r+1)!}\right\}\\ &= \frac{1}{2} - \frac{J_1(2x)}{2x}\end{aligned}$$

when use is made of equation (1.5).

2.6 Addition theorems

It is not possible to express $J_\nu(x+y)$ as an algebraic function of $J_\nu(x)$ and $J_\nu(y)$ and so the Bessel functions do not have addition theorems in the sense of those of the trigonometrical functions. There are, however, certain formulae which are usually referred to as addition theorems and these are briefly discussed in this section.

The simplest formula is obtained by starting with the identity

$$\exp\{\tfrac{1}{2}x(t-t^{-1})\}\exp\{\tfrac{1}{2}y(t-t^{-1})\} = \exp\{\tfrac{1}{2}(x+y)(t-t^{-1})\}$$

and using formula (1.35); this gives

$$\sum_{n=-\infty}^{\infty} J_n(x+y)t^n = \sum_{r=-\infty}^{\infty}\sum_{s=-\infty}^{\infty} J_r(x)J_s(y)t^{r+s}. \tag{2.22}$$

By equating coefficients of t^n, we have as the required addition formula

$$J_n(x+y) = \sum_{r=-\infty}^{\infty} J_r(x)J_{n-r}(y), \tag{2.23}$$

a result first given by C. G. Neumann.

Neumann also gave a formula for $J_0\{\sqrt{(x^2+y^2-2xy\cos\theta)}\}$. This was generalized by J. H. Graf and a formal derivation of Graf's result is given below. Since

$$\frac{1}{2}z\left(kt-\frac{1}{kt}\right) = \frac{1}{2}kz\left(t-\frac{1}{t}\right) + \frac{1}{2}\frac{z}{t}\left(k-\frac{1}{k}\right),$$

we have, using formula (1.35) firstly with kt in place of t and secondly with kz in place of z,

$$\begin{aligned}\sum_{r=-\infty}^{\infty} J_r(z)k^r t^r &= \exp\left\{\frac{1}{2}z\left(kt-\frac{1}{kt}\right)\right\}\\ &= \exp\left\{\frac{z}{2t}\left(k-\frac{1}{k}\right)\right\}\exp\left\{\frac{1}{2}kz\left(t-\frac{1}{t}\right)\right\}\\ &= \exp\left\{\frac{z}{2t}\left(k-\frac{1}{k}\right)\right\}\sum_{r=-\infty}^{\infty} J_r(kz)t^r.\end{aligned} \tag{2.24}$$

Writing $z = x$, $k = e^{i\alpha}$ and noting that

$$\exp\left\{\frac{z}{2t}\left(k-\frac{1}{k}\right)\right\} = \exp\left\{\frac{x}{2t}(e^{i\alpha}-e^{-i\alpha})\right\} = \exp\left(\frac{ix\sin\alpha}{t}\right),$$

equation (2.24) can be written in the form

$$\sum_{r=-\infty}^{\infty} e^{ri\alpha}J_r(x)t^r = \exp\left(\frac{ix\sin\alpha}{t}\right)\sum_{r=-\infty}^{\infty} J_r(xe^{i\alpha})t^r.$$

Similarly with $z = y$, $k = e^{i\beta}$, equation (2.24) gives

$$\sum_{s=-\infty}^{\infty} e^{si\beta}J_s(y)t^s = \exp\left(\frac{iy\sin\beta}{t}\right)\sum_{s=-\infty}^{\infty} J_s(ye^{i\beta})t^s,$$

so that, division by the exponentials and multiplication of these two results gives

$$\begin{aligned}&\sum_{r=-\infty}^{\infty} J_r(xe^{i\alpha})t^r \sum_{s=-\infty}^{\infty} J_s(ye^{i\beta})t^s\\ &= \exp\left\{\frac{-i(x\sin\alpha+y\sin\beta)}{t}\right\}\sum_{r=-\infty}^{\infty} e^{ri\alpha}J_r(x)t^r\sum_{s=-\infty}^{\infty} e^{si\beta}J_s(y)t^s.\end{aligned}$$

Using (2.22), $J_n(xe^{i\alpha}+ye^{i\beta})$ is therefore the coefficient of t^n in the expansion of

$$\exp\left\{\frac{-i(x\sin\alpha+y\sin\beta)}{t}\right\}\sum_{r=-\infty}^{\infty}\sum_{s=-\infty}^{\infty} e^{ri\alpha+si\beta}J_r(x)J_s(y)t^{r+s}. \tag{2.25}$$

Now let $xe^{i\alpha} + ye^{i\beta} = R$ and assume that x, y, α, β, R are real quantities. Then $x \sin \alpha + y \sin \beta = 0$ and it is easy to show that

$$R^2 = x^2 + y^2 + 2xy \cos (\alpha - \beta);$$

hence (2.25) gives

$$J_n[\sqrt{\{x^2 + y^2 + 2xy \cos (\alpha - \beta)\}}] = \sum_{s=-\infty}^{\infty} e^{(n-s)i\alpha+si\beta} J_{n-s}(x)J_s(y).$$

Putting $\alpha - \beta = \pi - \theta$, this can be written

$$J_n\{\sqrt{(x^2 + y^2 - 2xy \cos \theta)}\} = e^{ni\alpha} \sum_{s=-\infty}^{\infty} e^{-si(\pi-\theta)} J_{n-s}(x)J_s(y)$$

$$= e^{ni\alpha} \sum_{r=-\infty}^{\infty} J_{n+r}(x)J_r(y)e^{-ir\theta}, \qquad (2.26)$$

where, in the last step, we have put $r = -s$ and used the result $e^{-is\pi}J_s(y) = J_{-s}(y)$. Now

$$R = xe^{i\alpha} + ye^{i\beta} = xe^{i\alpha} + ye^{i(\alpha+\theta-\pi)} = e^{i\alpha}(x - ye^{i\theta})$$

and

$$R^2 = x^2 + y^2 - 2xy \cos \theta = x^2 + y^2 - xy(e^{i\theta} + e^{-i\theta})$$
$$= (x - ye^{i\theta})(x - ye^{-i\theta}),$$

so that

$$e^{2i\alpha} = \frac{x - ye^{-i\theta}}{x - ye^{i\theta}}.$$

Substituting for $e^{i\alpha}$, equation (2.26) can be written

$$J_n\{\sqrt{(x^2 + y^2 - 2xy \cos \theta)}\} = \left(\frac{x - ye^{-i\theta}}{x - ye^{i\theta}}\right)^{\frac{1}{2}n} \sum_{r=-\infty}^{\infty} J_{n+r}(x)J_r(y)e^{-ir\theta} \qquad (2.27)$$

and this is Graf's formula.

It is sometimes useful to transform formula (2.27) by introducing an angle ψ defined by

$$x - y \cos \theta = R \cos \psi, \quad y \sin \theta = R \sin \psi,$$

where $R^2 = x^2 + y^2 - 2xy \cos \theta$ (see Fig. 5). Then it follows that

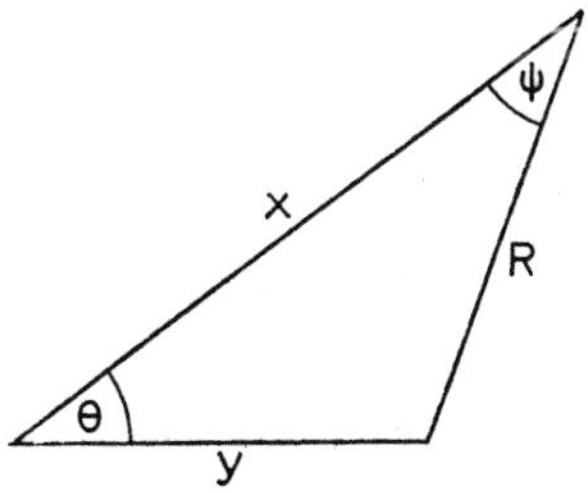

FIG. 5

$$\frac{x - ye^{-i\theta}}{x - ye^{i\theta}} = \frac{x - y \cos \theta + iy \sin \theta}{x - y \cos \theta - iy \sin \theta} = \frac{R \cos \psi + iR \sin \psi}{R \cos \psi - iR \sin \psi} = e^{2i\psi}$$

and Graf's formula becomes

$$e^{-ni\psi}J_n(R) = \sum_{r=-\infty}^{\infty} J_{n+r}(x)J_r(y)e^{-ir\theta}.$$

By equating real and imaginary parts, this can be written

$$J_n(R)\begin{matrix}\cos\\ \sin\end{matrix} n\psi = \sum_{r=-\infty}^{\infty} J_{n+r}(x)J_r(y)\begin{matrix}\cos\\ \sin\end{matrix} r\theta, \tag{2.28}$$

and the special case ($n = 0$) giving Neumann's formula

$$\begin{aligned} J_0\{\sqrt{(x^2 + y^2 - 2xy\cos\theta)}\} &= \sum_{r=-\infty}^{\infty} J_r(x)J_r(y)\cos r\theta \\ &= J_0(x)J_0(y) + 2\sum_{r=1}^{\infty} J_r(x)J_r(y)\cos r\theta \end{aligned} \tag{2.29}$$

should be noted.

The formulae (2.28) have here been derived only when the Bessel function on the left is of integral order and when the quantities x, y, θ are real. They are, however, valid when these restrictions are removed provided then that $|ye^{\pm i\theta}| < |x|$ and, under such conditions,

$$J_\nu(R)\begin{matrix}\cos\\ \sin\end{matrix} \nu\psi = \sum_{r=-\infty}^{\infty} J_{\nu+r}(x)J_r(y)\begin{matrix}\cos\\ \sin\end{matrix} r\theta \tag{2.30}$$

but the reader is referred to works more comprehensive* than this for the details. By changing the signs of ν and r and using (1.12), it follows that

$$Y_\nu(R)\begin{matrix}\cos\\ \sin\end{matrix} \nu\psi = \sum_{r=-\infty}^{\infty} Y_{\nu+r}(x)J_r(y)\begin{matrix}\cos\\ \sin\end{matrix} r\theta \tag{2.31}$$

and it can then be seen from formulae (1.27) that the functions of the second kind can be replaced by either of the Hankel functions. Since from (1.51) and (1.59) $I_\nu(z) = e^{-\frac{1}{2}\nu\pi i}J_\nu(iz)$, $K_\nu(z) = \frac{1}{2}\pi i e^{\frac{1}{2}\nu\pi i}H_\nu^{(1)}(iz)$, it follows by replacing R, x, y in the above formulae by iR, ix and iy that

$$I_\nu(R)\begin{matrix}\cos\\ \sin\end{matrix} \nu\psi = \sum_{r=-\infty}^{\infty} (-1)^r I_{\nu+r}(x)I_r(y)\begin{matrix}\cos\\ \sin\end{matrix} r\theta, \tag{2.32}$$

and

$$K_\nu(R)\begin{matrix}\cos\\ \sin\end{matrix} \nu\psi = \sum_{r=-\infty}^{\infty} K_{\nu+r}(x)I_r(y)\begin{matrix}\cos\\ \sin\end{matrix} r\theta. \tag{2.33}$$

Another addition formula can be obtained by differentiating Neumann's formula (2.29) n times with respect to $\cos\theta$. Since $R^2 = x^2 + y^2 - 2xy\cos\theta$, we have $R\,\mathrm{d}R = -xy\,\mathrm{d}(\cos\theta)$ and use of formula (1.34) with $\nu = 0$ gives

$$\frac{\mathrm{d}^n}{\mathrm{d}(\cos\theta)^n}J_0(R) = (-xy)^n\left(\frac{\mathrm{d}}{R\,\mathrm{d}R}\right)^n J_0(R) = \left(\frac{xy}{R}\right)^n J_n(R).$$

* See G. N. Watson, *Theory of Bessel Functions* (Cambridge, 1944), §11.3.

Hence (2.29) yields

$$\frac{J_n(R)}{R^n} = \frac{2}{x^n y^n} \sum_{r=1}^{\infty} J_r(x) J_r(y) \frac{d^n}{d(\cos\theta)^n} (\cos r\theta)$$
$$= \frac{2}{x^n y^n} \sum_{s=0}^{\infty} J_{n+s}(x) J_{n+s}(y) \frac{d^n}{d(\cos\theta)^n} \{\cos(n+s)\theta\}, \tag{2.34}$$

when we write $r = n + s$ and note that, since $\cos r\theta$ is a polynomial of degree r in $\cos\theta$, the nth differential of $\cos r\theta$ with respect to $\cos\theta$ vanishes when $r < n$. It can be shown that

$$\frac{d^n}{d(\cos\theta)^n} \{\cos(n+s)\theta\} = 2^{n-1}(n+s)(n-1)!\,C_s^n(\cos\theta)$$

where $C_s^n(\cos\theta)$ is the coefficient of α^s in the expansion of $(1 - 2\alpha\cos\theta + \alpha^2)^{-n}$, and (2.34) can therefore be written

$$\frac{J_n(R)}{R^n} = \frac{2^n(n-1)!}{x^n y^n} \sum_{s=0}^{\infty} (n+s) J_{n+s}(x) J_{n+s}(y) C_s^n(\cos\theta). \tag{2.35}$$

This is known as L. Gegenbauer's addition theorem and $C_s^n(\cos\theta)$ as Gegenbauer's polynomial.

Formula (2.35) has again been derived only when the order of the Bessel function on the left is an integer and when x, y, θ are real. It is sometimes valid when these restrictions are removed and details of the derivation of the formula

$$\frac{J_\nu(R)}{R^\nu} = \frac{2^\nu\Gamma(\nu)}{x^\nu y^\nu} \sum_{s=0}^{\infty} (\nu+s) J_{\nu+s}(x) J_{\nu+s}(y) C_s^\nu(\cos\theta), \tag{2.36}$$

which is true for all values of ν except $0, -1, -2, \ldots$ and for all values of x, y, θ can be found in Watson's treatise (§11.4). The similar formula

$$\frac{J_{-\nu}(R)}{R^\nu} = \frac{2^\nu\Gamma(\nu)}{x^\nu y^\nu} \sum_{s=0}^{\infty} (-1)^s(\nu+s) J_{-\nu-s}(x) J_{\nu+s}(y) C_s^\nu(\cos\theta), \tag{2.37}$$

which is true only when $|ye^{\pm i\theta}| < |x|$ can also be established. By combining (2.36), (2.37) and using formula (1.12), it is easy to deduce that, for values of x, y, θ so restricted,

$$\frac{Y_\nu(R)}{R^\nu} = \frac{2^\nu\Gamma(\nu)}{x^\nu y^\nu} \sum_{s=0}^{\infty} (\nu+s) Y_{\nu+s}(x) J_{\nu+s}(y) C_s^\nu(\cos\theta). \tag{2.38}$$

Replacing R, x, y by iR, ix, iy and using (1.51), (1.59), the formulae

$$\frac{I_\nu(R)}{R^\nu} = \frac{2^\nu\Gamma(\nu)}{x^\nu y^\nu} \sum_{s=0}^{\infty} (-1)^s(\nu+s) I_{\nu+s}(x) I_{\nu+s}(y) C_s^\nu(\cos\theta), \tag{2.39}$$

$$\frac{K_\nu(R)}{R^\nu} = \frac{2^\nu\Gamma(\nu)}{x^\nu y^\nu} \sum_{s=0}^{\infty} (\nu+s) K_{\nu+s}(x) I_{\nu+s}(y) C_s^\nu(\cos\theta), \tag{2.40}$$

are easily obtained.

Certain special cases of these formulae are of interest and of use in physical problems. Thus since $J_{\frac{1}{2}}(R) = (2/\pi R)^{\frac{1}{2}} \sin R$ and since $C_s^{\frac{1}{2}}(\cos\theta)$, being the coefficient of α^s in the expansion of $(1 - 2\alpha\cos\theta + \alpha^2)^{-\frac{1}{2}}$, is the Legendre polynomial $P_s(\cos\theta)$, equation (2.36) gives with $\nu = \frac{1}{2}$

$$\frac{\sin R}{R} = \frac{\pi}{2\sqrt{(xy)}} \sum_{s=0}^{\infty} (2s + 1) J_{s+\frac{1}{2}}(x) J_{s+\frac{1}{2}}(y) P_s(\cos\theta). \tag{2.41}$$

Since, from (1.20), $Y_{\frac{1}{2}}(R) = -J_{-\frac{1}{2}}(R) = -(2/\pi R)^{\frac{1}{2}}\cos R$, equation (2.38) with $\nu = \frac{1}{2}$ similarly gives

$$\frac{\cos R}{R} = \frac{-\pi}{2\sqrt{(xy)}} \sum_{s=0}^{\infty} (2s + 1) Y_{s+\frac{1}{2}}(x) J_{s+\frac{1}{2}}(y) P_s(\cos\theta). \tag{2.42}$$

Multiplication of (2.41) by i and addition to (2.42) then gives

$$\frac{e^{iR}}{R} = \frac{\pi i}{2\sqrt{(xy)}} \sum_{s=0}^{\infty} (2s + 1) H_{s+\frac{1}{2}}^{(1)}(x) J_{s+\frac{1}{2}}(y) P_s(\cos\theta). \tag{2.43}$$

Example 4. *Use Gegenbauer's addition theorem to obtain the expansion*

$$x^{2\nu} = \frac{2^{2\nu}\Gamma(\nu)\Gamma(\nu + 1)}{\Gamma(2\nu)} \sum_{s=0}^{\infty} (\nu + s) \frac{\Gamma(2\nu + s)}{s!} J_{\nu+s}{}^2(x). \tag{2.44}$$

Writing $y = x$, $\theta = 0$ in formula (2.36), we have $R = 0$ and the left-hand side becomes

$$\lim_{R\to 0} \left\{\frac{J_\nu(R)}{R^\nu}\right\} = \frac{1}{2^\nu\Gamma(\nu + 1)},$$

by (1.5). The Gegenbauer polynomial on the right of (2.36) is now $C_s^\nu(1)$ and this is the coefficient of α^s in the expansion of $(1 - \alpha)^{-2\nu}$, that is

$$\frac{\Gamma(2\nu + s)}{s!\Gamma(2\nu)}.$$

Hence with these values of y and θ, formula (2.36) gives

$$\frac{1}{2^\nu\Gamma(\nu + 1)} = \frac{2^\nu\Gamma(\nu)}{x^{2\nu}} \sum_{s=0}^{\infty} (\nu + s) J_{\nu+s}{}^2(x) \frac{\Gamma(2\nu + s)}{s!\Gamma(2\nu)}$$

and the required result (2.44) follows after a trivial rearrangement.

Exercises 2

1. Show that

$$\int z^{\nu+1} I_\nu(z)\, dz = z^{\nu+1} I_{\nu+1}(z),$$

$$\int z^{-\nu+1} I_\nu(z)\, dz = z^{-\nu+1} I_{\nu-1}(z).$$

2. Establish the results

$$\int z^{\nu+1}K_\nu(z)\,dz = -z^{\nu+1}K_{\nu+1}(z),$$

$$\int z^{-\nu+1}K_\nu(z)\,dz = -z^{-\nu+1}K_{\nu-1}(z).$$

3. Show that

$$(4\nu + 2)\int z^{2\nu+1}J_\nu^2(z)\,dz = z^{2\nu+2}\{J_\nu^2(z) + J_{\nu+1}^2(z)\}.$$

4. Prove that

$$\int \frac{dz}{zJ_\nu(z)J_{-\nu}(z)} = -\frac{\pi}{2\sin\nu\pi}\log_e\left\{\frac{J_{-\nu}(z)}{J_\nu(z)}\right\}.$$

5. Show that, if $R(\nu) > -1$,

$$(\lambda^2 - \mu^2)\int zI_\nu(\lambda z)I_\nu(\mu z)\,dz = -z\{\mu I_\nu(\lambda z)I_\nu'(\mu z) - \lambda I_\nu(\mu z)I_\nu'(\lambda z)\}$$

and deduce that

$$\int zI_\nu^2(\lambda z)\,dz = -\frac{z^2}{2}\left[\{I_\nu'(\lambda z)\}^2 - \left(1 + \frac{\nu^2}{\lambda^2 z^2}\right)I_\nu^2(\lambda z)\right].$$

6. Establish Rayleigh's result

$$2\int_0^x J_1^2(z)\frac{dz}{z} = 1 - J_0^2(x) - J_1^2(x).$$

7. Show that

$$(\tfrac{1}{2}z)^\mu = \sum_{r=0}^{\infty}\frac{(-1)^r(\mu + 2r)\Gamma(\mu + r)}{r!}\,I_{\mu+2r}(z).$$

8. Establish the formulae:

(i) $\frac{1}{2}z^2 = 2^2J_2(z) + 4^2J_4(z) + 6^2J_6(z) + \ldots,$

(ii) $\frac{1}{2}z^3 = 2\,.\,3\,.\,4\,J_3(z) + 4\,.\,5\,.\,6\,J_5(z) + 6\,.\,7\,.\,8\,J_7(z) + \ldots.$

9. If $|h| < |z|$, prove that

$$(z + h)^{\frac{1}{2}\nu}J_\nu\{\sqrt{(z + h)}\} = \sum_{r=0}^{\infty}\frac{(\frac{1}{2}h)^r}{r!}\,z^{\frac{1}{2}(\nu-r)}J_{\nu-r}(\sqrt{z})$$

and deduce that, when $|t| < \frac{1}{2}|x|$,

$$\left(\frac{2}{\pi x}\right)^{\frac{1}{2}}\sin\sqrt{(x^2 + 2xt)} = \sum_{r=0}^{\infty}\frac{t^r}{r!}J_{\frac{1}{2}-r}(x).$$

10. Deduce from the addition formula (2.23) that

$$J_n(2z) = \sum_{r=0}^{n}J_r(z)J_{n-r}(z) + 2\sum_{r=1}^{\infty}(-1)^rJ_r(z)J_{n+r}(z).$$

11. Show that

$$J_0(z \sin \alpha) = J_0^2(\tfrac{1}{2}z) + 2\sum_{r=1}^{\infty} J_r^2(\tfrac{1}{2}z) \cos 2r\alpha.$$

12. If n is an integer (or zero), x and y are real and if $\tan \psi = y/x$, show that

$$J_n\{\sqrt{(x^2 + y^2)}\} \cos n\psi = \sum_{r=-\infty}^{\infty} (-1)^r J_{n+2r}(x) J_{2r}(y),$$

$$J_n\{\sqrt{(x^2 + y^2)}\} \sin n\psi = \sum_{r=-\infty}^{\infty} (-1)^r J_{n+2r+1}(x) J_{2r+1}(y).$$

13. Deduce from Gegenbauer's addition formula that

(i) $$\frac{J_\nu(x+y)}{(x+y)^\nu} = \frac{2^\nu \Gamma(\nu)}{x^\nu y^\nu \Gamma(2\nu)} \sum_{s=0}^{\infty} (-1)^s \frac{(\nu+s)\Gamma(2\nu+s)}{s!} J_{\nu+s}(x) J_{\nu+s}(y),$$

(ii) $$\frac{J_\nu\{\sqrt{(x^2+y^2)}\}}{(x^2+y^2)^{\frac{1}{2}\nu}} = \frac{2^\nu}{x^\nu y^\nu} \sum_{s=0}^{\infty} (-1)^s \frac{(\nu+2s)\Gamma(\nu+s)}{s!} J_{\nu+2s}(x) J_{\nu+2s}(y).$$

14. Show that when $r = 0, 1, 2, 3, \ldots$

$$\pi J_r(x) J_r(y) = \int_0^\pi J_0\{\sqrt{(x^2 + y^2 - 2xy \cos \theta)}\} \cos r\theta \, d\theta.$$

15. Show that $J_0(re^{i\theta}) = \xi + i\eta$ where

$$\xi = J_0(r) + r \sin \theta \sin \theta \, J_1(r) - \frac{r^2 \sin^2 \theta \cos 2\theta}{2!} J_2(r) - \frac{r^3 \sin^3 \theta \sin 3\theta}{3!} J_3(r) + \ldots,$$

$$\eta = -r \sin \theta \cos \theta \, J_1(r) - \frac{r^2 \sin^2 \theta \sin 2\theta}{2!} J_2(r) + \frac{r^3 \sin^3 \theta \cos 3\theta}{3!} J_3(r) + \ldots.$$

and deduce that

$$I_0(r) = J_0(r) + rJ_1(r) + \frac{r^2}{2!} J_2(r) + \frac{r^3}{3!} J_3(r) + \ldots.$$

16. Given that $(\tfrac{1}{2}\pi x)^{\frac{1}{2}} i^{s+1} e^{-ix} H_{s+\frac{1}{2}}^{(1)}(x)$ tends to unity as x tends to infinity, deduce from equation (2.43) that

$$\exp(iy \cos \theta) = \left(\frac{\pi}{2y}\right)^{\frac{1}{2}} \sum_{s=0}^{\infty} i^s (2s+1) J_{s+\frac{1}{2}}(y) P_s(\cos \theta)$$

17. Use Graf's addition formula (2.27) to show that, n being an integer or zero,

$$t^n J_n\{x(t+t^{-1})\} = \sum_{r=-\infty}^{\infty} t^{2r} J_{n-r}(x) J_r(x).$$

Deduce that

$$t^n I_n\{x(t^{-1}-t)\} = \sum_{r=-\infty}^{\infty} (-1)^r t^{2r} J_{n-r}(x) J_r(x).$$

18. Use Exercise 14 above to show that, when $r = 0, 1, 2, 3, \ldots$,

$$J_r^2(x) = \frac{1}{\pi}\int_0^{\pi} J_0(2x \sin\phi)\cos 2r\phi \, d\phi.$$

Deduce that

$$J_0^2(x) = \sum_{s=0}^{\infty} \frac{(-1)^s (2s)!}{(s!)^4} (\tfrac{1}{2}x)^{2s}.$$

CHAPTER 3

INTEGRAL REPRESENTATIONS AND ASYMPTOTIC EXPANSIONS

3.1 Introduction

Bessel functions can be usefully represented by a wide variety of integrals. Although their representation by contour integrals often gives greater generality and validity over wider regions of the argument z and order ν, integrals with respect to a real variable are usually of greater use in applications to physical problems and the first part of this chapter is mainly concerned with the derivation of such definite integrals.

Series which approximate to the value of Bessel functions for *large* values of their arguments are also important in physical applications. The rigorous analysis required to derive such (asymptotic) series is rather outside the scope of this work and a formal approach is used to obtain the results given in the later parts of the chapter. Conditions under which these results are valid are, however, given, as also are references to more detailed discussions.

3.2 Bessel's integral for $J_n(z)$

When n is zero or a positive integer, the Bessel function $J_n(z)$ can be represented by a certain definite integral, usually referred to as *Bessel's integral.* This can be deduced from equations (1.37), viz.

$$\cos (z \sin \theta) = J_0(z) + 2\sum_{n=1}^{\infty} J_{2n}(z) \cos 2n\theta,$$

$$\sin (z \sin \theta) = 2\sum_{n=0}^{\infty} J_{2n+1}(z) \sin (2n+1)\theta,$$

by multiplying respectively by $\cos 2n\theta$, $\sin (2n+1)\theta$ and integrating with respect to θ between 0 and π. Thus since, when m and n are integers or zero,

$$\int_0^{\pi} \cos 2n\theta \cos 2m\theta \, d\theta = \begin{cases} 0 & (m \neq n), \\ \frac{1}{2}\pi & (m = n \neq 0), \\ \pi & (m = n = 0), \end{cases}$$

and

$$\int_0^{\pi} \sin (2n+1)\theta \sin (2m+1)\theta \, d\theta = \begin{cases} 0 & (m \neq n), \\ \frac{1}{2}\pi & (m = n), \end{cases}$$

we find

$$J_{2n}(z) = \frac{1}{\pi}\int_0^{\pi} \cos (z \sin \theta) \cos 2n\theta \, d\theta, \tag{3.1}$$

$$J_{2n+1}(z) = \frac{1}{\pi}\int_0^{\pi} \sin (z \sin \theta) \sin (2n+1)\theta \, d\theta. \tag{3.2}$$

Because of the periodic properties of the trigonometrical functions involved,

$$\int_0^\pi \cos(z\sin\theta)\cos(2n+1)\theta\,d\theta = 0 = \int_0^\pi \sin(z\sin\theta)\sin 2n\theta\,d\theta,$$

so that for all integral values of n (including zero) we can write

$$J_n(z) = \frac{1}{\pi}\int_0^\pi \{\cos(z\sin\theta)\cos n\theta + \sin(z\sin\theta)\sin n\theta\}\,d\theta$$

$$= \frac{1}{\pi}\int_0^\pi \cos(n\theta - z\sin\theta)\,d\theta \tag{3.3}$$

and this is Bessel's integral for $J_n(z)$.

It is worth noticing that formulae (3.1), (3.2) can be written in the form

$$\tfrac{1}{2}\pi J_n(z) = \begin{cases} \displaystyle\int_0^{\frac{1}{2}\pi} \cos(z\sin\theta)\cos n\theta\,d\theta & (n \text{ even}), \\ \displaystyle\int_0^{\frac{1}{2}\pi} \sin(z\sin\theta)\sin n\theta\,d\theta & (n \text{ odd}). \end{cases}$$

Replacement of θ by $\frac{1}{2}\pi - \theta$ then leads to

$$\tfrac{1}{2}\pi J_n(z) = \begin{cases} (-1)^{\frac{1}{2}n}\displaystyle\int_0^{\frac{1}{2}\pi} \cos(z\cos\theta)\cos n\theta\,d\theta & (n \text{ even}), \\ (-1)^{\frac{1}{2}(n-1)}\displaystyle\int_0^{\frac{1}{2}\pi} \sin(z\cos\theta)\cos n\theta\,d\theta & (n \text{ odd}). \end{cases}$$

3.3 Poisson's integral for $J_\nu(z)$

From the manner of its derivation, Bessel's integral (3.3) represents $J_\nu(z)$ only when ν is a positive integer or zero. An integral representation of $J_\nu(z)$ valid when the real* part of ν is greater than $-\frac{1}{2}$ but when ν is otherwise unrestricted is due to Poisson and can be obtained from the series (1.5) for the Bessel function.

Since $\Gamma(r+\frac{1}{2})r! = \pi^{\frac{1}{2}}2^{-2r}(2r)!$, we have with a little manipulation,

$$J_\nu(z) = \sum_{r=0}^{\infty} \frac{(-1)^r(z/2)^{\nu+2r}}{r!\,\Gamma(\nu+r+1)}$$

$$= \sum_{r=0}^{\infty} \frac{(-1)^r(z/2)^\nu}{\pi^{\frac{1}{2}}\Gamma(\nu+\frac{1}{2})}\cdot\frac{z^{2r}}{(2r)!}\cdot\frac{\Gamma(\nu+\frac{1}{2})\Gamma(r+\frac{1}{2})}{\Gamma(\nu+r+1)}.$$

Using the well-known property of the gamma function that, provided $R(\nu) > -\frac{1}{2}$ and $R(r) > -\frac{1}{2}$,

$$\frac{\Gamma(\nu+\frac{1}{2})\Gamma(r+\frac{1}{2})}{\Gamma(\nu+r+1)} = \int_0^1 t^{\nu-\frac{1}{2}}(1-t)^{r-\frac{1}{2}}\,dt$$

it follows that $J_\nu(z)$ can be written in the form

$$J_\nu(z) = \frac{(z/2)^\nu}{\pi^{\frac{1}{2}}(\nu+\frac{1}{2})}\sum_{r=0}^{\infty}\frac{(-1)^r z^{2r}}{(2r)!}\int_0^1 t^{\nu-\frac{1}{2}}(1-t)^{r-\frac{1}{2}}\,dt, \quad R(\nu) > -\tfrac{1}{2}.$$

* From now onwards, the symbols $R(\ )$ will, for brevity, be used to denote "the real part of."

Although the details are rather intricate (the reader is referred to §3.3 of Watson's treatise for a full discussion), it is possible to show that the order of integration and summation in this result may be interchanged so that

$$J_\nu(z) = \frac{(z/2)^\nu}{\pi^{\frac{1}{2}}\Gamma(\nu+\frac{1}{2})}\int_0^1 t^{\nu-\frac{1}{2}}\left\{\sum_{r=0}^{\infty}\frac{(-1)^r z^{2r}(1-t)^{r-\frac{1}{2}}}{(2r)!}\right\}dt$$

$$= \frac{(z/2)^\nu}{\pi^{\frac{1}{2}}\Gamma(\nu+\frac{1}{2})}\int_0^{\pi/2} \sin^{2\nu-1}\theta\left\{\sum_{r=0}^{\infty}\frac{(-1)^r z^{2r}\cos^{2r-1}\theta}{(2r)!}\right\}2\sin\theta\cos\theta\,d\theta$$

when we write $t = \sin^2\theta$. On summing the series this gives *Poisson's integral*

$$J_\nu(z) = \frac{2(z/2)^\nu}{\pi^{\frac{1}{2}}\Gamma(\nu+\frac{1}{2})}\int_0^{\pi/2}\cos(z\cos\theta)\sin^{2\nu}\theta\,d\theta$$

$$= \frac{(z/2)^\nu}{\pi^{\frac{1}{2}}\Gamma(\nu+\frac{1}{2})}\int_0^{\pi}\cos(z\cos\theta)\sin^{2\nu}\theta\,d\theta, \quad R(\nu) > -\tfrac{1}{2}. \tag{3.4}$$

Various transformations of this integral can be made. Thus, since

$$\int_0^\pi \sin(z\cos\theta)\sin^{2\nu}\theta\,d\theta = 0,$$

equation (3.4) can be written in the form

$$J_\nu(z) = \frac{(z/2)^\nu}{\pi^{\frac{1}{2}}\Gamma(\nu+\frac{1}{2})}\int_0^{\pi}\exp(iz\cos\theta)\sin^{2\nu}\theta\,d\theta. \tag{3.5}$$

Again, by writing $\cos\theta = t$ in (3.5) we have

$$J_\nu(z) = \frac{(z/2)^\nu}{\pi^{\frac{1}{2}}\Gamma(\nu+\frac{1}{2})}\int_{-1}^{1}(1-t^2)^{\nu-\frac{1}{2}}\exp(izt)\,dt, \tag{3.6}$$

and the particular case, obtained by writing $\nu = 0$,

$$J_0(z) = \frac{1}{\pi}\int_{-1}^{1}\frac{\cos(zt)\,dt}{\sqrt{(1-t^2)}} = \frac{2}{\pi}\int_0^1\frac{\cos(zt)\,dt}{\sqrt{(1-t^2)}} \tag{3.7}$$

is worth noting. Still further transformations of (3.4) will be found in Exercises 3, Nos. 2, 3, and, using the relation between $I_\nu(z)$ and $J_\nu(iz)$ given in §1.14, the following results are easily obtained:

$$\left.\begin{aligned}\pi^{\frac{1}{2}}\Gamma(\nu+\tfrac{1}{2})(z/2)^{-\nu}I_\nu(z) &= \int_0^\pi \cosh(z\cos\theta)\sin^{2\nu}\theta\,d\theta\\ &= \int_0^\pi \exp(-z\cos\theta)\sin^{2\nu}\theta\,d\theta\\ &= \int_{-1}^{1}(1-t^2)^{\nu-\frac{1}{2}}\exp(-zt)\,dt,\end{aligned}\right\} \tag{3.8}$$

the restriction $R(\nu) > -\frac{1}{2}$ being necessary in all cases.

Example 1. *If $u > 0$, show that*

$$\int_0^\infty \exp(-z \sinh u) J_0(z)\, dz = \operatorname{sech} u.$$

From (3.5) with $\nu = 0$,

$$J_0(z) = \frac{1}{\pi}\int_0^\pi \exp(iz\cos\theta)\, d\theta$$

so that, interchanging the order of integrations, we have

$$\begin{aligned}\int_0^\infty \exp(-z\sinh u) J_0(z)\, dz &= \frac{1}{\pi}\int_0^\pi d\theta \int_0^\infty \exp\{(-\sinh u + i\cos\theta)z\}\, dz \\ &= \frac{1}{\pi}\int_0^\pi \frac{d\theta}{\sinh u - i\cos\theta} = \frac{1}{\pi}\cdot\frac{\pi}{(\sinh^2 u + 1)^{\frac{1}{2}}} \\ &= \operatorname{sech} u.\end{aligned}$$

3.4 Generalization of Bessel's integral

Bessel's integral (3.3) is valid only when the order ν of the Bessel function is a positive integer or zero and Poisson's integral (3.4) only when the real part of ν is greater than $-\frac{1}{2}$. We now obtain an integral representing $J_\nu(z)$ free from all restrictions on ν.

We start with the expansion

$$\exp(-z^2/4t) = \sum_{r=0}^\infty (-1)^r \frac{(z/2)^{2r} t^{-r}}{r!}$$

and we use Hankel's contour integral for the gamma function

$$\frac{1}{\Gamma(\nu + r + 1)} = \frac{1}{2\pi i}\int_{-\infty}^{(0+)} e^t t^{-\nu-r-1}\, dt \tag{3.9}$$

where the initial and final values of $\arg t$ in the integral are $-\pi$, π and the contour encircles the origin O in a counter-clockwise direction (Fig. 6). Hence we have formally

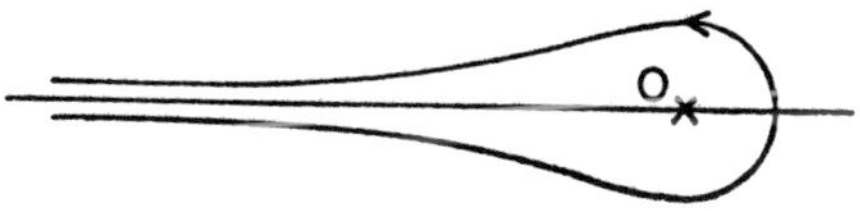

FIG. 6. t-plane

$$\begin{aligned}\frac{(z/2)^\nu}{2\pi i}\int_{-\infty}^{(0+)} \exp\left(t - \frac{z^2}{4t}\right) t^{-\nu-1}\, dt &= \frac{(z/2)^\nu}{2\pi i}\int_{-\infty}^{(0+)} e^t t^{-\nu-1} \sum_{r=0}^\infty \frac{(-1)^r (z/2)^{2r} t^{-r}}{r!}\, dt \\ &= \frac{1}{2\pi i}\sum_{r=0}^\infty \frac{(-1)^r (z/2)^{\nu+2r}}{r!}\int_{-\infty}^{(0+)} e^t t^{-\nu-r-1}\, dt \\ &= \sum_{r=0}^\infty \frac{(-1)^r (z/2)^{\nu+2r}}{r!\,\Gamma(\nu + r + 1)} = J_\nu(z).\end{aligned} \tag{3.10}$$

When $R(\nu) > -1$ the contour in the integral in this result may be deformed into a straight line to the right of and parallel to the imaginary axis. Hence

$$J_\nu(z) = \frac{(z/2)^\nu}{2\pi i}\int_{c-i\infty}^{c+i\infty} \exp\left(t - \frac{z^2}{4t}\right) t^{-\nu-1}\, dt \tag{3.11}$$

where $R(\nu) > -1$ and $c > 0$.

Changing the variable in the integral in (3.10) to w where $w = \log_e(2t/z)$, we find

$$J_\nu(z) = \frac{1}{2\pi i}\int_{\infty-\pi i}^{\infty+\pi i} \exp(z \sinh w - \nu w)\, dw \tag{3.12}$$

is valid when $|\arg z| < \frac{1}{2}\pi$, the contour being three sides of a rectangle with vertices at the points $\infty - \pi i$, $-\pi i$, πi and $\infty + \pi i$ (Fig. 7). If now we write

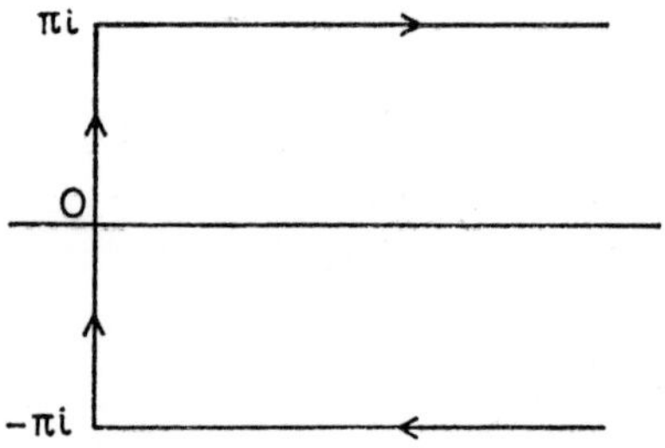

FIG. 7. w-plane

$\tau \mp i\pi$ for w on the sides parallel to the real axis and $\pm i\theta$ for w on the lines joining the origin O to the points $\pm\pi i$, we obtain

$$J_\nu(z) = \frac{1}{\pi}\int_0^\pi \cos(\nu\theta - z\sin\theta)\, d\theta - \frac{\sin\nu\pi}{\pi}\int_0^\infty \exp(-\nu\tau - z\sinh\tau)\, d\tau. \tag{3.13}$$

This formula is a generalization of Bessel's integral (3.3) to which it reduces when ν is a positive integer. It is valid when $|\arg z| < \frac{1}{2}\pi$ and it is due to L. Schläfli.

An integral representation of $Y_\nu(z)$ can now be found by using (3.13) in the formula (1.12) defining it. This is

$$\sin\nu\pi\; Y_\nu(z) = J_\nu(z)\cos\nu\pi - J_{-\nu}(z),$$

so that

$$\pi\sin\nu\pi\, Y_\nu(z) = \cos\nu\pi\int_0^\pi \cos(\nu\theta - z\sin\theta)\, d\theta - \int_0^\pi \cos(\nu\theta + z\sin\theta)\, d\theta$$

$$- \cos\nu\pi\sin\nu\pi\int_0^\infty \exp(-\nu\tau - z\sinh\tau)\, d\tau - \sin\nu\pi\int_0^\infty \exp(\nu\tau - z\sinh\tau)\, d\tau.$$

Replacing θ by $\pi - \theta$ in the second integral and making a few reductions, this gives

$$Y_\nu(z) = \frac{1}{\pi}\int_0^\pi \sin(z\sin\theta - \nu\theta)\,d\theta - \frac{1}{\pi}\int_0^\infty (e^{\nu\tau} + e^{-\nu\tau}\cos\nu\pi)\exp(-z\sinh\tau)\,d\tau, \tag{3.14}$$

a result again valid for $|\arg z| < \frac{1}{2}\pi$.

3.5 An integral representation of $K_\nu(z)$

From (1.53)

$$\frac{2}{\pi}K_\nu(z) = \frac{I_{-\nu}(z) - I_\nu(z)}{\sin\nu\pi} \tag{3.15}$$

and $I_\nu(z)$ is given as a definite integral by equation (3.8). Hence an integral representation of $K_\nu(z)$ can be found by finding one of $I_{-\nu}(z)$. To do this we start by modifying Hankel's contour integral for the gamma function [equation (3.9)] by replacing t by $zte^{-i\pi}$, $-\nu$ by 2ν and r by $2r$. If we take r to be an integer this gives, when $|\arg z| < \frac{1}{2}\pi$

$$\int_\infty^{(0+)} e^{-zt}t^{2\nu-2r-1}\,dt = \frac{2\pi i e^{2\nu\pi i}z^{2r-2\nu}}{\Gamma(-2\nu+2r+1)} \tag{3.16}$$

where the initial and final values of arg t in the integral are 0, 2π and the contour encircles the origin O in a counter-clockwise direction (Fig. 8). If this

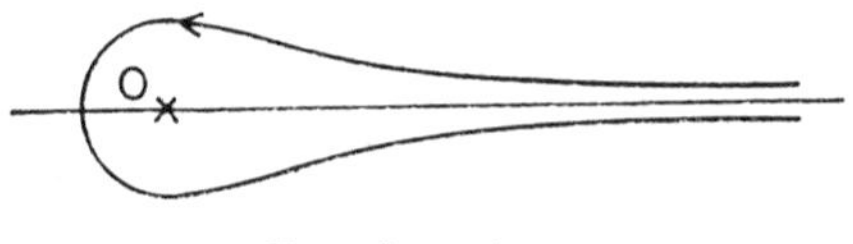

FIG. 8. t-plane

contour lies outside the circle $|t| = 1$, $(t^2-1)^{\nu-\frac{1}{2}}$ can be expanded in a series of descending powers of t, uniformly convergent on the contour, and we have

$$\Gamma(\tfrac{1}{2}-\nu)(t^2-1)^{\nu-\frac{1}{2}} = \sum_{r=0}^\infty \frac{\Gamma(\frac{1}{2}-\nu+r)}{r!}t^{2\nu-2r-1}$$

so that, using (3.16) and formally integrating term by term

$$\Gamma(\tfrac{1}{2}-\nu)\int_\infty^{(0+)}(t^2-1)^{\nu-\frac{1}{2}}e^{-zt}\,dt = 2\pi i e^{2\nu\pi i}\sum_{r=0}^\infty \frac{\Gamma(\frac{1}{2}-\nu+r)z^{2r-2\nu}}{r!\,\Gamma(-2\nu+2r+1)}.$$

Since $\Gamma(-2\nu+2r+1) = 2^{-2\nu+2r}\pi^{-\frac{1}{2}}\Gamma(-\nu+r+\frac{1}{2})\Gamma(-\nu+r+1)$, this can be written

$$\Gamma(\tfrac{1}{2}-\nu)\int_\infty^{(0+)}(t^2-1)^{\nu-\frac{1}{2}}e^{-zt}\,dt = 2\pi^{\frac{3}{2}}ie^{2\nu\pi i}\sum_{r=0}^\infty \frac{(z/2)^{2r-2\nu}}{r!\,\Gamma(-\nu+r+1)}$$
$$= 2\pi^{\frac{3}{2}}ie^{2\nu\pi i}(z/2)^{-\nu}I_{-\nu}(z) \tag{3.17}$$

when use is made of equation (1.51).

If we take $R(\nu + \frac{1}{2}) > 0$ to secure convergence, the contour of the integral in (3.17) can be deformed into that shown in Fig. 9 and the radii of the two circles

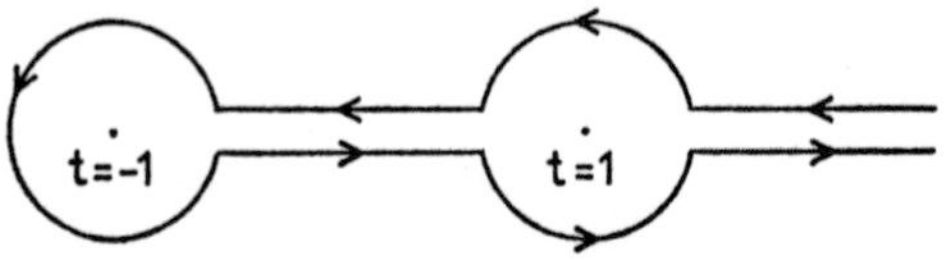

FIG. 9. t-plane

can be made to tend to zero. As the point describes the small semi-circle above $t = 1$, $\arg(t - 1)$ increases by π and we replace $(t^2 - 1)^{\nu-\frac{1}{2}}$ by $(1 - t^2)^{\nu-\frac{1}{2}} \times e^{(\nu-\frac{1}{2})\pi i}$; as the point describes the small circle about $t = -1$, $\arg(t + 1)$ increases by 2π so that $(t^2 - 1)^{\nu-\frac{1}{2}}$ is to be replaced by $(1 - t^2)^{\nu-\frac{1}{2}}e^{(\nu-\frac{1}{2})3\pi i}$; finally when the point describes the semi-circle below $t = 1$, the value of $(t^2 - 1)^{\nu-\frac{1}{2}}$ is to be replaced by $(t^2 - 1)^{\nu-\frac{1}{2}}e^{(\nu-\frac{1}{2})4\pi i}$. Hence (3.17) can be written,

$$I_{-\nu}(z) = \frac{\Gamma(\frac{1}{2} - \nu)e^{-2\nu\pi i}(z/2)^\nu}{2\pi^{\frac{3}{2}}i}\left\{\int_\infty^1 (t^2 - 1)^{\nu-\frac{1}{2}}e^{-zt}\,dt - ie^{\nu\pi i}\int_1^{-1}(1 - t^2)^{\nu-\frac{1}{2}}e^{-zt}\,dt\right.$$
$$\left. + ie^{3\nu\pi i}\int_{-1}^1 (1 - t^2)^{\nu-\frac{1}{2}}e^{-zt}\,dt + e^{4\nu\pi i}\int_1^\infty (t^2 - 1)^{\nu-\frac{1}{2}}e^{-zt}\,dt\right\}$$
$$= \frac{\Gamma(\frac{1}{2} - \nu)(z/2)^\nu}{\pi^{\frac{3}{2}}}\left\{\sin 2\nu\pi\int_1^\infty (t^2 - 1)^{\nu-\frac{1}{2}}e^{-zt}\,dt\right.$$
$$\left. + \cos\nu\pi\int_{-1}^1 (1 - t^2)^{\nu-\frac{1}{2}}e^{-zt}\,dt\right\}. \qquad (3.18)$$

Using equation (3.8) and the well-known property $\Gamma(\frac{1}{2} - \nu)\Gamma(\frac{1}{2} + \nu) = \pi \sec \nu\pi$ of the gamma function, this gives

$$I_{-\nu}(z) = \frac{2(z/2)^\nu}{\pi^{\frac{1}{2}}\Gamma(\frac{1}{2} + \nu)}\sin\nu\pi\int_1^\infty (t^2 - 1)^{\nu-\frac{1}{2}}e^{-zt}\,dt + I_\nu(z)$$

and the formula

$$\Gamma(\tfrac{1}{2} + \nu)K_\nu(z) = \pi^{\frac{1}{2}}(z/2)^\nu\int_1^\infty (t^2 - 1)^{\nu-\frac{1}{2}}e^{-zt}\,dt, \qquad (3.19)$$

which is valid when $R(\nu) > -\frac{1}{2}$ and $|\arg z| < \frac{1}{2}\pi$, then follows immediately from equation (3.15).

By writing $t = \cosh\theta$, equation (3.19) is easily transformed into the alternative form

$$\Gamma(\tfrac{1}{2} + \nu)K_\nu(z) = \pi^{\frac{1}{2}}(z/2)^\nu\int_0^\infty \exp(-z\cosh\theta)\sinh^{2\nu}\theta\,d\theta. \qquad (3.20)$$

Yet another transformation of the integral in (3.19) is obtained by setting $t = 1 + (\xi/z)$. This gives

$$\Gamma(\tfrac{1}{2} + \nu)K_\nu(z) = \sqrt{\left(\frac{\pi}{2z}\right)}\,e^{-z}\int_0^\infty e^{-\xi}\xi^{\nu-\frac{1}{2}}\left(1 + \frac{\xi}{2z}\right)^{\nu-\frac{1}{2}}d\xi \qquad (3.21)$$

and this formula is used in the next section.

Example 2. *If x is real and positive, deduce from equation* (3.19) *that*

$$J_0(x) = \frac{2}{\pi}\int_1^\infty \frac{\sin(xt)}{\sqrt{(t^2-1)}}\,\mathrm{d}t. \tag{3.22}$$

Equation (1.59) gives $H_0^{(1)}(iz) = (2/\pi i)K_0(z)$, so that writing $z = -xi$ and using (3.19) with $\nu = 0$ (for which value of ν the restriction on z is not necessary),

$$H_0^{(1)}(x) = \frac{2}{\pi i}K_0(-ix) = \frac{2}{\pi i}\int_1^\infty \frac{e^{ixt}}{\sqrt{(t^2-1)}}\,\mathrm{d}t.$$

The result (3.22) then follows by equating the real parts.

3.6 The asymptotic expansion of $K_\nu(z)$

In many physical problems it is useful to know the values of Bessel functions for *large* values of their arguments and we give below a purely formal expansion of $K_\nu(z)$ in powers of $1/z$ when $|z| \gg |\nu|$ and $|z| \gg 1$. We start with the integral representation (3.21) and assume that it is permissible to expand $(1 + \xi/2z)^{\nu-\frac{1}{2}}$ by the binomial theorem and to interchange the order of integration and summation. Hence

$$\Gamma(\tfrac{1}{2}+\nu)K_\nu(z) = \sqrt{\left(\frac{\pi}{2z}\right)}\,e^{-z}\sum_{s=0}^{\infty}\frac{\Gamma(\nu+\frac{1}{2})}{s!\,\Gamma(\nu+\frac{1}{2}-s)}\cdot\frac{1}{(2z)^s}\int_0^\infty e^{-\xi}\xi^{s+\nu-\frac{1}{2}}\,\mathrm{d}\xi$$

and, since (by the definition of the gamma function) the integral on the right-hand side is equal to $\Gamma(\nu + \frac{1}{2} + s)$, this leads to

$$K_\nu(z) = \sqrt{\left(\frac{\pi}{2z}\right)}\,e^{-z}\sum_{s=0}^{\infty}\frac{\Gamma(\nu+\frac{1}{2}+s)}{s!\,\Gamma(\nu+\frac{1}{2}-s)}\cdot\frac{1}{(2z)^s}. \tag{3.23}$$

The infinite series in (3.23) is divergent but, if it is written in the form

$$\sum_{s=0}^{m-1}\frac{\Gamma(\nu+\frac{1}{2}+s)}{s!\,\Gamma(\nu+\frac{1}{2}-s)}\cdot\frac{1}{(2z)^s} + R_m,$$

it can be shown that R_m can be made arbitrarily small by making $|z|$ sufficiently large. Series of this kind are called *asymptotic* expansions and we write

$$K_\nu(z) \sim \sqrt{\left(\frac{\pi}{2z}\right)}\,e^{-z}\sum_{s=0}^{\infty}\frac{(\nu, s)}{(2z)^s} \tag{3.24}$$

where (ν, s) is Hankel's symbol defined by $(\nu, 0) = 1$ and

$$(\nu, s) = \frac{\Gamma(\nu+\frac{1}{2}+s)}{s!\,\Gamma(\nu+\frac{1}{2}-s)} = \frac{2^{-2s}}{s!}\,[(4\nu^2-1^2)(4\nu^2-3^2)\ldots\{4\nu^2-(2s-1)^2\}] \tag{3.25}$$

when $s = 1, 2, 3, \ldots$. The expansion (3.24) can be shown to be valid for all values of ν when $|\arg z| < \frac{3}{2}\pi$ but for a rigorous derivation the reader must refer to a more comprehensive work such as Watson's treatise (Chapter 7).

3.7 Asymptotic expansions of the other Bessel functions

Similar asymptotic expansions for the other Bessel functions can be deduced from that of $K_\nu(z)$ by using equation (1.59). Replacing z by $ze^{-\frac{1}{2}\pi i}$, this equation gives

$$H_\nu^{(1)}(z) = -\frac{2i}{\pi}\, e^{-\frac{1}{2}\nu\pi i} K_\nu(ze^{-\frac{1}{2}\pi i})$$

and use of (3.24) then leads to

$$H_\nu^{(1)}(z) \sim \sqrt{\left(\frac{2}{\pi z}\right)}\, e^{i(z-\frac{1}{2}\nu\pi-\frac{1}{4}\pi)} \sum_{s=0}^{\infty} \frac{(\nu, s)}{(-2iz)^s} \quad (-\pi < \arg z < 2\pi). \tag{3.26}$$

Similarly,

$$H_\nu^{(2)}(z) \sim \sqrt{\left(\frac{2}{\pi z}\right)}\, e^{-i(z-\frac{1}{2}\nu\pi-\frac{1}{4}\pi)} \sum_{s=0}^{\infty} \frac{(\nu, s)}{(2iz)^s} \quad (-2\pi < \arg z < \pi), \tag{3.27}$$

and, by using the relations $H_\nu^{(1)}(z) = J_\nu(z) + i\,Y_\nu(z)$, $H_\nu^{(2)}(z) = J_\nu(z) - i\,Y_\nu(z)$, it then follows that the expansions

$$J_\nu(z) \sim \sqrt{\left(\frac{2}{\pi z}\right)}\left[\cos\left(z - \tfrac{1}{2}\nu\pi - \tfrac{1}{4}\pi\right) \sum_{s=0}^{\infty} \frac{(-1)^s(\nu, 2s)}{(2z)^{2s}} - \sin\left(z - \tfrac{1}{2}\nu\pi - \tfrac{1}{4}\pi\right) \sum_{s=0}^{\infty} \frac{(-1)^s(\nu, 2s+1)}{(2z)^{2s+1}}\right], \tag{3.28}$$

$$Y_\nu(z) \sim \sqrt{\left(\frac{2}{\pi z}\right)}\left[\sin\left(z - \tfrac{1}{2}\nu\pi - \tfrac{1}{4}\pi\right) \sum_{s=0}^{\infty} \frac{(-1)^s(\nu, 2s)}{(2z)^{2s}} + \cos\left(z - \tfrac{1}{2}\nu\pi - \tfrac{1}{4}\pi\right) \sum_{s=0}^{\infty} \frac{(-1)^s(\nu, 2s+1)}{(2z)^{2s+1}}\right], \tag{3.29}$$

are valid when $|\arg z| < \pi$.

Asymptotic expansions of $I_\nu(z)$ can be derived from the relations $I_\nu(z) = e^{-\frac{1}{2}\nu\pi i} J_\nu(ze^{\frac{1}{2}\pi i})$ when $-\pi < \arg z \leqslant \frac{1}{2}\pi$, $I_\nu(z) = e^{\frac{1}{2}\nu\pi i} J_\nu(ze^{-\frac{1}{2}\pi i})$ when $-\frac{1}{2}\pi \leqslant \arg z < \pi$, $2J_\nu(z) = H_\nu^{(1)}(z) + H_\nu^{(2)}(z)$ and formulae (3.26), (3.27). The results are

$$I_\nu(z) \sim \frac{e^z}{\sqrt{(2\pi z)}} \sum_{s=0}^{\infty} \frac{(\nu, s)}{(-2z)^s} + \frac{e^{-z-(\nu+\frac{1}{2})\pi i}}{\sqrt{(2\pi z)}} \sum_{s=0}^{\infty} \frac{(\nu, s)}{(2z)^s} \tag{3.30}$$

when $-\frac{3}{2}\pi < \arg z < \frac{1}{2}\pi$ and

$$I_\nu(z) \sim \frac{e^z}{\sqrt{(2\pi z)}} \sum_{s=0}^{\infty} \frac{(\nu, s)}{(-2z)^s} + \frac{e^{-z+(\nu+\frac{1}{2})\pi i}}{\sqrt{(2\pi z)}} \sum_{s=0}^{\infty} \frac{(\nu, s)}{(2z)^s} \tag{3.31}$$

when $-\frac{1}{2}\pi < \arg z < \frac{3}{2}\pi$. There is an apparent discrepancy in formulae (3.30), (3.31) when $-\frac{1}{2}\pi < \arg z < \frac{1}{2}\pi$ and this is an example of a phenomenon discovered by Stokes. Another and simpler example is that $\cosh z \sim \frac{1}{2}e^z$ as $|z| \to \infty$ when $|\arg z| < \frac{1}{2}\pi$ but $\cosh z \sim \frac{1}{2}e^{-z}$ when $\frac{1}{2}\pi < \arg z < \frac{3}{2}\pi$. A full explanation, which is outside the scope of this book, will be found in Chapter 7 of Watson's treatise; see also A. Erdélyi, *Asymptotic Expansions* (Dover, 1956).

Example 3. *If x is real, positive and large show that*

$$ber\,(x) = \frac{e^{\alpha}}{\sqrt{(2\pi x)}} \cos\beta, \quad bei\,(x) = \frac{e^{\alpha}}{\sqrt{(2\pi x)}} \sin\beta$$

where $\alpha \sim \dfrac{x}{\sqrt{2}} + \dfrac{1}{8x\sqrt{2}} - \ldots$ *and* $\beta \sim \dfrac{x}{\sqrt{2}} - \dfrac{\pi}{8} - \dfrac{1}{8x\sqrt{2}} - \dfrac{1}{16x^2} - \ldots.$

From (3.30) [or (3.31)] and (3.25)

$$I_0(z) \sim \frac{e^z}{\sqrt{(2\pi z)}} \sum_{s=0}^{\infty} \frac{(0, s)}{(-2z)^s} = \frac{e^z}{\sqrt{(2\pi z)}} \left\{1 + \frac{1^2}{1!(8z)} + \frac{1^2 \cdot 3^2}{2!(8z)^2} + \ldots\right\}$$

$$= \frac{1}{\sqrt{(2\pi z)}} \exp\left\{z + \log_e\left(1 + \frac{1}{8z} + \frac{9}{128z^2} + \ldots\right)\right\}$$

$$= \frac{1}{\sqrt{(2\pi z)}} \exp\left\{z + \left(\frac{1}{8z} + \frac{9}{128z^2} + \ldots\right) - \frac{1}{2}\left(\frac{1}{8z} + \frac{9}{128z^2} + \ldots\right)^2 + \ldots\right\}$$

$$= \frac{1}{\sqrt{(2\pi z)}} \exp\left(z + \frac{1}{8z} + \frac{1}{16z^2} + \ldots\right).$$

Hence

$$I_0(x\sqrt{i}) = I_0(xe^{i\pi/4})$$

$$\sim \frac{1}{\sqrt{(2\pi x)}} e^{-i\pi/8} \exp\left(xe^{i\pi/4} + \frac{1}{8x} e^{-i\pi/4} + \frac{1}{16x^2} e^{-i\pi/2} + \ldots\right)$$

$$= \frac{1}{\sqrt{(2\pi x)}} \exp\left\{-\frac{i\pi}{8} + x\left(\frac{1+i}{\sqrt{2}}\right) + \frac{1}{8x}\left(\frac{1-i}{\sqrt{2}}\right) - \frac{i}{16x^2} + \ldots\right\}$$

$$= \frac{1}{\sqrt{(2\pi x)}} \exp(\alpha + i\beta) = \frac{e^{\alpha}}{\sqrt{(2\pi x)}} (\cos\beta + i \sin\beta).$$

The required results then follow from the equation (1.75)

$$ber\,(x) + i\, bei\,(x) = I_0(x\sqrt{i})$$

by equating real and imaginary parts.

The series obtained in the foregoing are valid when $|z|$ is large and ν is fixed. Even when $|z|$ is not very large, values of the Bessel functions can be computed with considerable accuracy from the asymptotic formulae given. For example, for real positive values of z greater than 8, the first three terms of formulae (3.28) gives the value of $J_0(z)$ correct to six places of decimals.

When $|\nu|$ is large and z is fixed, approximations to the Bessel functions can be obtained from their power series and Stirling's formula for the gamma function of large argument

$$\log_e \Gamma(\nu + 1) \sim (\nu + \tfrac{1}{2}) \log_e \nu - \nu + \tfrac{1}{2} \log_e 2\pi,$$

an approximation which neglects terms of order ν^{-1} and above. Thus, using this approximation in formula (1.5), viz.

$$J_\nu(z) = \left(\frac{z}{2}\right)^\nu \sum_{r=0}^{\infty} \frac{(-1)^r (z/2)^{2r}}{r!\Gamma(\nu + r + 1)},$$

we find

$$J_\nu(z) \sim \frac{1}{\sqrt{(2\pi)}} \exp\{\nu + \nu \log_e(z/2) - (\nu + \tfrac{1}{2}) \log_e \nu\}$$

when terms of order ν^{-1} and higher powers are omitted. Approximations for the Bessel functions when both $|z|$ *and* $|\nu|$ are large are difficult to derive and the reader is referred to Chapter 8 of Watson's book for a detailed discussion.

Exercises 3

1. Show that when $n = 0, 1, 2, 3, \ldots$

$$\pi I_n(z) = (-1)^n \int_0^\pi \exp(-z\cos\theta)\cos n\theta \, d\theta$$

$$= \int_0^\pi \exp(z\cos\theta)\cos n\theta \, d\theta.$$

2. If $R(\nu) > -\frac{1}{2}$, show that $\frac{1}{2}\pi^{\frac{1}{2}}\Gamma(\nu + \frac{1}{2})(z/2)^{-\nu}J_\nu(z)$ can be represented by the following integrals:

(i) $\displaystyle\int_0^1 (1 - t^2)^{\nu - \frac{1}{2}} \cos(zt)\, dt,$

(ii) $\displaystyle\frac{1}{2}\int_0^1 t^{\nu - \frac{1}{2}}(1 - t)^{-\frac{1}{2}} \cos\{z(1 - t)^{\frac{1}{2}}\}\, dt.$

3. If $R(\nu) > \frac{1}{2}$, show, by integrating by parts, that Poisson's integral (3.4) gives

$$J_\nu(z) = \frac{(2\nu - 1)(z/2)^{\nu - 1}}{\pi^{\frac{1}{2}}\Gamma(\nu + \frac{1}{2})} \int_0^{\pi/2} \sin(z\cos\theta)\sin^{2\nu - 2}\theta\cos\theta \, d\theta.$$

4. If $R(\nu) > -\frac{1}{2}$, show that

$$I_\nu(z) = \frac{(z/2)^\nu}{\pi^{\frac{1}{2}}\Gamma(\nu + \frac{1}{2})} \int_{-1}^1 (1 - t^2)^{\nu - \frac{1}{2}} \cosh(zt)\, dt.$$

5. Given that $\displaystyle\int_0^\infty x^{-1}\sin ax\, dx = \pm \tfrac{1}{2}\pi$ according as a is positive or negative, use Bessel's integral to show that

$$\int_0^\infty t^{-1}J_0(rt)\sin t\, dt = \begin{cases} \frac{1}{2}\pi, & r \leqslant 1, \\ \sin^{-1}\left(\dfrac{1}{r}\right), & r \geqslant 1. \end{cases}$$

6. If x is real and positive, show that

$$Y_0(x) = \frac{2}{\pi}\int_0^\infty \cos(x\cosh\theta)\, d\theta.$$

7. If x and z are real and positive, show that

$$e^{\frac{3}{4}\pi i}\sqrt{\left(\frac{\pi x}{2z}\right)}\, H_{\frac{1}{2}}{}^{(1)}(ixz) = \frac{e^{-xz}}{z} = \frac{2}{\pi}\int_0^\infty \frac{\cos xu\, du}{u^2+z^2}.$$

8. Deduce from equations (1.59) and (3.19) that

$$\pi H_0{}^{(1)}(kx) = -i\int_{-\infty}^{\infty} (x^2+u^2)^{-\frac{1}{2}} \exp\{ik(x^2+u^2)^{\frac{1}{2}}\}\, du,$$

k and x being real and positive.

9. If x is real and positive, use formula (3.19) to show that when $R(\nu) > -\frac{1}{2}$

$$\Gamma(\tfrac{1}{2}+\nu)K_\nu(x) = (\tfrac{1}{2}\pi)^{\frac{1}{2}} x^\nu e^{-x}\int_0^\infty e^{-x\xi}\xi^{\nu-\frac{1}{2}}(1+\tfrac{1}{2}\xi)^{\nu-\frac{1}{2}}\, d\xi,$$

and deduce that $K_\nu(x)$ tends to zero when x tends to infinity.

10. Show that Bessel's integral for $J_0(z)$ can be written in the form

$$2\pi J_0(z) = \int_{-\pi}^{\pi} \exp(-iz\sin\theta)\, d\theta$$

and deduce that

$$\pi J_0{}^2(z) = \int_0^\pi J_0(2z\cos\alpha)\, d\alpha.$$

11. Deduce from formula (3.20) that

$$K_0{}^2(z) = 2\int_0^\infty K_0(2z\cosh t)\, dt.$$

12. Given that $\int_0^\infty \exp\{-a^2t^2 - b^2t^{-2}\}\, dt = (\sqrt{\pi}/2a)\exp(-2ab)$, deduce from Exercise 9 above that

$$2K_\nu(x) = \int_0^\infty \exp\{-\tfrac{1}{2}x(\lambda+\lambda^{-1})\}\lambda^{\nu-1}\, d\lambda,$$

x being real and positive and $R(\nu) > -\frac{1}{2}$.

13. If x is real, positive and large show that

$$ker\,(x) = \left(\frac{\pi}{2x}\right)^{\frac{1}{2}} e^\gamma\cos\delta, \quad kei\,(x) = \left(\frac{\pi}{2x}\right)^{\frac{1}{2}} e^\gamma\sin\delta,$$

where $\gamma \sim \dfrac{x}{\sqrt{2}} - \dfrac{1}{8x\sqrt{2}} + \ldots$ and $\delta \sim -\dfrac{x}{\sqrt{2}} - \dfrac{\pi}{8} + \dfrac{1}{8x\sqrt{2}} - \dfrac{1}{16x^2} + \ldots$

14. Deduce from the asymptotic expansion (3.28) that

$$\sqrt{(\tfrac{1}{2}\pi z)}J_{\frac{7}{2}}(z) = \left(\frac{105}{z^4} - \frac{45}{z^2} + 1\right)\sin z - \left(\frac{105}{z^3} - \frac{10}{z}\right)\cos z.$$

15. If n is a positive integer (or zero), show that

$$K_{n+\frac{1}{2}}(z) = \left(\frac{\pi}{2z}\right)^{\frac{1}{2}} e^{-z} \sum_{s=0}^{n} \frac{(n+s)!}{s!(n-s)!} (2z)^{-s}.$$

16. If x is sufficiently large for x^{-2}, x^{-3}, . . . to be neglected in comparison with x^{-1}, show that

$$\int_{\infty}^{x} \frac{J_0(t)}{t}\, dt = \left(\frac{2}{\pi x}\right)^{\frac{1}{2}} \frac{\sin(x - \pi/4)}{x}.$$

17. If x and n are real show that

$$J_n^2(x) + Y_n^2(x) \sim \frac{2}{\pi x}\left\{1 + \frac{1}{2} \cdot \frac{(4n^2-1)}{(2x)^2} + \frac{1\,.\,3}{2\,.\,4} \frac{(4n^2-1)(4n^2-9)}{(2x)^4} + \ldots\right\}.$$

18. If x is sufficiently large for x^{-2} and higher powers of x^{-1} to be neglected, show that

$$J_0(x) = \left(\frac{2}{\pi x}\right)^{\frac{1}{2}} \cos\left\{x - \frac{\pi}{4} - \tan^{-1}\left(\frac{1}{8x}\right)\right\}.$$

Deduce that $J_0(x)$ vanishes when

$$x = (s - \tfrac{1}{4})\pi + \frac{1}{2\pi(4s-1)}$$

approximately, s being a large integer.

CHAPTER 4

ZEROS OF BESSEL FUNCTIONS, FOURIER-BESSEL SERIES AND HANKEL TRANSFORMS

4.1 Introduction

In many of the applications of Bessel functions to practical problems, we require to know for what values of the argument the function vanishes, that is, we require a knowledge of the zeros of Bessel functions. We start by discussing some general properties such as the infinity of real zeros possessed by $J_\nu(z)$ when ν is real, the absence of complex and imaginary zeros of this function and so on. Next we briefly consider the zeros of the modified Bessel functions and we then give a useful representation of $J_\nu(z)$ as an infinite product. The discussion is completed by giving Stokes' method of finding approximate numerical values of the zeros and it is shown that, except perhaps for the smallest zeros, this method is sufficiently accurate for most practical purposes.

The second part of the chapter first deals with the expansion of a given function in a series of Bessel functions. This is the Fourier-Bessel expansion, so called from its analogue with the expansion of a function in a Fourier series of trigonometrical terms. After a purely formal discussion of such series we obtain, again without pretence to rigour, Hankel's repeated integral, this being the counterpart of Fourier's important integral formula. The chapter concludes by the re-expression of some of the results obtained in the form of integral transforms and their appropriate inversion formulae; this will prove useful in later applications.

4.2 The zeros of $J_\nu(z)$ when ν is real

The graphs given in Figs. 1 and 2 of Chapter 1 suggest that functions satisfying Bessel's equation have an infinite number of real zeros and we here adapt a method originally used by Bessel to show that this is indeed true for $J_\nu(z)$ when ν is real.

We start by taking $-\frac{1}{2} < \nu < \frac{1}{2}$ and write $(2m + 1)\cos\theta = t$, $z = (m + \frac{1}{2})\pi$, where $m = 0, 1, 2, 3, \ldots$, in Poisson's integral (§3.3). This gives

$$J_\nu(m\pi + \tfrac{1}{2}\pi) = \frac{2\{(\frac{1}{2}m + \frac{1}{4})\pi\}^\nu}{\pi^{\frac{1}{2}}\Gamma(\nu + \frac{1}{2})}\int_0^{2m+1} \cos(\tfrac{1}{2}\pi t)\left\{1 - \frac{t^2}{(2m + 1)^2}\right\}^{\nu-\frac{1}{2}} \frac{dt}{2m + 1},$$

and the definite integral can be written in the form

$$\tfrac{1}{2}u_0 - u_1 + u_2 - \ldots + (-1)^m u_m$$

where

$$u_r = (-1)^r \int_{2r-1}^{2r+1} \cos\left(\tfrac{1}{2}\pi t\right)\left\{1 - \frac{t^2}{(2m+1)^2}\right\}^{\nu-\frac{1}{2}} \frac{dt}{2m+1}$$
$$= \int_{-1}^{1} \cos\left(\tfrac{1}{2}\pi t\right)\left\{1 - \left(\frac{2r+t}{2m+1}\right)^2\right\}^{\nu-\frac{1}{2}} \frac{dt}{2m+1}$$

when t is replaced by $2r + t$. This shows that u_r is positive and, as $\nu < \frac{1}{2}$, $u_r < u_{r+1}$. Hence $J_\nu(m\pi + \frac{1}{2}\pi)$ is positive or negative according as m is even or odd. Consequently $J_\nu(z)$ changes sign as z increases from $(m - \frac{1}{2})\pi$ to $(m + \frac{1}{2})\pi$ and the function therefore vanishes for some values of z in that interval. We have therefore shown that when $-\frac{1}{2} < \nu < \frac{1}{2}$, $J_\nu(z)$ has an infinite number of real zeros and it is clear from formulae (1.38), (1.39) that the result remains valid when $\nu = \pm\frac{1}{2}$.

Since, from (1.34),

$$\frac{d}{dz}\{z^{-\nu}J_\nu(z)\} = -z^{-\nu}J_{\nu+1}(z)$$

and since $z^{-\nu}J_\nu(z)$ and $z^{-\nu}J_{\nu+1}(z)$ are both continuous functions of z, it follows from Rolle's theorem that there is at least one real zero of $z^{-\nu}J_{\nu+1}(z)$ between each consecutive pair of real zeros of $z^{-\nu}J_\nu(z)$. The relation (1.33) shows in a similar way that there is at least one real zero of $z^\nu J_{\nu-1}(z)$ between each consecutive pair of zeros of $z^\nu J_\nu(z)$. These considerations enable the restrictions on the values of ν in the result of the preceding paragraph to be removed and we have established the important result that, *when ν is real, $J_\nu(z)$ has an infinite number of real zeros*. If p is one of these real zeros then, since $z^{-\nu}J_\nu(z)$ is an even function of z, it follows that $-p$ is also a zero.

The above proposition can also be inferred from the asymptotic expansion for $J_\nu(z)$ given in (3.28). This expansion shows also that the large positive zeros approximate to those of $\cos(z - \frac{1}{2}\nu\pi - \frac{1}{4}\pi)$, that is, they are given by $z \simeq (s + \frac{1}{2}\nu - \frac{1}{4})\pi$ where s is a large positive integer. Thus, taking $s = 11$ and $\nu = 0$, we find that $J_0(z) = 0$ when $z \simeq 10{\cdot}75\pi = 33{\cdot}77$.

When ν is real and greater than -1, we can show that $J_\nu(z)$ *has no complex zeros* as follows. Suppose p is such a zero so that, since $J_\nu(z)$ is a real function of z, the conjugate quantity $\bar{p}$ must also be a zero. Using equation (2.8) with $\lambda = p$, $\mu = \bar{p}$,

$$(p^2 - \bar{p}^2)\int_0^1 zJ_\nu(pz)J_\nu(\bar{p}z)\,dz = \Big[z\Big\{pJ_\nu(\bar{p}z)J_{\nu+1}(pz) - \bar{p}J_\nu(pz)J_{\nu+1}(\bar{p}z)\Big\}\Big]_0^1$$
$$= 0, \tag{4.1}$$

the right-hand side vanishing at the upper limit as $J_\nu(p) = J_\nu(\bar{p}) = 0$ and at the lower limit because of the factor z. But $J_\nu(pz)$, $J_\nu(\bar{p}z)$ are conjugate complex quantities and the integrand on the left-hand side of equation (4.1) is therefore essentially positive. Hence we have established a contradiction and the proposition stated at the beginning of this paragraph is proved.

Writing $z = iq$ in the series (1.5), it is clear, if q and ν are real and $\nu > -1$, that all the terms on the right-hand side are of the same sign so that $J_\nu(z)$ *has no purely imaginary zeros.* Finally, $J_\nu(z)$ *has no repeated zeros* (*except possibly at* $z = 0$). For if p is a repeated zero, $J_\nu(p) = J_\nu'(p) = 0$ and, if $p \neq 0$, Bessel's equation (1.1) shows that $J_\nu''(p) = 0$. Repeated differentiation of Bessel's equation then shows that $J_\nu'''(p) = J_\nu^{(iv)}(p) = \ldots = 0$; hence, by Taylor's theorem, $J_\nu(z)$ vanishes identically and this is certainly not true.

Taking ν as real and positive, it can be seen from the series (1.5) and that obtained by differentiating it with respect to z that $J_\nu(z)$ and $J_\nu'(z)$ are both positive for sufficiently small positive real values of z. Bessel's equation (1.1) written in the form

$$z\frac{\mathrm{d}}{\mathrm{d}z}\left\{z\frac{\mathrm{d}J_\nu(z)}{\mathrm{d}z}\right\} = (\nu^2 - z^2)J_\nu(z)$$

shows, so long as $z < \nu$ and $J_\nu(z)$ is positive, that $zJ_\nu'(z)$ is positive and increasing and we can deduce that $J_\nu(z)$ increases with z. Hence we have established that, *when ν is real and positive, the smallest positive zeros of $J_\nu(z)$ and $J_\nu'(z)$ are each greater than ν.*

4.3 The zeros of other Bessel functions

Properties of the zeros of other Bessel functions can be investigated in similar ways (cf. Exercises 2, 4, 5, 6 at the end of this chapter) and we now discuss briefly some further results.

Firstly, formula (1.51) gives

$$I_\nu(z) = \sum_{r=0}^{\infty} \frac{(z/2)^{\nu+2r}}{r!\,\Gamma(\nu + r + 1)} \tag{4.2}$$

and it is clear that, *when ν is real and greater than -1, the function $I_\nu(z)$ has no real zeros.* Secondly, equations (1.73) and (3.21) give

$$K_{-\nu}(z) = K_\nu(z) = \frac{\pi^{\frac{1}{2}}e^{-z}}{(2z)^{\frac{1}{2}}\Gamma(\frac{1}{2} + \nu)}\int_0^\infty e^{-\xi}\xi^{\nu-\frac{1}{2}}\left(1 + \frac{\xi}{2z}\right)^{\nu-\frac{1}{2}} \mathrm{d}\xi \tag{4.3}$$

and it follows that, *when ν is real, $K_\nu(z)$ has no positive real zeros.*

The equation

$$J_\nu(az)Y_\nu(bz) = J_\nu(bz)Y_\nu(az), \tag{4.4}$$

where a, b are real and positive, is of considerable importance in the application of Bessel functions to physical problems and we now discuss the nature of its roots for real values of ν.

Writing

$$\left.\begin{aligned} u &= J_\nu(az)Y_\nu(rz) - J_\nu(rz)Y_\nu(az),\\ v &= J_\nu(a\bar{z})Y_\nu(r\bar{z}) - J_\nu(r\bar{z})Y_\nu(a\bar{z}),\end{aligned}\right\} \tag{4.5}$$

where $\bar{z}$ is the conjugate of z, u and v satisfy the differential equations

$$r^2u'' + ru' + (r^2z^2 - \nu^2)u = 0,$$
$$r^2v'' + rv' + (r^2\bar{z}^2 - \nu^2)v = 0,$$

dashes denoting derivatives with respect to r. Multiplying respectively by v/r, u/r and subtracting, these give

$$-(z^2 - \bar{z}^2)ruv = r(vu'' - uv'') + vu' - uv'$$
$$= \frac{\mathrm{d}}{\mathrm{d}r}\{r(vu' - uv')\}. \tag{4.6}$$

If z (and therefore also $\bar{z}$) is a complex root of equation (4.4), u and v both vanish when $r = b$ and, since they also both vanish when $r = a$, we have

$$-(z^2 - \bar{z}^2)\int_a^b ruv\,\mathrm{d}r = \Big[r(vu' - uv')\Big]_{r=a}^{r=b} = 0.$$

But, since u, v are conjugate complex quantities, the left-hand side of this equation does not vanish and the contradiction established shows that *equation* (4.4) *has no complex roots.* Since $H_\nu^{(1)}(z) = J_\nu(z) + iY_\nu(z)$, equation (4.4) can be written $J_\nu(az)H_\nu^{(1)}(bz) = J_\nu(bz)H_\nu^{(1)}(az)$ and the relation $I_\nu(z) = e^{-\frac{1}{2}\nu\pi i}J_\nu(iz)$ and that giving $K_\nu(z)$ in terms of $H_\nu^{(1)}(iz)$ [equation (1.59)] show that, if $z = iq$ is a purely imaginary zero of equation (4.4), then

$$I_\nu(aq)K_\nu(bq) = I_\nu(bq)K_\nu(aq).$$

But if $\nu > -1$ and $b > a$, equation (4.2) shows that $I_\nu(aq)/I_\nu(bq) < 1$ and if $\nu \geqslant 0$ equation (4.3) shows that $K_\nu(aq)/K_\nu(bq) > 1$. Again a contradiction has been established so that *equation* (4.4) *has no purely imaginary roots and all its roots are therefore real.* It is left to the reader (Exercises 4, No. 8) to show that *the equation has no repeated roots.* The corollary that the roots of the equation

$$I_\nu(az)K_\nu(bz) = I_\nu(bz)K_\nu(az) \tag{4.7}$$

are all purely imaginary and simple is worth noting.

4.4 The infinite product for $J_\nu(z)$

It is possible to express $J_\nu(z)$ by the formula

$$J_\nu(z) = \frac{(z/2)^\nu}{\Gamma(\nu + 1)}\prod_{s=1}^{\infty}\left(1 - \frac{z^2}{p_s^2}\right), \tag{4.8}$$

where the p_s are the real zeros of $J_\nu(z)$. Full details of the rigorous derivation of this result will be found in Watson's treatise (p. 497) and only the formal steps will be given here.

We consider the contour integral

$$\frac{1}{2\pi i}\int_D \frac{t}{w(w - t)} \cdot \frac{J_{\nu+1}(w)}{J_\nu(w)}\,\mathrm{d}w \tag{4.9}$$

where D is a suitable contour containing t and the zeros $\pm p_s$ $(s = 1, 2, 3, \ldots, m)$ which are supposed to be arranged in non-descending magnitudes of their moduli. The poles of the integrand are at $w = t$ and $w = \pm p_s$ and the residues at these poles are $J_{\nu+1}(t)/J_\nu(t)$ and

$$\frac{\mp t}{p_s(\pm p_s - t)}$$

since, by the first of equations (1.31), $J_{\nu+1}(w) = -J_\nu'(w)$ when $w = \pm p_s$. By expanding the contour to avoid the zeros $\pm p_s$ when $s > m$ and showing that $J_{\nu+1}(w)/J_\nu(w)$ is bounded on the contour so that the integral in (4.9) is ultimately zero, the theory of residues gives

$$\frac{J_{\nu+1}(t)}{J_\nu(t)} - \sum_{s=1}^{\infty} \frac{t}{p_s(p_s - t)} - \sum_{s=1}^{\infty} \frac{t}{p_s(p_s + t)} = 0.$$

Since, by (1.34), $J_{\nu+1}(t) = -t^\nu \dfrac{\mathrm{d}}{\mathrm{d}t}\{t^{-\nu}J_\nu(t)\}$, this can be written

$$\frac{\dfrac{\mathrm{d}}{\mathrm{d}t}\{t^{-\nu}J_\nu(t)\}}{t^{-\nu}J_\nu(t)} = \sum_{s=1}^{\infty}\left\{\frac{1}{t - p_s} + \frac{1}{p_s}\right\} + \sum_{s=1}^{\infty}\left\{\frac{1}{t + p_s} - \frac{1}{p_s}\right\}.$$

By (1.5) $t^{-\nu}J_\nu(t)$ tends to $1/\{2^\nu\Gamma(\nu + 1)\}$ as t tends to zero, so that by integration with respect to t between 0 and z we have

$$\log_e\{z^{-\nu}J_\nu(z)\} + \log_e\{2^\nu\Gamma(\nu + 1)\} = \sum_{s=1}^{\infty}\left\{\log_e\left(\frac{z - p_s}{-p_s}\right) + \frac{z}{p_s}\right\}$$
$$+ \sum_{s=1}^{\infty}\left\{\log_e\left(\frac{z + p_s}{p_s}\right) - \frac{z}{p_s}\right\}$$

and the result (4.8) follows on removing the logarithms.

Example 1. *If the zeros of $J_0(z)$ are p_s $(s = 1, 2, 3, \ldots)$, show that*

$$\sum_{s=1}^{\infty}\frac{1}{p_s^2} = \frac{1}{4}, \quad \sum_{s=1}^{\infty}\frac{1}{p_s^4} = \frac{1}{32}.$$

Putting $\nu = 0$ in (4.8) and taking logarithms,

$$\log_e J_0(z) = \sum_{s=1}^{\infty} \log_e\left(1 - \frac{z^2}{p_s^2}\right)$$

so that, remembering that $J_0'(z) = -J_1(z)$, differentiation with respect to z gives

$$\frac{J_1(z)}{J_0(z)} = \sum_{s=1}^{\infty}\frac{2z}{p_s^2 - z^2}.$$

Provided $|z| < p_1$ this can be written

$$J_1(z) = 2zJ_0(z)\sum_{s=1}^{\infty}\sum_{m=0}^{\infty}\frac{z^{2m}}{p_s^{2m+2}} = 2zJ_0(z)\sum_{m=0}^{\infty}\sigma_{m+1}z^{2m}$$

where $\sigma_m = \sum_{s=1}^{\infty} p_s^{-2m}$. Substituting

$$J_0(z) = 1 - \frac{z^2}{4} + \ldots, \quad J_1(z) = \frac{z}{2} - \frac{z^3}{16} + \ldots,$$

and equating the coefficients of z and z^3 we have

$$\tfrac{1}{2} = 2\sigma_1, \quad -\tfrac{1}{16} = 2\sigma_2 - \tfrac{1}{2}\sigma_1,$$

giving $\sigma_1 = \frac{1}{4}$, $\sigma_2 = \frac{1}{32}$ as required.

4.5 Stokes' method of calculating the zeros of Bessel functions

We have indicated in §4.2 that the large positive zeros of $J_\nu(z)$ approximate to those of $\cos(z - \frac{1}{2}\nu\pi - \frac{1}{4}\pi)$ and we now give Stokes' method of improving the approximation. His method is illustrated here for the case of $J_0(z)$ but it can be extended to cover other values of the order of the function and to other Bessel functions such as $Y_\nu(z)$, $J_\nu(az)Y_\nu(bz) - J_\nu(bz)Y_\nu(az)$, etc.

We start with equations (3.28) and (3.25) which give

$$J_0(z) \sim \left(\frac{2}{\pi z}\right)^{\frac{1}{2}} \{P_0(z)\cos(z - \tfrac{1}{4}\pi) - Q_0(z)\sin(z - \tfrac{1}{4}\pi)\}$$

where

$$\left.\begin{aligned} P_0(z) &= 1 - \frac{1^2 . 3^2}{2!(8z)^2} + \frac{1^2 . 3^2 . 5^2 . 7^2}{4!(8z)^4} - \ldots, \\ Q_0(z) &= -\frac{1^2}{1!(8z)} + \frac{1^2 . 3^2 . 5^2}{3!(8z)^3} - \ldots \quad . \end{aligned}\right\}$$

This can be written in the form

$$\left(\frac{\pi z}{2}\right)^{\frac{1}{2}} J_0(z) \sim \{P_0^2(z) + Q_0^2(z)\}^{\frac{1}{2}} \cos(z - \tfrac{1}{4}\pi - \theta)$$

where

$$\tan\theta = -\frac{Q_0(z)}{P_0(z)} = \frac{1}{8z} - \frac{33}{512z^3} + \ldots$$

when terms in z^{-5}, etc., are neglected. Hence the positive zeros are given by $z - \frac{1}{4}\pi - \theta = (s - \frac{1}{2})\pi$ where s is a positive integer so that

$$\begin{aligned} z &= (s - \tfrac{1}{4})\pi + \tan^{-1}\left(\frac{1}{8z} - \frac{33}{512z^3} + \ldots\right) \\ &= (s - \tfrac{1}{4})\pi + \frac{1}{8z} - \frac{25}{384z^3} + \ldots \end{aligned} \quad (4.10)$$

when we use the formula $\tan^{-1} x = x - \frac{1}{3}x^3 + \ldots$. Writing $\alpha = (s - \frac{1}{4})\pi$

and assuming that $z = \alpha + \frac{\lambda}{\alpha} + \frac{\mu}{\alpha^3} + \ldots$, substituting in (4.10) and neglecting α^{-5}, etc., we have

$$\alpha + \frac{\lambda}{\alpha} + \frac{\mu}{\alpha^3} + \ldots = \alpha + \frac{1}{8}\left(\frac{1}{\alpha} - \frac{\lambda}{\alpha^3} + \ldots\right) - \frac{25}{384}\left(\frac{1}{\alpha^3} - \ldots\right) + \ldots$$

so that, equating the coefficients of α^{-1} and α^{-3},

$$\lambda = \frac{1}{8}, \qquad \mu = -\frac{1}{8}\lambda - \frac{25}{384} = -\frac{31}{384}.$$

Hence the zeros of $J_0(z)$ are given by

$$z \sim (s - \tfrac{1}{4})\pi + \frac{1}{8(s - \frac{1}{4})\pi} - \frac{31}{384(s - \frac{1}{4})^3\pi^3} + \ldots \tag{4.11}$$

and it is possible, by retaining powers of z^{-1} and α^{-1} above the third, to obtain further terms in the asymptotic expansion (4.11) of the zeros.

The formula

$$z \sim (s + \tfrac{1}{4})\pi - \frac{3}{8(s + \frac{1}{4})\pi} + \frac{9}{384(s + \frac{1}{4})^3\pi^3} - \ldots \tag{4.12}$$

for the zeros of $J_1(z)$ can be obtained in the same way and the corresponding formulae for the zeros of the Bessel functions of the second kind can be found similarly. They are

(i) $Y_0(z) = 0$ when

$$z \sim (s - \tfrac{3}{4})\pi + \frac{1}{8(s - \frac{3}{4})\pi} - \frac{31}{384(s - \frac{3}{4})^3\pi^3} + \ldots, \tag{4.13}$$

(ii) $Y_1(z) = 0$ when

$$z \sim (s - \tfrac{1}{4})\pi - \frac{3}{8(s - \frac{1}{4})\pi} + \frac{9}{384(s - \frac{1}{4})^3\pi^3} - \ldots. \tag{4.14}$$

Values of the zeros for $s = 1, 2, 3, 4, 5$ calculated from formulae (4.11), (4.12), (4.13) and (4.14) are given in the following table:

s	Values of z making:			
	$J_0(z) = 0$	$J_1(z) = 0$	$Y_0(z) = 0$	$Y_1(z) = 0$
1	2·403	3·832	0·778	2·199
2	5·520	7·016	3·958	5·430
3	8·654	10·173	7·086	8·596
4	11·792	13·324	10·222	11·749
5	14·931	16·471	13·361	14·897

With the exception of the first line ($s = 1$) of this table, the entries agree (to three places of decimals) with values obtained by more elaborate methods. Such methods have been used to compile very extensive tables of the zeros and those given in the British Association Mathematical Tables referred to in §1.7 show that the first positive zeros of $J_0(z)$, $J_1(z)$, $Y_0(z)$, $Y_1(z)$ are, in fact, 2·405, 3·832, 0·894 and 2·197.

4.6 Fourier-Bessel series

The Fourier series for a function $f(x)$ from $x = -\pi$ to $x = \pi$ is

$$f(x) = \tfrac{1}{2}a_0 + \sum_{s=1}^{\infty}(a_s \cos sx + b_s \sin sx), \tag{4.15}$$

where the coefficients a_s, b_s are determined from

$$\pi a_s = \int_{-\pi}^{\pi} f(x) \cos sx \, dx, \quad \pi b_s = \int_{-\pi}^{\pi} f(x) \sin sx \, dx, \tag{4.16}$$

and this expansion is very useful in mathematical physics. The analogous expansion

$$f(r) = \sum_{s=1}^{\infty} c_s J_\nu(p_s r) \tag{4.17}$$

where the p_s are zeros of $J_\nu(pa)$ and where the coefficients c_s are determined by integrals similar to those in (4.16) is called the *Fourier-Bessel expansion* of $f(r)$ and it is also of use in applications of Bessel functions to physical problems. Just as a rigorous treatment of the theory of Fourier series is a difficult problem in analysis so also is that of Fourier-Bessel series and we shall not attempt it here. A full discussion will be found in Chapter XVIII of Watson's treatise and we give below simply a formal derivation of the formulae for the coefficients.

We start by writing $\lambda = p_s$, $\mu = p_t$, $z = r$ in (2.8) so that

$$(p_s^2 - p_t^2)\int_0^a rJ_\nu(p_s r)J_\nu(p_t r)\, dr$$
$$= \Big[rp_t J_\nu(p_s r)J_\nu'(p_t r) - rp_s J_\nu(p_t r)J_\nu'(p_s r)\Big]_0^a \tag{4.18}$$

and it follows, if ν is real and greater than -1 and if p_s, p_t are different zeros of $J_\nu(pa)$, that

$$\int_0^a rJ_\nu(p_s r)J_\nu(p_t r)\, dr = 0, \quad t \neq s. \tag{4.19}$$

Writing $\lambda = p_s$, $z = r$ in equation (2.9), we have

$$2\int_0^a rJ_\nu^2(p_s r)\, dr = \left[r^2\{J_\nu'(p_s r)\}^2 + \left(r^2 - \frac{\nu^2}{p_s^2}\right) J_\nu^2(p_s r)\right]_0^a \tag{4.20}$$

so that, since $J_\nu(p_s a) = 0$,

$$\int_0^a rJ_\nu^2(p_s r)\, dr = \tfrac{1}{2}a^2\{J_\nu'(p_s a)\}^2. \tag{4.21}$$

If we now *assume* the possibility of the expansion (4.17)

$$f(r) = \sum_{s=1}^{\infty} c_s J_\nu(p_s r), \quad 0 < r < a,$$

multiplication by $rJ_\nu(p_s r)$, integration with respect to r between 0, a and use of (4.19), (4.21) gives

$$\begin{aligned} c_s &= \frac{2}{a^2\{J_\nu'(p_s a)\}^2} \int_0^a rf(r) J_\nu(p_s r)\,\mathrm{d}r \\ &= \frac{2}{a^2 J_{\nu+1}^2(p_s a)} \int_0^a rf(r) J_\nu(p_s r)\,\mathrm{d}r \end{aligned} \tag{4.22}$$

since, in the last step, the first of equations (1.31) shows that $J_\nu'(p_s a) = -J_{\nu+1}(p_s a)$ when $J_\nu(p_s a) = 0$.

Formula (4.22) for the coefficients in the Fourier-Bessel expansion (4.17) corresponds to formulae (4.16) for the coefficients in the Fourier expansion (4.15). The formal derivation given here omits all reference to the conditions of validity and a full statement of the theorem proved by Watson is as follows: "Let $f(t)$ be a function defined arbitrarily in the interval $(0, a)$ and let $\int_0^a t^{\frac{1}{2}} f(t)\,\mathrm{d}t$ exist and (if it is an improper integral) let it be absolutely convergent. Let

$$c_s = \frac{2}{a^2 J_{\nu+1}^2(p_s a)} \int_0^a tf(t) J_\nu(p_s t)\,\mathrm{d}t, \quad \nu + \tfrac{1}{2} \geqslant 0,$$

and let r be any internal point of an interval (h, k) such that $0 < h < k < a$ and such that $f(t)$ has limited total fluctuation in (h, k). Then the series $\sum_{s=1}^{\infty} c_s J_\nu(p_s r)$ is convergent and its sum is $\frac{1}{2}\{f(r+0) + f(r-0)\}$".

Example 2. *If* p_s $(s = 1, 2, 3, \ldots)$ *are the positive zeros of* $J_1(p) = 0$ *and* $0 < r < 1$, *show that*

$$r = \sum_{s=1}^{\infty} \frac{2J_1(p_s r)}{p_s J_2(p_s)}. \tag{4.23}$$

Writing $f(r) = r$, $\nu = 1$, $a = 1$ in (4.17), (4.22), $r = \sum_{s=1}^{\infty} c_s J_1(p_s r)$ where

$$\begin{aligned} c_s &= \frac{2}{J_2^2(p_s)} \int_0^1 r^2 J_1(p_s r)\,\mathrm{d}r \\ &= \frac{2}{p_s^3 J_2^2(p_s)} \int_0^{p_s} z^2 J_1(z)\,\mathrm{d}z \quad (p_s r = z) \\ &= \frac{2}{p_s^3 J_2^2(p_s)} \Big[z^2 J_2(z) \Big]_0^{p_s}, \quad \text{by equation (2.2)}, \\ &= \frac{2}{p_s J_2(p_s)}, \end{aligned}$$

and the required result has been established.

4.7 Some other series in terms of Bessel functions

In the Fourier-Bessel expansion, the summation is over the zeros of $J_\nu(pa)$ and we now consider the corresponding expansion involving the zeros of the function

$$paJ_\nu'(pa) + hJ_\nu(pa) \tag{4.24}$$

where h is a given constant. Such an expansion is known as a *Dini series* and formal expressions for its coefficients can be obtained from equations (4.18) and (4.20). Thus (4.18) shows that if p_s and p_t are zeros of the function (4.24)

$$\int_0^a rJ_\nu(p_s r)J_\nu(p_t r)\,dr = 0, \quad t \neq s, \tag{4.25}$$

while (4.20) gives

$$2\int_0^a rJ_\nu^2(p_s r)\,dr = a^2\{J_\nu'(p_s a)\}^2 + \left(a^2 - \frac{\nu^2}{p_s^2}\right) J_\nu^2(p_s a).$$

Since $p_s aJ_\nu'(p_s a) + hJ_\nu(p_s a) = 0$, by eliminating $J_\nu'(p_s a)$ this can be written

$$\int_0^a rJ_\nu^2(p_s r)\,dr = \frac{1}{2}\left(\frac{h^2}{p_s^2} + a^2 - \frac{\nu^2}{p_s^2}\right) J_\nu^2(p_s a). \tag{4.26}$$

Hence, assuming the possibility of the expansion

$$f(r) = \sum_{s=1}^{\infty} c_s J_\nu(p_s r), \quad 0 < r < a, \tag{4.27}$$

multiplication by $rJ_\nu(p_s r)$, integration with respect to r between 0, a and use of (4.25), (4.26) gives

$$c_s = \frac{2p_s^2}{(h^2 + a^2p_s^2 - \nu^2)J_\nu^2(p_s a)} \int_0^a rf(r)J_\nu(p_s r)\,dr. \tag{4.28}$$

Conditions similar to those necessary for the validity of the Fourier-Bessel expansion are required in the case of Dini's expansion and full details can again be found in Chapter XVIII of Watson's book.

Example 3. *If p_s satisfies the equation $J_0(p_s) = J_2(p_s)$ when $s = 1, 2, 3, \ldots$ show that*

$$\tfrac{1}{2}r = \sum_{s=1}^{\infty} \frac{p_s J_1(p_s r)J_2(p_s)}{(p_s^2 - 1)J_1^2(p_s)}, \quad 0 < r < 1.$$

From the last of equations (1.31) with $\nu = 1$, $J_0(p_s) - J_2(p_s) = 2J_1'(p_s)$ so that p_s is a zero of the function (4.24) with $\nu = 1$, $h = 0$. Hence taking $\nu = 1$, $h = 0$, $a = 1$, $f(r) = r$, equations (4.27), (4.28) give $r = \sum_{s=1}^{\infty} c_s J_1(p_s r)$ where

$$c_s = \frac{2p_s^2}{(p_s^2 - 1)J_1^2(p_s)} \int_0^1 r^2 J_1(p_s r)\,dr.$$

The value of the definite integral is found as in Example 2 to be $p_s^{-1}J_2(p_s)$ and the required result then follows immediately.

Another expansion of practical importance is

$$f(r) = \sum_{s=1}^{\infty} c_s B_\nu(p_s r), \quad a < r < b, \tag{4.29}$$

where

$$B_\nu(p_s r) = J_\nu(p_s r)Y_\nu(p_s a) - Y_\nu(p_s r)J_\nu(p_s a), \tag{4.30}$$

and p_s $(s = 1, 2, 3, \ldots)$ are the positive roots of the equation $B_\nu(p_s b) = 0$. Working as before we find

$$\int_a^b rB_\nu(p_s r)B_\nu(p_t r)\,\mathrm{d}r = 0, \quad t \neq s,$$

and

$$\int_a^b rB_\nu^2(p_s r)\,\mathrm{d}r = \frac{2}{\pi^2 p_s^2}\left\{\frac{J_\nu^2(p_s a)}{J_\nu^2(p_s b)} - 1\right\}.$$

Use of these results shows that the coefficients c_s in the expansion (4.29) are formally given by

$$\frac{2}{\pi^2}c_s = \frac{p_s^2 J_\nu^2(p_s b)}{J_\nu^2(p_s a) - J_\nu^2(p_s b)}\int_a^b rf(r)B_\nu(p_s r)\,\mathrm{d}r. \tag{4.31}$$

4.8 Hankel's integral formula

We have already seen that Fourier-Bessel series are analogous to Fourier series and we now obtain a formula which is the counterpart of Fourier's famous integral formula. This is usually known as *Hankel's integral formula* or *Hankel's repeated integral.*

Starting from equation (2.8) with $z = p$, $\lambda = R$, $\mu = r$,

$$\int_0^h pJ_\nu(Rp)J_\nu(rp)\,\mathrm{d}p = \frac{h}{R^2 - r^2}\{RJ_\nu(rh)J_{\nu+1}(Rh) - rJ_\nu(Rh)J_{\nu+1}(rh)\}, \tag{4.32}$$

if we assume that the real part of ν is greater than -1 so that the Bessel functions $J_{\nu+1}(Rp)$, $J_{\nu+1}(rp)$ vanish when $p = 0$. When h is large equation (3.28) gives $J_\nu(rh) \sim (2/\pi rh)^{\frac{1}{2}}\{\cos(rh - \frac{1}{2}\nu\pi - \frac{1}{4}\pi) + O(h^{-1})\}$ so that

$$\begin{aligned} hJ_\nu(rh)J_{\nu+1}(Rh) &\sim \frac{2}{\pi(rR)^{\frac{1}{2}}}\cos(rh - \tfrac{1}{2}\nu\pi - \tfrac{1}{4}\pi)\sin(Rh - \tfrac{1}{2}\nu\pi - \tfrac{1}{4}\pi) + O(h^{-1}) \\ &= \frac{1}{\pi(rR)^{\frac{1}{2}}}[\sin\{(R + r)h - \nu\pi - \tfrac{1}{2}\pi\} + \sin(R - r)h] + O(h^{-1}) \\ &= \frac{1}{\pi(rR)^{\frac{1}{2}}}[\sin(R - r)h - \cos\{(R + r)h - \nu\pi\}] + O(h^{-1}), \end{aligned}$$

with a similar expression for $J_\nu(Rh)J_{\nu+1}(rh)$. Substituting in (4.32) we find

$$\pi(R^2 - r^2)\int_0^h pJ_\nu(Rp)J_\nu(rp)\,\mathrm{d}p$$

$$= \left(\frac{R}{r}\right)^{\frac{1}{2}}[\sin(R-r)h - \cos\{(R+r)h - \nu\pi\}]$$

$$- \left(\frac{r}{R}\right)^{\frac{1}{2}}[\sin(r-R)h - \cos\{(r+R)h - \nu\pi\}] + O(h^{-1})$$

$$= \frac{R+r}{(rR)^{\frac{1}{2}}}\sin(R-r)h - \frac{R-r}{(rR)^{\frac{1}{2}}}\cos\{(R+r)h - \nu\pi\} + O(h^{-1}).$$

Hence

$$\int_0^\infty Rf(R)\,\mathrm{d}R\int_0^h pJ_\nu(Rp)J_\nu(rp)\,\mathrm{d}p$$

$$= \frac{1}{\pi r^{\frac{1}{2}}}\left[\int_0^\infty \frac{R^{\frac{1}{2}}f(R)}{R-r}\sin(R-r)h\,\mathrm{d}R - \int_0^\infty \frac{R^{\frac{1}{2}}f(R)}{R+r}\cos\{(R+r)h-\nu\pi\}\,\mathrm{d}R\right]$$
$$+ O(h^{-1})$$

$$= \frac{1}{\pi r^{\frac{1}{2}}}\left[\int_{-rh}^\infty \left(r+\frac{x}{h}\right)^{\frac{1}{2}} f\left(r+\frac{x}{h}\right)\frac{\sin x}{x}\,\mathrm{d}x\right.$$
$$\left. - \int_{rh}^\infty \left(-r+\frac{x}{h}\right)^{\frac{1}{2}} f\left(-r+\frac{x}{h}\right)\frac{\cos(x-\nu\pi)}{x}\,\mathrm{d}x\right] + O(h^{-1}) \qquad (4.33)$$

when we write $(R - r)h = x$ in the first integral and $(R + r)h = x$ in the second.

Provided the function f satisfies appropriate conditions, the first integral on the right of (4.33) tends to the limit $\frac{1}{2}\pi r^{\frac{1}{2}}\{f(r+0) + f(r-0)\}$ as h tends to infinity (r being assumed positive) and the second integral tends to zero. Hence (4.33) gives

$$\tfrac{1}{2}\{f(r+0) + f(r-0)\} = \int_0^\infty Rf(R)\,\mathrm{d}R\int_0^\infty pJ_\nu(Rp)J_\nu(rp)\,\mathrm{d}p \qquad (4.34)$$

and this is Hankel's integral formula.

The above derivation of formula (4.34) is substantially that originally given by Hankel and it is, of course, open to several objections from the point of view of rigour. A satisfactory derivation under the assumptions that (i) $\int_0^\infty R^{\frac{1}{2}}f(R)\,\mathrm{d}R$ exists and is absolutely convergent and (ii) the positive quantity r lies inside an interval in which $f(R)$ has limited total fluctuation, is given by Watson (§14.4). Watson also assumes that the order ν of the Bessel functions is not less than $-\frac{1}{2}$ but he states that it is likely to be sufficient for ν to be greater than -1.

4.9 Hankel transforms

Integral transforms defined by

$$F(p) = \int_a^b f(r)K(p, r)\,\mathrm{d}r \tag{4.35}$$

where $K(p, r)$ is a given function of p and r, called the *kernel* of the transform, have recently proved to be very useful in the solution of some problems of mathematical physics. Transforms in which the kernel is a Bessel function are usually known as *Hankel transforms* and here we use some of the results derived in the last few sections to give some formulae involving them.

We start by assuming that $f(R)$ satisfies the conditions (stated above) required for a rigorous derivation of Hankel's integral formula (4.34). Under these conditions, the order of integration in the double integral of equation (4.34) can be interchanged and we have, if we further assume that $f(R)$ is continuous when $R = r$,

$$f(r) = \int_0^\infty pJ_\nu(rp)\,\mathrm{d}p \int_0^\infty Rf(R)J_\nu(pR)\,\mathrm{d}R. \tag{4.36}$$

Defining the Hankel transform $F(p)$ of order ν of the function $f(r)$ by

$$F(p) = \int_0^\infty rf(r)J_\nu(pr)\,\mathrm{d}r, \tag{4.37}$$

equation (4.36) gives, since $\int_0^\infty rf(r)J_\nu(pr)\,\mathrm{d}r = \int_0^\infty Rf(R)J_\nu(pR)\,\mathrm{d}R$,

$$f(r) = \int_0^\infty pF(p)J_\nu(rp)\,\mathrm{d}p. \tag{4.38}$$

Formulae (4.37), (4.38) constitute what is often called *Hankel's inversion theorem* and (4.38) enables the original function $f(r)$ to be found from its Hankel transform $F(p)$. The inversion theorem, besides being useful in the solution of partial differential equations, can be employed to evaluate certain definite integrals and an example is given below.

Example 4. *Find the Hankel transform of order zero of $f(r)$ where $f(r) = 1$ when $0 < r < a$ and $f(r) = 0$ when $r > a$. Deduce the value of the definite integral* $\int_0^\infty J_1(ap)J_0(rp)\,\mathrm{d}p$.

By (4.37) with $\nu = 0$,

$$\begin{aligned} F(p) &= \int_0^a rJ_0(pr)\,\mathrm{d}r = \frac{1}{p^2}\int_0^{pa} zJ_0(z)\,\mathrm{d}z \quad (z = rp), \\ &= \frac{1}{p^2}\Big[zJ_1(z)\Big]_0^{pa}, \quad \text{by (2.2)} \\ &= \frac{a}{p}J_1(ap). \end{aligned}$$

Substitution in (4.38) then gives

$$\int_0^\infty J_1(ap)J_0(rp)\,\mathrm{d}p = \begin{cases} a^{-1}, & 0 < r < a, \\ 0, & r > a. \end{cases} \tag{4.39}$$

Since $J_{\frac{1}{2}}(pr) = (2/\pi pr)^{\frac{1}{2}} \sin pr$, the special case $\nu = \frac{1}{2}$ of formulae (4.37), (4.38) is

$$F(p) = \left(\frac{2}{\pi p}\right)^{\frac{1}{2}} \int_0^\infty r^{\frac{1}{2}} f(r) \sin pr\,\mathrm{d}r, \quad f(r) = \left(\frac{2}{\pi r}\right)^{\frac{1}{2}} \int_0^\infty p^{\frac{1}{2}} F(p) \sin rp\,\mathrm{d}p.$$

Replacing $F(p)$ by $(2/\pi p)^{\frac{1}{2}} G(p)$ and $r^{\frac{1}{2}} f(r)$ by $g(r)$ these equations can be written

$$G(p) = \int_0^\infty g(r) \sin pr\,\mathrm{d}r \tag{4.40}$$

and

$$g(r) = \frac{2}{\pi} \int_0^\infty G(p) \sin rp\,\mathrm{d}p. \tag{4.41}$$

Equation (4.40) defines the *Fourier sine transform* of $g(r)$ and equation (4.41) is the inversion formula for this transform. In the same way $\nu = -\frac{1}{2}$ leads to the *Fourier cosine transform* defined by

$$G(p) = \int_0^\infty g(r) \cos pr\,\mathrm{d}r \tag{4.42}$$

with its inversion formula

$$g(r) = \frac{2}{\pi} \int_0^\infty G(p) \cos rp\,\mathrm{d}p. \tag{4.43}$$

Example 5. *Starting from Poisson's integral for $J_0(p)$, show that*

$$\int_0^\infty J_0(p) \cos rp\,\mathrm{d}p = \begin{cases} (1 - r^2)^{-\frac{1}{2}}, & 0 < r < 1, \\ 0, & r > 1. \end{cases} \tag{4.44}$$

Poisson's integral for $J_0(p)$ in the form given by equation (3.7) can be written

$$J_0(p) = \frac{2}{\pi} \int_0^1 \frac{\cos pr}{\sqrt{(1 - r^2)}}\,\mathrm{d}r.$$

This shows that $G(p) = J_0(p)$ is the cosine transform of a function $g(r)$ defined by

$$g(r) = \begin{cases} \dfrac{2}{\pi} \cdot \dfrac{1}{\sqrt{(1 - r^2)}}, & 0 < r < 1, \\ 0, & r > 1, \end{cases}$$

and substitution of these expressions for $g(r)$ and $G(p)$ in equation (4.43) gives the required result.

The function $F(p)$ given by

$$F(p) = \int_0^a rf(r)J_\nu(pr)\,\mathrm{d}r \tag{4.45}$$

is said to be the *finite Hankel transform of order* ν of the function $f(r)$. If p is chosen to be a positive zero p_s of the function $J_\nu(pa)$ and if the conditions set out in §4.6 are satisfied, equations (4.17) and (4.22) show that

$$f(r) = \frac{2}{a^2}\sum_{s=1}^{\infty}\frac{F(p_s)}{J_{\nu+1}{}^2(p_s a)}J_\nu(p_s r) \tag{4.46}$$

and this is the inversion formula for the finite transform (4.45) when $J_\nu(p_s a) = 0$.

Other finite Hankel transforms can be similarly defined. For example, suppose we define the transform by equation (4.45) but, instead of taking p_s to be a zero of $J_\nu(pa)$, we take it as a zero of the function $paJ_\nu'(pa) + hJ_\nu(pa)$ where h is a given constant. For such a transform, equation (4.28) shows that the appropriate inversion formula is

$$f(r) = 2\sum_{s=1}^{\infty}\frac{p_s{}^2F(p_s)}{(h^2 + a^2p_s{}^2 - \nu^2)J_\nu{}^2(p_s a)}J_\nu(p_s r). \tag{4.47}$$

Again, for the transform defined by

$$F(p) = \int_a^b rf(r)B_\nu(pr)\,\mathrm{d}r \tag{4.48}$$

where $B_\nu(pr) = J_\nu(pr)Y_\nu(pa) - Y_\nu(pr)J_\nu(pa)$ and p_s is taken to be a zero of the function $B_\nu(pb)$, equation (4.31) gives the inversion formula

$$f(r) = \tfrac{1}{2}\pi^2\sum_{s=1}^{\infty}\frac{p_s{}^2J_\nu{}^2(p_s b)F(p_s)}{J_\nu{}^2(p_s a) - J_\nu{}^2(p_s b)}B_\nu(p_s r). \tag{4.49}$$

Exercises 4

1. If $\nu \geqslant 0$ and is real, show that there is one and only one zero of $J_\nu'(z)$ between two consecutive zeros of $J_\nu(z)$.

2. If A, B, ν are real and $\nu > -1$, show that the function $AJ_\nu(z) + BzJ_\nu'(z)$ has no complex zeros.

3. If ν is real show that $J_\nu(x)$ and $J_\nu'(x)$ have no roots in common except possibly at $x = 0$.

4. If ν is real and greater than -1, show that $I_\nu(z)$ has no complex zeros.

5. Infer from its asymptotic expansion that, when ν is real, $Y_\nu(z)$ has an infinite number of real zeros and deduce that $Y_0(z) = 0$ when $z \simeq 32{\cdot}2$.

6. If ν is real and $R(\lambda + \mu) > 0$, show that

$$(\lambda^2 - \mu^2)\int_z^\infty zK_\nu(\lambda z)K_\nu(\mu z)\,\mathrm{d}z = z\{\mu K_\nu(\lambda z)K_\nu'(\mu z) - \lambda K_\nu(\mu z)K_\nu'(\lambda z)\}.$$

Deduce that $K_\nu(z)$ cannot have a complex zero with its real part positive.

7. Show that

$$4x^{\frac{3}{2}}\frac{\mathrm{d}}{\mathrm{d}x}\left[\sin(x-p)\frac{\mathrm{d}}{\mathrm{d}x}\{\sqrt{x}J_0(x)\}-\cos(x-p)\sqrt{x}J_0(x)\right]=-\sin(x-p)J_0(x).$$

Deduce that when p is a positive zero of $J_0(x)$

$$4\sqrt{(\pi+p)}J_0(\pi+p)=-\int_p^{\pi+p}x^{-\frac{3}{2}}\sin(x-p)J_0(x)\,\mathrm{d}x,$$

and hence show that the difference between two consecutive zeros of $J_0(x)$ is less than π.

8. If u and v are the functions defined in equations (4.5), deduce from equation (4.6) that

$$-2z\int_a^b ru^2\,\mathrm{d}r=\left[r\left(u\frac{\partial^2 u}{\partial r\partial z}-\frac{\partial u}{\partial r}\frac{\partial u}{\partial z}\right)\right]_{r=b}.$$

Hence show that equation (4.4) has no repeated roots.

9. If the zeros of $J_\nu(z)$ are p_s $(s=1,2,3,\ldots)$ show that

$$\sum_{s=1}^{\infty}\frac{1}{p_s^{\,2}}=\frac{1}{2^2(\nu+1)},\quad \sum_{s=1}^{\infty}\frac{1}{p_s^{\,4}}=\frac{1}{2^4(\nu+1)^2(\nu+2)}.$$

10. If λ, μ are positive quantities such that $0\leqslant\lambda\leqslant\mu\leqslant 1$ and $R(z)>0$, it can be assumed that the integral

$$\int\frac{H_\nu^{(1)}(\mu w)H_\nu^{(2)}(w)-H_\nu^{(2)}(\mu w)H_\nu^{(1)}(w)}{z^2-w^2}\cdot\frac{J_\nu(\lambda w)}{J_\nu(w)}\,\mathrm{d}w$$

taken round a rectangle indented at the origin and with vertices $A\pm Bi$, $\pm Bi$ tends to zero as A and B tend to infinity. Deduce the *Kneser-Sommerfeld formula*

$$\sum_{s=1}^{\infty}\frac{J_\nu(p_s\lambda)J_\nu(p_s\mu)}{(z^2-p_s^{\,2})p_sJ_\nu'^2(p_s)}=\frac{\pi J_\nu(\lambda z)}{4zJ_\nu(z)}\{J_\nu(z)Y_\nu(\mu z)-Y_\nu(z)J_\nu(\mu z)\},$$

where the p_s are the zeros of $J_\nu(z)$.

11. Show that, when $b>a>0$, the large positive real roots of the equation $J_\nu(az)Y_\nu(bz)=J_\nu(bz)Y_\nu(az)$ are given by $z\simeq s\pi/(b-a)$ where s is a positive integer. Deduce that 5·24 is an approximate root of the equation when $a=1$ and $b=4$.

12. Show that the zeros of $J_\nu'(z)$ are given approximately by

$$z\simeq(s+\tfrac{1}{2}\nu+\tfrac{1}{4})\pi-\frac{4\nu^2+3}{8(s+\frac{1}{2}\nu+\frac{1}{4})\pi}.$$

By taking $s=2,3,4,5,6$ show that 8·54, 11·71, 14·86, 18·02 and 21·16 are approximate zeros of $J_1'(z)$.

13. If $0<r<1$ and p_s are the zeros of $J_0(p)=0$ show that

(i) $$1=\sum_{s=1}^{\infty}\frac{2J_0(p_sr)}{p_sJ_1(p_s)},$$

(ii) $$\frac{J_0(rz)}{J_0(z)}=\sum_{s=1}^{\infty}\frac{2p_sJ_0(p_sr)}{(p_s^{\,2}-z^2)J_1(p_s)}.$$

14. If $a < r < b$, $B_1(pr) = J_1(pr)\,Y_1(pa) - Y_1(pr)J_1(pa)$ and if p_s $(s = 1, 2, 3, \ldots)$ are positive roots of the equation $B_1(pb) = 0$, show that

$$\frac{r^2 - a^2}{r} = \pi\left(\frac{b^2 - a^2}{b}\right)\sum_{s=1}^{\infty}\frac{J_1(p_s a)J_1(p_s b)}{J_1^{\,2}(p_s a) - J_1^{\,2}(p_s b)}\,B_1(p_s r).$$

15. Find the Hankel transform of order ν (with real part greater than -1) of the function $f(r)$ given by $f(r) = r^\nu$ when $0 < r < a$ and $f(r) = 0$ when $r > a$. Deduce that

$$\int_0^\infty J_{\nu+1}(ap)J_\nu(rp)\,\mathrm{d}p = \begin{cases} r^\nu/a^{\nu+1}, & 0 < r < a, \\ 0, & r > a. \end{cases}$$

16. By taking $R(\nu) > 0$ and first finding the Hankel transform of order ν of the function defined by

$$f(r) = (r/a)^\nu \text{ when } 0 < r < a \quad\text{and}\quad f(r) = (a/r)^\nu \text{ when } r > a,$$

show that $f(r)$ is represented by the integral

$$2\nu\int_0^\infty p^{-1}J_\nu(ap)J_\nu(rp)\,\mathrm{d}p.$$

17. The Hankel transform of order ν of $f(r)$ is denoted by $F(p;\nu)$. Show that the transform of order ν of $2\nu r^{-1}f(r)$ is

$$pF(p;\nu - 1) + pF(p;\nu + 1)$$

and that this can also be written in the form

$$2\nu p^{-\nu}\int_0^p t^\nu F(t;\nu - 1)\,\mathrm{d}t.$$

18. If the real part of ν is greater than -1, if $0 < r < a$ and if p_s $(s = 1, 2, 3, \ldots)$ are the positive roots of the equation $J_\nu(pa) = 0$ where $a > 1$, show that

$$\sum_{s=1}^{\infty}\frac{J_{\nu+1}(p_s)J_\nu(p_s r)}{p_s J_{\nu+1}^{\,2}(p_s a)} = \tfrac{1}{2}a^2\int_0^\infty J_{\nu+1}(p)J_\nu(rp)\,\mathrm{d}p.$$

CHAPTER 5

SOME FINITE AND INFINITE DEFINITE INTEGRALS CONTAINING BESSEL FUNCTIONS

5.1 Introduction

Finite and infinite definite integrals involving Bessel functions are of considerable importance in mathematical physics and this chapter gives a small selection of the very many different integrals which may appear in the solution of physical problems. Most of the integrals considered here can be evaluated either by expanding the Bessel function in powers of its argument and integrating term by term or by replacing the Bessel function by an integral representation and changing the order of integration. Both of these processes are such that a detailed discussion is required to obtain a rigorous evaluation of the integrals. Lack of space prevents such details being given here and the reader who is interested in this aspect is referred to the excellent thirteenth chapter of G. N. Watson's well-known treatise.

5.2 Sonine's finite integral and its extension

A formula expressing $J_{\mu+\nu+1}(z)$ in terms of a Bessel function of *lower* order μ was first given by N. J. Sonine and is often known as *Sonine's finite integral.* The formula, which is valid when the real parts of both μ and ν are greater than -1, is

$$J_{\mu+\nu+1}(z) = \frac{z^{\nu+1}}{2^{\nu}\Gamma(\nu+1)}\int_0^{\pi/2} J_\mu(z\sin\theta)\sin^{\mu+1}\theta\cos^{2\nu+1}\theta\,d\theta \tag{5.1}$$

and can be obtained as follows. Using the series (1.5) for $J_\mu(z\sin\theta)$ and changing the order of integration and summation, the right-hand side of equation (5.1) is

$$\sum_{r=0}^{\infty}\frac{(-1)^r z^{\mu+\nu+2r+1}}{2^{\mu+\nu+2r}r!\,\Gamma(\nu+1)\Gamma(\mu+r+1)}\int_0^{\pi/2}\sin^{2\mu+2r+1}\theta\cos^{2\nu+1}\theta\,d\theta.$$

Using the known result

$$\int_0^{\pi/2}\sin^{2\mu+2r+1}\theta\cos^{2\nu+1}\theta\,d\theta = \frac{\Gamma(\mu+r+1)\Gamma(\nu+1)}{2\Gamma(\mu+\nu+r+2)},$$

this becomes

$$\sum_{r=0}^{\infty}\frac{(-1)^r z^{\mu+\nu+2r+1}}{2^{\mu+\nu+2r+1}r!\,\Gamma(\mu+\nu+r+2)}$$

and this, by (1.5), is $J_{\mu+\nu+1}(z)$.

Example 1. *Show, in a similar manner to the above, that when* $R(\nu) > -\frac{1}{2}$

$$J_\nu^2(z) = \frac{2z^\nu}{\pi^{\frac{1}{2}}\Gamma(\nu + \frac{1}{2})} \int_0^{\pi/2} J_\nu(2z \sin \theta) \sin^\nu \theta \cos^{2\nu} \theta \, d\theta. \tag{5.2}$$

Using (1.5) and changing the order of integration and summation, the right-hand side of (5.2) is

$$\frac{2}{\pi^{\frac{1}{2}}\Gamma(\nu + \frac{1}{2})} \sum_{r=0}^{\infty} \frac{(-1)^r z^{2\nu+2r}}{r!\Gamma(\nu + r + 1)} \int_0^\infty \sin^{2\nu+2r} \theta \cos^{2\nu} \theta \, d\theta$$

$$= \frac{2}{\pi^{\frac{1}{2}}\Gamma(\nu + \frac{1}{2})} \sum_{r=0}^{\infty} \frac{(-1)^r z^{2\nu+2r}}{r!\Gamma(\nu + r + 1)} \cdot \frac{\Gamma(\nu + r + \frac{1}{2})\Gamma(\nu + \frac{1}{2})}{2\Gamma(2\nu + r + 1)}$$

when we replace the integral by its value in terms of gamma functions. But

$$\Gamma(2\nu + 2r + 1) = \pi^{-\frac{1}{2}}2^{2\nu+2r}\Gamma(\nu + r + \tfrac{1}{2})\Gamma(\nu + r + 1),$$

so that substitution for $\Gamma(\nu + r + \frac{1}{2})$ makes the right-hand side of (5.2) to be

$$\sum_{r=0}^{\infty} \frac{(-1)^r \Gamma(2\nu + 2r + 1)(z/2)^{2\nu+2r}}{r!\Gamma^2(\nu + r + 1)\Gamma(2\nu + r + 1)}$$

and this, by equation (2.21), is $J_\nu^2(z)$.

Sonine also obtained the formula

$$J_{\mu-\nu-1}(z) = \frac{z^{\nu+1}}{2^\nu\Gamma(\nu + 1)} \int_0^\infty J_\mu(z \cosh \theta) \cosh^{1-\mu} \theta \sinh^{2\nu+1} \theta \, d\theta, \tag{5.3}$$

valid when $R(\frac{1}{2}\mu - \frac{1}{4}) > R(\nu) > -1$ and z is a positive real quantity. This can be regarded as an extension of formula (5.1) for it expresses a Bessel function in terms of one of *higher* order. A formal derivation of this formula starts by using equation (3.11) giving

$$2\pi i J_\mu\{\sqrt{(t^2 + z^2)}\} = 2^{-\mu}(t^2 + z^2)^{\frac{1}{2}\mu} \int_{c-i\infty}^{c+i\infty} \exp\left(w - \frac{t^2 + z^2}{4w}\right) w^{-\mu-1} \, dw$$

where $c > 0$. Hence, after changing the order of integration

$$2\pi i \int_0^\infty \frac{J_\mu\{\sqrt{(t^2 + z^2)}\}}{(t^2 + z^2)^{\frac{1}{2}\mu}} t^{2\nu+1} \, dt$$

$$= 2^{-\mu} \int_{c-i\infty}^{c+i\infty} w^{-\mu-1} \exp\left(w - \frac{z^2}{4w}\right) dw \int_0^\infty t^{2\nu+1} e^{-t^2/4w} \, dt. \tag{5.4}$$

Setting $t^2 = 4w\alpha$, we find that

$$\int_0^\infty t^{2\nu+1} e^{-t^2/4w} \, dt = 2^{2\nu+1} w^{\nu+1} \int_0^\infty \alpha^\nu e^{-\alpha} \, d\alpha = 2^{2\nu+1} w^{\nu+1} \Gamma(\nu + 1)$$

so that the integral on the left of (5.4) becomes

$$2^{2\nu-\mu+1}\Gamma(\nu + 1) \int_{c-i\infty}^{c+i\infty} w^{\nu-\mu} \exp\left(w - \frac{z^2}{4w}\right) dw.$$

Again using (3.11), we therefore have

$$\int_0^\infty \frac{J_\mu\{\sqrt{(t^2+z^2)}\}}{(t^2+z^2)^{\frac{1}{2}\mu}}\, t^{2\nu+1}\, dt = \frac{2^\nu\Gamma(\nu+1)}{z^{\mu-\nu-1}} J_{\mu-\nu-1}(z) \tag{5.5}$$

and the result (5.3) follows when we write $t = z\sinh\theta$ and make a few reductions.

5.3 Some exponential integrals containing Bessel functions

Special cases of the general integral

$$\int_0^\infty e^{-pt} J_\nu(at) t^{\mu-1}\, dt, \quad R(p) > 0, \quad R(\mu+\nu) > 0, \tag{5.6}$$

often occur in the solution of physical problems. It can be evaluated by expanding the Bessel function, interchanging the order of integration and summation, and expressing the resulting integral in terms of gamma functions. Thus we find, assuming that $|a| < |p|$,

$$\begin{aligned}\int_0^\infty e^{-pt} J_\nu(at) t^{\mu-1}\, dt &= \sum_{r=0}^\infty \frac{(-1)^r(\frac{1}{2}a)^{\nu+2r}}{r!\,\Gamma(\nu+r+1)} \int_0^\infty t^{\mu+\nu+2r-1} e^{-pt}\, dt \\ &= \sum_{r=0}^\infty \frac{(-1)^r(\frac{1}{2}a)^{\nu+2r}}{r!\,\Gamma(\nu+r+1)} \cdot \frac{\Gamma(\mu+\nu+2r)}{p^{\mu+\nu+2r}} \\ &= \frac{(a/2p)^\nu}{p^\mu} \sum_{r=0}^\infty \frac{(-1)^r\Gamma(\mu+\nu+2r)}{r!\,\Gamma(\nu+r+1)} \left(\frac{a^2}{4p^2}\right)^r,\end{aligned} \tag{5.7}$$

and it can be shown that this result remains true when the restrictions $R(p) > 0$ and $|a| < |p|$ are replaced by $R(p \pm ia) > 0$.

The series in (5.7) can be expressed in terms of the hypergeometric function introduced in §2.3 but the details will not be given here. For certain values of μ and ν the series reduces to an elementary function. For example, taking $\nu = 0$, $\mu = 1$, we have

$$\begin{aligned}\int_0^\infty e^{-pt} J_0(at)\, dt &= \frac{1}{p} \sum_{r=0}^\infty \frac{(-1)^r\Gamma(1+2r)}{r!\,\Gamma(1+r)} \left(\frac{a^2}{4p^2}\right)^r \\ &= \frac{1}{p}\left\{1 - \frac{a^2}{2p^2} + \frac{3a^4}{8p^4} - \frac{5a^6}{16p^6} + \dots\right\} \\ &= \frac{1}{p}\left(1 + \frac{a^2}{p^2}\right)^{-\frac{1}{2}} = \frac{1}{(p^2+a^2)^{\frac{1}{2}}}.\end{aligned} \tag{5.8}$$

Also, with $\nu = 1$, $\mu = 2$

$$\begin{aligned}\int_0^\infty e^{-pt} J_1(at) t\, dt &= \frac{a}{2p^3} \sum_{r=0}^\infty \frac{(-1)^r\Gamma(3+2r)}{r!\,\Gamma(2+r)} \left(\frac{a^2}{4p^2}\right)^r \\ &= \frac{a}{2p^3}\left\{2 - \frac{3a^2}{p^2} + \frac{15a^4}{4p^4} - \frac{35a^6}{8p^6} + \dots\right\} \\ &= \frac{a}{(p^2+a^2)^{\frac{3}{2}}},\end{aligned} \tag{5.9}$$

and integration with respect to p from p to ∞ then gives

$$\int_0^\infty e^{-pt} J_1(at)\, dt = \frac{(p^2+a^2)^{\frac{1}{2}} - p}{a(p^2+a^2)^{\frac{1}{2}}}. \tag{5.10}$$

It can be shown that the more general result

$$\int_0^\infty e^{-pt} J_\nu(at)\, dt = \frac{\{(p^2+a^2)^{\frac{1}{2}} - p\}^\nu}{a^\nu(p^2+a^2)^{\frac{1}{2}}} \tag{5.11}$$

is valid when $R(\nu) > -1$ and this formula gives the Laplace transform of the function $J_\nu(at)$.

Example 2. *Show that*

$$\int_0^\infty \frac{p}{\sqrt{(a^2+p^2)}} J_0(rp)\, dp = \frac{e^{-ar}}{r}, \quad R(p \pm ia) > 0. \tag{5.12}$$

Writing $t = r$ and interchanging a with p, equation (5.8) gives

$$\int_0^\infty e^{-ar} J_0(pr)\, dr = \frac{1}{\sqrt{(a^2+p^2)}}$$

showing that $(a^2+p^2)^{-\frac{1}{2}}$ is the Hankel transform of order zero of the function e^{-ar}/r. The inversion theorem (4.38) then gives the required result at once.

The integral

$$\int_0^\infty e^{-p^2t^2} J_\nu(at) t^{\nu+1}\, dt, \quad R(\nu) > -1 \tag{5.13}$$

can be evaluated in a similar way. Thus, replacing the Bessel function by its expansion and changing the order of integration and summation,

$$\int_0^\infty e^{-p^2t^2} J_\nu(at) t^{\nu+1}\, dt = \sum_{r=0}^\infty \frac{(-1)^r(\frac{1}{2}a)^{\nu+2r}}{r!\,\Gamma(\nu+r+1)} \int_0^\infty t^{2\nu+2r+1} e^{-p^2t^2}\, dt.$$

By writing $p^2t^2 = \alpha$, the integral on the right becomes

$$\tfrac{1}{2}p^{-2(\nu+r+1)} \int_0^\infty \alpha^{\nu+r} e^{-\alpha}\, d\alpha = \frac{\Gamma(\nu+r+1)}{2p^{2(\nu+r+1)}}$$

and we find

$$\begin{aligned}\int_0^\infty e^{-p^2t^2} J_\nu(at) t^{\nu+1}\, dt &= \frac{(\frac{1}{2}a)^\nu}{2p^{2(\nu+1)}} \sum_{r=0}^\infty \frac{(-1)^r(\frac{1}{4}a^2)^r}{r!\,p^{2r}} \\ &= \frac{a^\nu}{(2p^2)^{\nu+1}} \exp\left(-\frac{a^2}{4p^2}\right).\end{aligned} \tag{5.14}$$

The special case in which $\nu = 0$ was first discussed by H. Weber and is usually known as *Weber's first exponential integral.* More general integrals in which the index of t in the integrand of (5.13) is unrelated to the order of the Bessel function can be evaluated in the same way but the resulting series cannot usually be replaced by an elementary function.

Example 3. *Show that, when $R(\nu) > -1$ and a, x are real and positive,*

$$\Gamma(\nu+1)\int_0^\infty \frac{J_\nu(at)t^{\nu+1}}{(t^2+x^2)^{\nu+1}}\,dt = (\tfrac{1}{2}a)^\nu K_0(ax). \tag{5.15}$$

From the integral defining the gamma function we have, when $R(\nu) > -1$,

$$\Gamma(\nu+1) = \int_0^\infty e^{-\alpha}\alpha^\nu\,d\alpha = (t^2+x^2)^{\nu+1}\int_0^\infty \beta^\nu \exp\{-(t^2+x^2)\beta\}\,d\beta$$

where, in the last step, we have written $\alpha = (t^2+x^2)\beta$. Using this result

$$\Gamma(\nu+1)\int_0^\infty \frac{J_\nu(at)t^{\nu+1}}{(t^2+x^2)^{\nu+1}}\,dt = \int_0^\infty J_\nu(at)t^{\nu+1}\,dt\int_0^\infty \beta^\nu \exp\{-(t^2+x^2)\beta\}\,d\beta$$

$$= \int_0^\infty \beta^\nu \exp(-x^2\beta)\,d\beta\int_0^\infty \exp(-t^2\beta)J_\nu(at)t^{\nu+1}\,dt$$

$$= (\tfrac{1}{2}a)^\nu \,.\, \tfrac{1}{2}\int_0^\infty \exp\left(-x^2\beta - \frac{a^2}{4\beta}\right)\frac{d\beta}{\beta}$$

using (5.14). Writing $\frac{1}{2}ae^\theta = x\beta$ so that $d\beta/\beta = d\theta$ and

$$x^2\beta + \frac{a^2}{4\beta} = \tfrac{1}{2}axe^\theta + \tfrac{1}{2}axe^{-\theta} = ax\cosh\theta,$$

this gives

$$\Gamma(\nu+1)\int_0^\infty \frac{J_\nu(at)t^{\nu+1}}{(t^2+x^2)^{\nu+1}}\,dt = (\tfrac{1}{2}a)^\nu \,.\, \tfrac{1}{2}\int_{-\infty}^\infty \exp(-ax\cosh\theta)\,d\theta$$

$$= (\tfrac{1}{2}a)^\nu K_0(ax)$$

when use is made of equation (3.20).

If we apply Gegenbauer's addition theorem (2.36) in the form

$$\frac{J_\nu(Rt)}{(Rt)^\nu} = \frac{2^\nu\Gamma(\nu)}{(abt^2)^\nu}\sum_{s=0}^\infty (\nu+s)J_{\nu+s}(at)J_{\nu+s}(bt)C_s^\nu(\cos\theta), \tag{5.16}$$

where $R^2 = a^2 + b^2 - 2ab\cos\theta$, to Weber's first exponential integral we can evaluate an exponential integral containing the product of two Bessel functions. To do this we use the result*

$$\int_0^\pi \sin^{2\nu}\theta\, C_s^\nu(\cos\theta)C_r^\nu(\cos\theta)\,d\theta = \begin{cases} 0, & \text{when } r \neq s, \\ \dfrac{\pi\Gamma(2\nu+s)}{2^{2\nu-1}(\nu+s)\,.\,s!\,\Gamma^2(\nu)}, & \text{when } r = s, \end{cases}$$

* See W. Magnus and F. Oberhettinger (translated by J. Wermer), *Special Functions of Mathematical Physics* (Chelsea Pub. Co., New York, 1949), p. 77.

and apply this to (5.16) to give, since $C_0^\nu(\cos\theta) = 1$ and $\Gamma(2\nu) = 2^{2\nu-1}\pi^{-\frac{1}{2}}\Gamma(\nu) \times \Gamma(\nu+\frac{1}{2})$,

$$\int_0^\pi \frac{J_\nu(Rt)\sin^{2\nu}\theta}{R^\nu t^\nu}\,d\theta = 2^\nu \pi^{\frac{1}{2}}\Gamma(\nu+\tfrac{1}{2})\frac{J_\nu(at)}{(at)^\nu}\cdot\frac{J_\nu(bt)}{(bt)^\nu}. \tag{5.17}$$

Hence

$$\begin{aligned}\int_0^\infty e^{-p^2t^2}J_\nu(at)J_\nu(bt)t\,dt &= \frac{(\frac{1}{2}ab)^\nu}{\pi^{\frac{1}{2}}\Gamma(\nu+\frac{1}{2})}\int_0^\pi \sin^{2\nu}\theta\,d\theta\int_0^\infty e^{-p^2t^2}\frac{J_\nu(Rt)}{R^\nu}t^{\nu+1}\,dt\\ &= \frac{(\frac{1}{4}ab/p^2)^\nu}{2p^2\pi^{\frac{1}{2}}\Gamma(\nu+\frac{1}{2})}\int_0^\pi \exp\left(-\frac{R^2}{4p^2}\right)\sin^{2\nu}\theta\,d\theta\\ &= \frac{(\frac{1}{4}ab/p^2)^\nu}{2p^2\pi^{\frac{1}{2}}\Gamma(\nu+\frac{1}{2})}\exp\left(-\frac{a^2+b^2}{4p^2}\right)\\ &\quad\times\int_0^\pi \exp\left(\frac{ab\cos\theta}{2p^2}\right)\sin^{2\nu}\theta\,d\theta \end{aligned} \tag{5.18}$$

when we use (5.14) in the penultimate step. Expanding the exponential and interchanging the order of integration and summation

$$\begin{aligned}\int_0^\pi \exp\left(\frac{ab\cos\theta}{2p^2}\right)\sin^{2\nu}\theta\,d\theta &= \sum_{s=0}^\infty\left(\frac{ab}{2p^2}\right)^s\frac{1}{s!}\int_0^\pi \cos^s\theta\sin^{2\nu}\theta\,d\theta\\ &= \sum_{s=0}^\infty\left(\frac{ab}{2p^2}\right)^{2s}\cdot\frac{1}{(2s)!}\cdot\frac{\Gamma(s+\frac{1}{2})\Gamma(\nu+\frac{1}{2})}{\Gamma(s+\nu+1)}\\ &= \pi^{\frac{1}{2}}\Gamma(\nu+\tfrac{1}{2})\sum_{s=0}^\infty\frac{(\frac{1}{4}ab/p^2)^{2s}}{s!\Gamma(s+\nu+1)}.\end{aligned}$$

Substituting in (5.18) and using formula (1.51) we therefore have

$$\int_0^\infty e^{-p^2t^2}J_\nu(at)J_\nu(bt)t\,dt = \frac{1}{2p^2}\exp\left(-\frac{a^2+b^2}{4p^2}\right)I_\nu\left(\frac{ab}{2p^2}\right) \tag{5.19}$$

and this result, valid when $R(\nu) > -1$, is known as *Weber's second exponential integral.*

5.4 Sonine's discontinuous integral

Formula (5.14) can also be used in evaluating an interesting discontinuous integral which was first investigated by Sonine. We start with formula (3.11) writing az in place of z and setting $t = \frac{1}{2}au$ so that, with $c, c' > 0$,

$$\begin{aligned}J_\nu(az) &= \frac{(\frac{1}{2}az)^\nu}{2\pi i}\int_{c-i\infty}^{c+i\infty}\exp\left(t-\frac{a^2z^2}{4t}\right)t^{-\nu-1}\,dt\\ &= \frac{z^\nu}{2\pi i}\int_{c'-i\infty}^{c'+i\infty}\exp\left\{\tfrac{1}{2}a\left(u-\frac{z^2}{u}\right)\right\}u^{-\nu-1}\,du.\end{aligned} \tag{5.20}$$

Using this formula with $z = \sqrt{(t^2 + x^2)}$ and formally interchanging the order of integration

$$\int_0^\infty J_\mu(bt)J_\nu\{a\sqrt{(t^2 + x^2)}\}(t^2 + x^2)^{-\frac{1}{2}\nu}t^{\mu+1}\,dt$$

$$= \frac{1}{2\pi i}\int_{c'-i\infty}^{c'+i\infty} u^{-\nu-1}\exp\left\{\tfrac{1}{2}a\left(u - \frac{x^2}{u}\right)\right\}du\int_0^\infty J_\mu(bt)t^{\mu+1}\exp\left(-\frac{at^2}{2u}\right)dt$$

$$= \frac{b^\mu}{2\pi i a^{\mu+1}}\int_{c'-i\infty}^{c'+i\infty} u^{\mu-\nu}\exp\left\{\frac{(a^2 - b^2)u}{2a} - \frac{ax^2}{2u}\right\}du \tag{5.21}$$

when use is made of (5.14). When $a < b$, the contour involved can be deformed into a semi-circle on the right of the imaginary axis and the integral along this is zero. When $a > b$, the integral in (5.21) becomes, writing $\sqrt{(a^2 - b^2)}u = au'$,

$$\frac{b^\mu}{2\pi i a^{\mu+1}}\frac{a^{\mu-\nu+1}}{\{\sqrt{(a^2 - b^2)}\}^{\mu-\nu+1}}\int_{c-i\infty}^{c+i\infty}(u')^{\mu-\nu}\exp\left\{\tfrac{1}{2}\sqrt{(a^2 - b^2)}\left(u' - \frac{x^2}{u'}\right)\right\}du'$$

and this integral can be evaluated by again using (5.20). The final result is

$$\int_0^\infty J_\mu(bt)\frac{J_\nu\{a\sqrt{(t^2 + x^2)}\}}{(t^2 + x^2)^{\frac{1}{2}\nu}}t^{\mu+1}\,dt$$

$$= \begin{cases} \dfrac{b^\mu}{a^\nu}\left\{\dfrac{\sqrt{(a^2 - b^2)}}{x}\right\}^{\nu-\mu-1} J_{\nu-\mu-1}\{x\sqrt{(a^2 - b^2)}\}, & 0 < b \leqslant a, \\ 0, & b > a, \end{cases} \tag{5.22}$$

and a more detailed consideration than that given here shows that this formula is valid when $R(\nu) > R(\mu) > -1$ with $a \neq b$ and when $R(\nu) > R(\mu + 1) > 0$ with $a = b$.

Special cases of (5.22) which are of interest include the following:

(i) Dividing by b^μ and letting b tend to zero

$$\int_0^\infty \frac{J_\nu\{a\sqrt{(t^2 + x^2)}\}}{(t^2 + x^2)^{\frac{1}{2}\nu}}t^{2\mu+1}\,dt = \frac{2^\mu\Gamma(\mu + 1)}{a^{\mu+1}x^{\nu-\mu-1}}J_{\nu-\mu-1}(ax), \tag{5.23}$$

and this is, in effect, Sonine's formula (5.5).

(ii) Letting x tend to zero

$$\int_0^\infty J_\nu(at)J_\mu(bt)t^{\mu-\nu+1}\,dt = \begin{cases} \dfrac{b^\mu(a^2 - b^2)^{\nu-\mu-1}}{2^{\nu-\mu-1}\Gamma(\nu - \mu)a^\nu}, & 0 < b \leqslant a, \\ 0, & b > a. \end{cases} \tag{5.24}$$

(iii) Taking $\mu = -\frac{1}{2}$, $\nu = 0$,

$$\int_0^\infty J_0\{a\sqrt{(t^2 + x^2)}\}\cos bt\,dt = \begin{cases} \dfrac{\cos\{x\sqrt{a^2 - b^2)}\}}{\sqrt{(a^2 - b^2)}}, & 0 < b < a, \\ 0, & b > a. \end{cases} \tag{5.25}$$

5.5 Weber's infinite integral

The result

$$\int_0^\infty t^{\mu-\nu-1} J_\nu(t)\,dt = \frac{2^{\mu-\nu-1}\Gamma(\frac{1}{2}\mu)}{\Gamma(\nu - \frac{1}{2}\mu + 1)} \tag{5.26}$$

was first obtained by H. Weber for the case in which ν is an integer and it was generalized later by P. Schafheitlin. It can be formally established for a limited range of values of the parameters μ and ν by using Poisson's integral representation (3.4) for $J_\nu(t)$ and interchanging the order of integrations. Thus

$$\begin{aligned}\int_0^\infty t^{\mu-\nu-1} J_\nu(t)\,dt &= \frac{2^{1-\nu}}{\pi^{\frac{1}{2}}\Gamma(\nu + \frac{1}{2})}\int_0^{\frac{1}{2}\pi} \sin^{2\nu}\theta\,d\theta \int_0^\infty t^{\mu-1}\cos(t\cos\theta)\,dt \\ &= \frac{2^{1-\nu}}{\pi^{\frac{1}{2}}\Gamma(\nu + \frac{1}{2})}\int_0^{\frac{1}{2}\pi} \sin^{2\nu}\theta\cos^{-\mu}\theta\,d\theta \int_0^\infty T^{\mu-1}\cos T\,dT,\end{aligned}$$

writing $T = t\cos\theta$ in the last line. Since

$$\int_0^{\frac{1}{2}\pi} \sin^{2\nu}\theta\cos^{-\mu}\theta\,d\theta = \frac{\Gamma(\nu + \frac{1}{2})\Gamma(\frac{1}{2} - \frac{1}{2}\mu)}{2\Gamma(\nu - \frac{1}{2}\mu + 1)},$$

$$\int_0^\infty T^{\mu-1}\cos T\,dT = \Gamma(\mu)\cos(\tfrac{1}{2}\mu\pi),$$

and since $\Gamma(\frac{1}{2} - \frac{1}{2}\mu)\Gamma(\frac{1}{2} + \frac{1}{2}\mu) = \pi\sec(\frac{1}{2}\mu\pi)$, $\Gamma(\mu) = 2^{\mu-1}\pi^{-\frac{1}{2}}\Gamma(\frac{1}{2}\mu)\Gamma(\frac{1}{2} + \frac{1}{2}\mu)$, this gives the result (5.26) for those values of μ and ν for which the formulae used in deriving it are valid. Generalization beyond these values can be obtained by using partial integrations and recurrence formulae and equation (5.26) can, in fact, be shown to hold when $R(\nu) + 3/2 > R(\mu) > 0$.

5.6 The Weber-Schafheitlin discontinuous integral

The integral

$$I(\nu, \mu, \lambda, a, b) = \int_0^\infty \frac{J_\nu(at)J_\mu(bt)}{t^\lambda}\,dt \tag{5.27}$$

in which a, b are positive, $R(\nu + \mu + 1) > R(\lambda) > -1$ when $a \neq b$ and $R(\nu + \mu + 1) > R(\lambda) > 0$ when $a = b$ was investigated in special cases by Weber and in its full generality by Schafheitlin. The case in which $\lambda = \nu - \mu - 1$ is of particular importance in physical applications and the value of the integral in this case has been given in (5.24). It can also then be found very simply by applying Hankel's inversion theorem to Sonine's first integral. Thus, replacing $\mu + \nu + 1$ by ν, z by p and writing $\sin\theta = r$ in (5.1),

$$J_\nu(p) = \frac{p^{\nu-\mu}}{2^{\nu-\mu-1}\Gamma(\nu - \mu)}\int_0^1 J_\mu(pr)r^{\mu+1}(1 - r^2)^{\nu-\mu-1}\,dr \tag{5.28}$$

showing that $2^{\nu-\mu-1}\Gamma(\nu - \mu)p^{\mu-\nu}J_\nu(p)$ is the Hankel transform of order μ of a function of r equal to $r^\mu(1 - r^2)^{\nu-\mu-1}$ when $0 < r < 1$ and to zero when $r > 1$. Hankel's inversion theorem (4.37), (4.38) then gives

$$\int_0^\infty \frac{J_\nu(p)J_\mu(rp)}{p^{\nu-\mu-1}}\,dp = \begin{cases} \dfrac{2^{\mu-\nu+1}}{\Gamma(\nu-\mu)}\, r^\mu(1-r^2)^{\nu-\mu-1}, & 0 < r < 1, \\ 0, & r > 1, \end{cases} \tag{5.29}$$

and formula (5.24) is obtained by writing $p = at$, $r = b/a$.

The value of the general integral in (5.27) can be found by first considering

$$\int_0^\infty e^{-ct}\,\frac{J_\nu(at)J_\mu(zt)}{t^\lambda}\,dt.$$

The Bessel function $J_\mu(zt)$ is then expanded in powers of zt and conditions are established under which the order of integration and summation may be interchanged. Formula (5.7), with a suitable transformation of the hypergeometric function contained in it, is then used to evaluate the resulting integrals. Consideration of the conditions of convergence then shows that we may set $z = b$ and allow c to tend to zero. The details, which are complicated and will not be given here, can be found in §13.4 of Watson's treatise. The final result is that, when $0 < b < a$, the value of the integral $I(\nu, \mu, \lambda, a, b)$ is

$$\frac{b^\mu \Gamma(\frac{1}{2}\nu + \frac{1}{2}\mu - \frac{1}{2}\lambda + \frac{1}{2})}{2^\lambda a^{\mu-\lambda+1}\Gamma(\mu+1)\Gamma(\frac{1}{2}\lambda + \frac{1}{2}\nu - \frac{1}{2}\mu + \frac{1}{2})} \times {}_2F_1\left(\frac{\nu+\mu-\lambda+1}{2}, \frac{\mu-\lambda-\nu+1}{2}; \mu+1; \frac{b^2}{a^2}\right). \tag{5.30}$$

Interchanging a, b and also μ, ν, we find that, when $0 < a < b$, the integral takes the value

$$\frac{a^\nu \Gamma(\frac{1}{2}\mu + \frac{1}{2}\nu - \frac{1}{2}\lambda + \frac{1}{2})}{2^\lambda b^{\nu-\lambda+1}\Gamma(\nu+1)\Gamma(\frac{1}{2}\lambda + \frac{1}{2}\mu - \frac{1}{2}\nu + \frac{1}{2})} \times {}_2F_1\left(\frac{\mu+\nu-\lambda+1}{2}, \frac{\nu-\lambda-\mu+1}{2}; \nu+1; \frac{a^2}{b^2}\right). \tag{5.31}$$

Formulae (5.30) and (5.31) show that the value of the integral is a function of a/b which is not analytic at $a/b = 1$. A complete investigation of the integral in this case is again complicated and the details may be found in §13.41 of Watson's book; the result is

$$\int_0^\infty \frac{J_\nu(at)J_\mu(at)}{t^\lambda}\,dt = \frac{(\frac{1}{2}a)^{\lambda-1}\Gamma(\lambda)\Gamma\left(\dfrac{\nu+\mu-\lambda+1}{2}\right)}{2\Gamma\left(\dfrac{\lambda+\nu-\mu+1}{2}\right)\Gamma\left(\dfrac{\lambda+\nu+\mu+1}{2}\right)\Gamma\left(\dfrac{\lambda-\nu+\mu+1}{2}\right)}. \tag{5.32}$$

In the case $\lambda = 1$, which is of importance in some practical applications, we have

$$\int_0^\infty \frac{J_\nu(at)J_\mu(at)}{t}\,dt$$
$$= \frac{\Gamma(\frac{1}{2}\nu + \frac{1}{2}\mu)}{2\Gamma(1 + \frac{1}{2}\nu - \frac{1}{2}\mu)\Gamma(1 + \frac{1}{2}\nu + \frac{1}{2}\mu)\Gamma(1 - \frac{1}{2}\nu + \frac{1}{2}\mu)}$$
$$= \frac{2}{\pi}\cdot\frac{\sin\frac{1}{2}(\mu - \nu)\pi}{\mu^2 - \nu^2}, \tag{5.33}$$

the formulae $\Gamma(1 + z) = z\Gamma(z)$, $\Gamma(z)\Gamma(1 - z) = \pi \operatorname{cosec} z\pi$ having been used in the last step.

It is worth noticing that if $\lambda + \nu - \mu + 1$ or $\lambda + \mu - \nu + 1$ is an even negative integer or zero, the right-hand sides of formulae (5.30) and (5.31) are respectively zero. Other special cases to be noted are:

$$\int_0^\infty J_0(at)\sin bt\,dt = \begin{cases} 1/\sqrt{(b^2 - a^2)}, & 0 < a < b, \\ \infty, & a = b, \\ 0, & a > b; \end{cases} \tag{5.34}$$

$$\int_0^\infty J_0(at)\cos bt\,dt = \begin{cases} 0, & 0 < a < b, \\ \infty, & a = b, \\ 1/\sqrt{(a^2 - b^2)}, & a > b; \end{cases} \tag{5.35}$$

$$\int_0^\infty \frac{J_0(at)\sin bt}{t}\,dt = \begin{cases} \frac{1}{2}\pi, & 0 < a \leqslant b, \\ \sin^{-1}(b/a) & a \geqslant b; \end{cases} \tag{5.36}$$

$$\int_0^\infty \frac{J_\nu(at)J_\nu(bt)}{t}\,dt = \begin{cases} \dfrac{1}{2\nu}\left(\dfrac{a}{b}\right)^\nu, & 0 < a \leqslant b, \\ \dfrac{1}{2\nu}\left(\dfrac{b}{a}\right)^\nu, & a \geqslant b. \end{cases} \tag{5.37}$$

5.7 The Bessel-integral function

The integral

$$Ji_\nu(z) = -\int_z^\infty \frac{J_\nu(t)}{t}\,dt \tag{5.38}$$

is known as the *Bessel-integral function of order* ν and is usually denoted by the symbol shown on the left of equation (5.38). It is of frequent use in the practical applications of Bessel functions, particularly when $\nu = 0, 1, 2, 3, \ldots$ and z is a positive real quantity x, and we give below some of its properties in this case.

Putting $\mu = \nu = n$ (a positive integer) in (5.26), we have

$$\int_0^\infty \frac{J_n(t)}{t}\,dt = \frac{2^{-1}\Gamma(\frac{1}{2}n)}{\Gamma(\frac{1}{2}n + 1)} = \frac{1}{n} \tag{5.39}$$

so that

$$nJi_n(x) = -n\int_x^\infty t^{-1}J_n(t)\,\mathrm{d}t = -n\int_0^\infty t^{-1}J_n(t)\,\mathrm{d}t + n\int_0^x t^{-1}J_n(t)\,\mathrm{d}t$$

$$= -1 + n\int_0^x t^{-1}J_n(t)\,\mathrm{d}t. \tag{5.40}$$

Substitution of the series (1.5) in the integral on the right then gives, with formal change of the order of integration and summation,

$$nJi_n(x) = -1 + n\sum_{r=0}^\infty \frac{(-1)^r}{r!(n+r)!2^{n+2r}}\int_0^x t^{n+2r-1}\,\mathrm{d}t$$

$$= -1 + n\sum_{r=0}^\infty \frac{(-1)^r(\tfrac{1}{2}x)^{n+2r}}{r!(n+r)!(n+2r)}. \tag{5.41}$$

This can be written

$$Ji_n(x) = \frac{1}{n}\left\{-1 + \frac{(\tfrac{1}{2}x)^n}{n!}\right\} + \sum_{r=1}^\infty \frac{(-1)^r(\tfrac{1}{2}x)^{n+2r}}{r!(n+r)!(n+2r)}$$

and the value of this when n is zero is

$$Ji_0(x) = \gamma + \log_e(\tfrac{1}{2}x) + \sum_{r=1}^\infty \frac{(-1)^r(\tfrac{1}{2}x)^{2r}}{(r!)^2 2r}, \tag{5.42}$$

where $\gamma = 0{\cdot}5772\ldots$ is Euler's constant.

Formulae (5.41) and (5.42) permit the calculation of the Bessel integral functions for small values of the argument x. V. G. Smith's formula for $Ji_0(x)$, useful when x is large, can be obtained as follows. Noting that $tJ_0(t)$ is the derivative with respect to t of $tJ_1(t)$, integration by parts gives

$$\int_x^\infty \frac{J_0(t)}{t^n}\,\mathrm{d}t = \int_x^\infty \frac{\mathrm{d}\{tJ_1(t)\}}{t^{n+1}} = -\frac{J_1(x)}{x^n} + (n+1)\int_x^\infty \frac{J_1(t)}{t^{n+1}}\,\mathrm{d}t.$$

Since $J_1(t) = -J_0'(t)$ this gives, again integrating by parts,

$$\int_x^\infty \frac{J_0(t)}{t^n}\,\mathrm{d}t = -\frac{J_1(x)}{x^n} + (n+1)\frac{J_0(x)}{x^{n+1}} - (n+1)^2\int_x^\infty \frac{J_0(t)}{t^{n+2}}\,\mathrm{d}t. \tag{5.43}$$

Using this with $n = 1, 3, 5, \ldots$ in succession, we find

$$Ji_0(x) = -J_0(x)\left\{\frac{2}{x^2} - \frac{2^2.4}{x^4} + \frac{2^2.4^2.6}{x^6} - \ldots\right\}$$
$$+ J_1(x)\left\{\frac{1}{x} - \frac{2^2}{x^3} + \frac{2^2.4^2}{x^5} - \ldots\right\} \tag{5.44}$$

as the required formula.

The last two of formulae (1.31) give

$$(n-1)J_{n-1}(t) - (n+1)J_{n+1}(t) = 2n\left\{J_n'(t) - \frac{J_n(t)}{t}\right\} = 2nt\frac{\mathrm{d}}{\mathrm{d}t}\left\{\frac{J_n(t)}{t}\right\},$$

so that, dividing by t and integrating with respect to t between x and ∞, we have the recurrence formula

$$(n-1)Ji_{n-1}(x) - (n+1)Ji_{n+1}(x) = \frac{2n}{x} J_n(x). \tag{5.45}$$

Since the derivative with respect to x of $Ji_n(x)$ is $x^{-1}J_n(x)$, this can be written in the form

$$(n-1)Ji_{n-1}(x) - (n+1)Ji_{n+1}(x) = 2nJi_n'(x). \tag{5.46}$$

Example 4. *If n is a positive integer, show that*

$$-nxJi_{2n}(x) = J_1(x) + 3J_3(x) + \ldots + (2n-1)J_{2n-1}(x).$$

Replacing n in equation (5.45) by 1, 3, 5, . . ., $(2n-1)$, in succession, we have

$$\begin{aligned}
-\,2Ji_2(x) &= \frac{2}{x} J_1(x),\\
2Ji_2(x) - 4Ji_4(x) &= \frac{6}{x} J_3(x),\\
4Ji_4(x) - 6Ji_6(x) &= \frac{10}{x} J_5(x),\\
\ldots\ldots\ldots&\ldots\ldots,\\
(2n-2)Ji_{2n-2}(x) - 2nJi_{2n}(x) &= \frac{4n-2}{x} J_{2n-1}(x),
\end{aligned}$$

and the required result follows by addition and multiplication by $\frac{1}{2}x$.

Example 5. *Show that*

$$-\frac{1}{2}\left(\frac{\pi}{2}\right)^{\frac{1}{2}} Ji_{\frac{1}{2}}(x) = \frac{\sin x}{x^{\frac{1}{2}}} + 2C(x^{\frac{1}{2}})$$

where $C(x) = \int_x^\infty \cos u^2 \, du$ *is Fresnel's integral.*

Using the definition (5.38) of $Ji_{\frac{1}{2}}(x)$, the formula $J_{\frac{1}{2}}(t) = (2/\pi t)^{\frac{1}{2}} \sin t$ and integrating by parts

$$\begin{aligned}
-\frac{1}{2}\left(\frac{\pi}{2}\right)^{\frac{1}{2}} Ji_{\frac{1}{2}}(x) &= \frac{1}{2}\int_x^\infty \frac{\sin t}{t^{\frac{3}{2}}}\, dt\\
&= \left[-\frac{\sin t}{t^{\frac{1}{2}}}\right]_x^\infty + \int_x^\infty \frac{\cos t}{t^{\frac{1}{2}}}\, dt\\
&= \frac{\sin x}{x^{\frac{1}{2}}} + 2\int_{\sqrt{x}}^\infty \cos u^2\, du,
\end{aligned}$$

when we set $t = u^2$ in the integral on the right.

5.8. A general integral containing a Bessel function

A method of evaluating integrals of the type

$$\int_0^\infty f(t)J_\nu(rt)\,\mathrm{d}t,$$

useful when r is large, can be obtained from a treatment by H. F. Willis of more general integrals. Here we consider the integral

$$I(p, r) = \int_0^\infty e^{-pt}f(t)J_\nu(rt)\,\mathrm{d}t \tag{5.47}$$

and assume that $f(t)$ admits a Taylor series expansion around the origin and further that the radius of convergence of this expansion covers the entire range of integration. Hence

$$\begin{aligned} I(p, r) &= \int_0^\infty e^{-pt}\left\{\sum_{s=0}^\infty \frac{t^s}{s!}f^{(s)}(0)\right\} J_\nu(rt)\,\mathrm{d}t \\ &= \sum_{s=0}^\infty \frac{f^{(s)}(0)}{s!}\int_0^\infty e^{-pt}t^sJ_\nu(rt)\,\mathrm{d}t. \end{aligned} \tag{5.48}$$

We further impose limitations such that the value of the integral

$$\int_0^\infty e^{-pt}J_\nu(rt)\,\mathrm{d}t$$

admits expansion in positive integral powers of p so that

$$\int_0^\infty e^{-pt}J_\nu(rt)\,\mathrm{d}t = \phi(p), \text{ say, } = \sum_{s=0}^\infty A_sp^s \tag{5.49}$$

where $A_s = \phi^{(s)}(0)/s!$ Differentiation of (5.49) s times with respect to p gives

$$\int_0^\infty e^{-pt}t^sJ_\nu(rt)\,\mathrm{d}t = (-1)^s\phi^{(s)}(p),$$

and substitution in (5.48) leads to

$$I(p, r) = \sum_{s=0}^\infty (-1)^sf^{(s)}(0)\phi^{(s)}(p)/s!$$

Finally, allowing p to tend to zero, we have

$$\begin{aligned} \int_0^\infty f(t)J_\nu(rt)\,\mathrm{d}t = I(0, r) &= \sum_{s=0}^\infty (-1)^sf^{(s)}(0)\phi^{(s)}(0)/s! \\ &= \sum_{s=0}^\infty (-1)^sA_sf^{(s)}(0). \end{aligned} \tag{5.50}$$

In obtaining formula (5.50), no attempt has been made to justify it and it would be an intricate problem to obtain precise conditions under which the result is valid. We shall be content to consider particular cases on their own merits and give below two examples in which the formula yields useful results. To sum up, if we expand the integral $\int_0^\infty e^{-pt}J_\nu(rt)\,dt$ in the form $\sum_{s=0}^{\infty} A_s p^s$, then the integral $\int_0^\infty f(t)J_\nu(rt)\,dt$ may well possess an expansion of the form $\sum_{s=0}^{\infty}(-1)^s A_s f^{(s)}(0)$.

Proceeding to particular cases, equation (5.8) gives

$$\int_0^\infty e^{-pt}J_0(rt)\,dt = \frac{1}{(p^2+r^2)^{\frac{1}{2}}} = \frac{1}{r}\left(1+\frac{p^2}{r^2}\right)^{-\frac{1}{2}}$$
$$= \frac{1}{r}\left(1 - \frac{1}{2}\cdot\frac{p^2}{r^2} + \frac{1\,.\,3}{2^2 2!}\cdot\frac{p^4}{r^4} - \frac{1\,.\,3\,.\,5}{2^3 3!}\cdot\frac{p^6}{r^6} + \ldots\right),$$

so that, in the notation of the last paragraph,

$$A_1 = A_3 = A_5 = \ldots = 0,$$
$$A_0 = \frac{1}{r}, \quad A_2 = -\frac{1}{2}\cdot\frac{1}{r^3}, \quad A_4 = \frac{1\,.\,3}{2^2 2!}\cdot\frac{1}{r^5}, \quad \ldots$$

and (5.50) gives

$$\int_0^\infty f(t)J_0(rt)\,dt = \frac{f(0)}{r} - \frac{1}{2}\cdot\frac{f''(0)}{r^3} + \frac{1\,.\,3}{2^2 2!}\cdot\frac{f^{(iv)}(0)}{r^5} - \ldots . \tag{5.51}$$

Similarly, starting with equation (5.10) in the form

$$\int_0^\infty e^{-pt}J_1(rt)\,dt = \frac{(p^2+r^2)^{\frac{1}{2}} - p}{r(p^2+r^2)^{\frac{1}{2}}} = \frac{1}{r} - \frac{p}{r^2}\left(1+\frac{p^2}{r^2}\right)^{-\frac{1}{2}}$$
$$= \frac{1}{r}\left(1 - \frac{p}{r} + \frac{1}{2}\cdot\frac{p^3}{r^3} - \frac{1\,.\,3}{2^2 2!}\frac{p^5}{r^5} + \ldots\right),$$

we find

$$\int_0^\infty f(t)J_1(rt)\,dt = \frac{f(0)}{r} + \frac{f'(0)}{r^2} - \frac{1}{2}\cdot\frac{f'''(0)}{r^4} + \frac{1\,.\,3}{2^2 2!}\frac{f^{(v)}(0)}{r^6} - \ldots \tag{5.52}$$

Example 6. *Use formula* (5.52) *to evaluate*

$$\text{(i)} \int_0^\infty J_1(rt)\,dt, \quad \text{(ii)} \int_0^\infty \sin t\, J_1(rt)\,dt, \quad r > 1.$$

(i) Here $f(t) = 1$, so that $f(0) = 1$ and $f^{(s)}(0) = 0$, $s \geqslant 1$, and the required value of the integral is $1/r$.

(ii) With $f(t) = \sin t$,

$f(0) = 0,\ f'(0) = 1,\ f''(0) = 0,\ f'''(0) = -1,\ f^{(iv)}(0) = 0,\ f^{(v)}(0) = 1, \ldots$
and

$$\int_0^\infty \sin t\, J_1(rt)\, dt = \frac{1}{r^2} + \frac{1}{2}\cdot\frac{1}{r^4} + \frac{1.3}{2^2 2!}\cdot\frac{1}{r^6} + \ldots$$

$$= \frac{1}{r^2}\left(1 - \frac{1}{r^2}\right)^{-\frac{1}{2}} = \frac{1}{r\sqrt{(r^2-1)}},$$

the series being convergent when $r > 1$.

Exercises 5

1. Deduce Poisson's integral (3.4) as a special case of Sonine's finite integral (5.1).

2. Show that

(i) $\displaystyle\int_0^{\pi/2} J_0(z\sin\theta)\sin\theta\, d\theta = \frac{\sin z}{z},$

(ii) $\displaystyle\int_0^{\pi/2} J_1(z\sin\theta)\sin^2\theta\, d\theta = \frac{\sin z - z\cos z}{z^2}.$

3. If n is a positive integer, the real part of μ is greater than -1 and

$$I(n, \mu, z) = \int_0^1 (1-t^2)^n \frac{d}{dt}\{t^{\mu+1}J_{\mu+1}(tz)\}\, dt,$$

show that $I(n, \mu, z) = (2n/z)I(n-1, \mu+1, z)$. Deduce that

$$J_n(z) = \frac{z^n}{2^{n-1}(n-1)!}\int_0^1 t(1-t^2)^{n-1}J_0(zt)\, dt.$$

4. Starting from the formulae $K_{-\mu}(z) = K_\mu(z)$ and (Exercises 3, No. 12)

$$2K_\mu(x) = \int_0^\infty \exp\{-\tfrac{1}{2}x(\lambda + \lambda^{-1})\}\lambda^{\mu-1}\, d\lambda,$$

show that, when $R(\nu) > -1$ and z is real and positive,

$$K_{\mu-\nu-1}(z) = \frac{z^{\mu-\nu-1}}{2^\nu\Gamma(\nu+1)}\int_0^\infty \frac{K_\mu\{\sqrt{(t^2+z^2)}\}}{(t^2+z^2)^{\frac{1}{2}\mu}}\, t^{2\nu+1}\, dt,$$

[cf. formula (5.5)].

5. By using Bessel's integral (3.3) for $J_0(t)$ and interchanging the order of integration in the resulting double integral, show that

$$\int_0^\infty e^{-t}J_0(t)\, dt = \tfrac{1}{2}\sqrt{2}.$$

6. Deduce from formula (5.8) that

(i) $\displaystyle\int_0^\infty J_0(at)\cos bt\, dt = \begin{cases}(a^2-b^2)^{-\frac{1}{2}}, & 0 < b < a,\\ 0, & b > a,\end{cases}$

(ii) $$\int_0^\infty J_0(at)\sin bt\,dt = \begin{cases} 0, & 0 < b < a, \\ (b^2 - a^2)^{-\frac{1}{2}}, & b > a. \end{cases}$$

7. Deduce from equation (5.1) that

$$\frac{2}{\pi y}\int_0^y \frac{x \sin x}{\sqrt{(y^2 - x^2)}}\,dx = J_1(y) = y\int_0^1 xJ_0(yx)\,dx.$$

8. Use Weber's first exponential integral to show that

$$\int^\infty e^{-p^2t^2}J_0(at)t^3\,dt = \frac{1}{2p^4}\left(1 - \frac{a^2}{4p^2}\right)\exp\left(-\frac{a^2}{4p^2}\right).$$

9. Use the integral representation for $K_\nu(x)$ given in Exercises 3, No. 12, formula (1.73) and formula (5.14) to obtain the result

$$\int_0^\infty J_\mu(bt)\frac{K_\nu\{a\sqrt{(t^2 + x^2)}\}}{(t^2 + x^2)^{\frac{1}{2}\nu}}\,t^{\mu+1}\,dt = \frac{b^\mu}{a^\nu}\left\{\frac{\sqrt{(a^2 + b^2)}}{x}\right\}^{\nu-\mu-1} K_{\nu-\mu-1}\{x\sqrt{(a^2 + b^2)}\}.$$

10. Deduce from Exercise 9 that

$$\int_0^\infty \cos bt\,K_0(at)\,dt = \frac{\pi}{2\sqrt{(a^2 + b^2)}}.$$

By inverting this result and using formula (5.8), show also that

$$K_0(x) = \int_0^\infty \frac{\cos \xi\,d\xi}{\sqrt{(\xi^2 + x^2)}} = \int_0^\infty \frac{tJ_0(tx)}{1 + t^2}\,dt.$$

11. Use Sonine's formula (5.3) and the Hankel inversion theorem to obtain the result, valid when $R(\mu) > R(\nu) > -1$,

$$\int_0^\infty \frac{J_\nu(p)J_\mu(rp)}{p^{\mu-\nu-1}}\,dp = \begin{cases} 0, & 0 < r < 1, \\ \dfrac{2^{\nu-\mu+1}}{\Gamma(\mu - \nu)}\,r^{-\mu}(r^2 - 1)^{\mu-\nu-1}, & r > 1. \end{cases}$$

12. Given that the real parts of μ, ν exceed -1, that n is a positive integer (or zero) and that

$${}_2F_1(\mu + n + 1, -n - \nu; \mu + 1; r^2) = (1 - r^2)^\nu{}_2F_1(-n, \mu + \nu + n + 1; \mu + 1; r^2),$$

use the Weber-Schafheitlin discontinuous integral and Hankel's inversion theorem to obtain a generalization of Sonine's finite integral in the form

$$J_{\mu+\nu+2n+1}(z) = \frac{z^{\nu+1}\Gamma(\mu + n + 1)}{2^\nu\Gamma(\mu + 1)\Gamma(\nu + n + 1)}$$

$$\times\int_0^{\pi/2} J_\mu(z\sin\theta)\,{}_2F_1(-n,\ \mu + \nu + n + 1;\ \mu + 1;\ \sin^2\theta)\sin^{\mu+1}\theta\cos^{2\nu+1}\theta\,d\theta.$$

13. Deduce from formulae (5.30), (5.31) and (5.32) that

$$\int_0^\infty \frac{J_1(at)\cos bt}{t}\,dt = \begin{cases} 0, & 0 < a \leqslant b, \\ \dfrac{\sqrt{(a^2 - b^2)}}{a}, & a \geqslant b. \end{cases}$$

4

14. Use formula (2.4) to show that, when $R(\nu) > 0$,

$$\nu Ji_\nu(x) = \int_0^x J_{\nu-1}(t)\,dt - J_\nu(x) - 1.$$

15. If n is a positive integer, show that

$$(2n+1)Ji_{2n+1}(x) = -Ji_1(x) + \frac{4}{x}\{J_2(x) + 2J_4(x) + \ldots + nJ_{2n}(x)\}.$$

Deduce that

$$Ji_{2n+1}(x) + Ji_{2n+1}(-x) = -\frac{2}{2n+1}.$$

16. Given that the sine and cosine integrals $Si(x)$ and $Ci(x)$ are defined respectively by

$$Si(x) = \int_0^x \frac{\sin t}{t}\,dt, \quad Ci(x) = -\int_x^\infty \frac{\cos t}{t}\,dt,$$

use formulae (1.37) to show that

$$Si(x) = \tfrac{1}{2}\pi + 2Ji_1(x) - 2Ji_3(x) + 2Ji_5(x) - \ldots,$$
$$Ci(x) = Ji_0(x) - 2Ji_2(x) + 2Ji_4(x) - \ldots.$$

17. Show that $xJi_2(x) = -J_1(x)$ and obtain the integral representation

$$\pi J_1(x) = -x\int_0^\pi \cos 2\theta\; Ci(x\sin\theta)\,d\theta$$

where $Ci(x)$ is the cosine integral defined in Exercise 16.

18. Use the method of §5.8 to show that, assuming $r > p$,

$$\int_0^\infty te^{-pt}J_0(rt)\,dt = \frac{p}{r^3} - \frac{3}{2}\frac{p^3}{r^5} + \frac{15}{8}\frac{p^5}{r^7} - \ldots$$
$$= p(r^2 + p^2)^{-\frac{3}{2}}.$$

CHAPTER 6

DUAL INTEGRAL AND DUAL SERIES EQUATIONS

6.1 Introduction

The solution of certain physical problems can be reduced to the determination of the function $F(p)$ from the integral equation

$$\int_0^\infty pF(p)J_\nu(rp)\,\mathrm{d}p = f(r), \quad 0 < r < \infty,$$

where $f(r)$ is a known function of r and $R(\nu) > -1$. In such cases, Hankel's inversion theorem gives

$$F(p) = \int_0^\infty rf(r)J_\nu(pr)\,\mathrm{d}r$$

and the complete solution of the physical problem follows. More general problems can be reduced to the determination of $F(p)$ from so-called "dual" integral equations of the form

$$\left.\begin{aligned}\int_0^\infty G(p)F(p)J_\nu(rp)\,\mathrm{d}p &= f(r), \quad 0 < r < 1,\\ \int_0^\infty pF(p)J_\nu(rp)\,\mathrm{d}p &= g(r), \quad 1 < r < \infty,\end{aligned}\right\} \tag{6.1}$$

where $G(p)$ is a prescribed function of p and $f(r)$, $g(r)$ are known functions of r.

It is the purpose of this chapter to discuss such dual integral equations and the corresponding equations in which the integrals are replaced by series. It is a seemingly formidable problem to establish precise conditions on $f(r)$, $g(r)$ for which a solution of these dual equations exists and such is not attempted here. We content ourselves with a formal approach throughout this chapter and only give obviously necessary conditions as these arise during the work.

6.2 The reduction of dual equations to canonical form

In many of the applications which give rise to dual integral equations $g(r) = 0$, and we give below a formal method which reduces the more general equations (6.1) to this form.

Let a function $F_2(p)$ be such that

$$\int_0^\infty pF_2(p)J_\nu(rp)\,dp = \begin{cases} h(r), & 0 < r < 1,\\ g(r), & 1 < r < \infty,\end{cases} \tag{6.2}$$

where $h(r)$ is an arbitrary function of r in $0 < r < 1$, so that it follows from Hankel's inversion theorem (4.37), (4.38) that

$$F_2(p) = \int_0^1 rh(r)J_\nu(pr)\,dr + \int_1^\infty rg(r)J_\nu(pr)\,dr. \tag{6.3}$$

Writing $F(p) = F_1(p) + F_2(p)$, the dual equations (6.1) become

$$\int_0^\infty G(p)F_1(p)J_\nu(rp)\,dp = f(r) - \int_0^\infty G(p)F_2(p)J_\nu(rp)\,dp$$
$$= f_1(r) \quad \text{(say)}, \qquad 0 < r < 1, \tag{6.4}$$

$$\int_0^\infty pF_1(p)J_\nu(rp)\,dp = g(r) - \int_0^\infty pF_2(p)J_\nu(rp)\,dp$$
$$= g(r) - g(r) = 0, \quad 1 < r < \infty. \tag{6.5}$$

Hence the equations (6.1) have been effectively reduced to a pair of equations in which $g(r) = 0$ and in what follows this will be taken as the canonical form of the dual equations. The reduction given above requires, of course, that $h(r)$ is so selected that the integrals involved exist.

Example 1. *Reduce the dual integral equations*

$$\left.\begin{aligned} \int_0^\infty F(p)J_1(rp)\,dp &= 0, & 0 < r < 1,\\ \int_0^\infty pF(p)J_1(rp)\,dp &= r^{-1}, & 1 < r < \infty, \end{aligned}\right\}$$

to canonical form.

Take $h(r) = r^{-1}$, so that equation (6.3) gives

$$F_2(p) = \int_0^1 J_1(pr)\,dr + \int_1^\infty J_1(pr)\,dr$$
$$= \int_0^\infty J_1(pr)\,dr = p^{-1}\int_0^\infty J_1(z)\,dz, \quad (z = pr),$$
$$= -p^{-1}\int_0^\infty J_0'(z)\,dz = p^{-1},$$

since $J_0(0) = 1$. Writing $F(p) = p^{-1} + F_1(p)$, the given dual equations reduce to

$$\int_0^\infty F_1(p)J_1(rp)\,dp = -\int_0^\infty p^{-1}J_1(rp)\,dp = -1, \quad 0 < r < 1,$$

using equation (5.39), and

$$\int_0^\infty pF_1(p)J_1(rp)\,dp = 0, \qquad 1 < r < \infty,$$

and these equations are in the required form.

6.3 Abel's integral equation

The integral equation

$$\int_0^x \frac{g(\xi)\,\mathrm{d}\xi}{(x^2-\xi^2)^k} = f(x), \quad 0 < k < 1, \tag{6.6}$$

in which $f(x)$ is a given continuous function of x with a continuous first derivative in $0 \leqslant x \leqslant a$, is a simple transformation of Abel's integral equation. It is of use in discussing the dual integral equations (6.1) and we now consider its solution.

Starting with the following properties of the gamma function

$$\pi \operatorname{cosec} k\pi = \Gamma(k)\Gamma(1-k) = 2\int_0^{\pi/2} \sin^{2k-1}\theta \cos^{1-2k}\theta \,\mathrm{d}\theta$$

and writing $\tan^2\theta = (z^2-x^2)/(x^2-\xi^2)$, we find after a little reduction that

$$2\int_\xi^z \frac{x\,\mathrm{d}x}{(x^2-\xi^2)^k(z^2-x^2)^{1-k}} = \frac{\pi}{\sin k\pi}. \tag{6.7}$$

Setting

$$\phi(z) = \int_0^z g(\xi)\,\mathrm{d}\xi, \tag{6.8}$$

multiplication of (6.7), (6.8) and change of the order of integration gives

$$\begin{aligned}\frac{\pi}{\sin k\pi}\phi(z) &= 2\int_0^z g(\xi)\,\mathrm{d}\xi \int_\xi^z \frac{x\,\mathrm{d}x}{(x^2-\xi^2)^k(z^2-x^2)^{1-k}} \\ &= 2\int_0^z \frac{x\,\mathrm{d}x}{(z^2-x^2)^{1-k}} \int_0^x \frac{g(\xi)\,\mathrm{d}\xi}{(x^2-\xi^2)^k} \\ &= 2\int_0^z \frac{xf(x)\,\mathrm{d}x}{(z^2-x^2)^{1-k}}\end{aligned} \tag{6.9}$$

when we substitute from (6.6). But (6.8) gives $g(z) = \phi'(z)$ and use of (6.9) yields

$$g(z) = \frac{2\sin k\pi}{\pi}\cdot\frac{\mathrm{d}}{\mathrm{d}z}\int_0^z \frac{xf(x)\,\mathrm{d}x}{(z^2-x^2)^{1-k}}. \tag{6.10}$$

This formula, which expresses the function g in terms of the given function f, is the required solution of the integral equation (6.6).

6.4 The reduction of dual integral equations to a Fredholm integral equation

In canonical form, the dual equations for solution are

$$\left.\begin{aligned}\int_0^\infty G(p)F(p)J_\nu(rp)\,\mathrm{d}p &= f(r), \quad 0 < r < 1, \\ \int_0^\infty pF(p)J_\nu(rp)\,\mathrm{d}p &= 0, \qquad 1 < r < \infty,\end{aligned}\right\} \tag{6.11}$$

and, now that electronic computers are available for the numerical solution of standard integral equations, it is worth while to reduce equations (6.11) to such an equation.

We start by letting $\int_0^\infty pF(p)J_\nu(rp)\,dp = \sigma(r)$ when $0 < r < 1$ so that, using Hankel's inversion theorem and the second of equations (6.11),

$$F(p) = \int_0^1 r\sigma(r)J_\nu(pr)\,dr. \tag{6.12}$$

Replacing $\mu + \nu + 1$ by ν, μ by $\nu - k$ and writing $z = pr$, $\sin\theta = x/r$ in Sonine's finite integral (5.1), we find that, when $R(k) > 0$, $R(\nu - k) > -1$,

$$J_\nu(pr) = \frac{p^k r^{-\nu}}{2^{k-1}\Gamma(k)} \int_0^r x^{\nu-k+1}(r^2 - x^2)^{k-1} J_{\nu-k}(px)\,dx. \tag{6.13}$$

Substitution in (6.12) and change of the order of integration then leads to

$$\begin{aligned} F(p) &= \frac{p^k}{2^{k-1}\Gamma(k)} \int_0^1 x^{\nu-k+1} J_{\nu-k}(px)\,dx \int_x^1 r^{1-\nu}(r^2 - x^2)^{k-1}\sigma(r)\,dr \\ &= p^k \int_0^1 H(x) J_{\nu-k}(px)\,dx, \end{aligned} \tag{6.14}$$

where

$$H(x) = \frac{x^{\nu-k+1}}{2^{k-1}\Gamma(k)} \int_x^1 r^{1-\nu}(r^2 - x^2)^{k-1}\sigma(r)\,dr, \tag{6.15}$$

and, when $F(p)$ is given by equations (6.14), (6.15), the second of the dual equations (6.11) is automatically satisfied.

Substituting from (6.14), the first of the dual equations will be satisfied if

$$\int_0^1 H(x)\,dx \int_0^\infty p^k G(p) J_\nu(rp) J_{\nu-k}(xp)\,dp = f(r), \quad 0 < r < 1. \tag{6.16}$$

We write

$$G(p) = p^{1-2k} + G^*(p), \tag{6.17}$$

hoping to be able to determine the parameter k so that $G^*(p)$ is small. Equation (6.16) then becomes

$$\begin{aligned} f(r) = \int_0^1 H(x)\,dx \int_0^\infty p^{1-k} J_\nu(rp) J_{\nu-k}(xp)\,dp \\ + \int_0^1 H(x)\,dx \int_0^\infty p^k G^*(p) J_\nu(rp) J_{\nu-k}(xp)\,dp, \quad 0 < r < 1, \end{aligned} \tag{6.18}$$

and, evaluating the infinite integral by (5.24), the first term on the right-hand side becomes

$$\frac{r^{-\nu}}{2^{k-1}\Gamma(k)} \int_0^r x^{\nu-k}(r^2 - x^2)^{k-1} H(x)\,dx.$$

Using (6.13) and (to avoid subsequent confusion) changing the variable of integration to t, we have after interchange of the order of integrations,

$$\int_0^\infty p^k G^*(p) J_\nu(rp) J_{\nu-k}(xp)\,dp$$
$$= \frac{r^{-\nu}}{2^{k-1}\Gamma(k)} \int_0^r t^{\nu-k+1}(r^2 - t^2)^{k-1}\,dt \int_0^\infty p^{2k} G^*(p) J_{\nu-k}(xp) J_{\nu-k}(tp)\,dp$$
$$= \frac{r^{-\nu}}{2^{k-1}\Gamma(k)} \int_0^r t^{\nu-k+1}(r^2 - t^2)^{k-1} K(x, t)\,dt \tag{6.19}$$

where

$$K(x, t) = \int_0^\infty p^{2k} G^*(p) J_{\nu-k}(xp) J_{\nu-k}(tp)\,dp. \tag{6.20}$$

Noticing that $K(x, t) = K(t, x)$, these results give, when substituted in equation (6.18) and when x is interchanged with t,

$$\int_0^r x^{\nu-k}(r^2 - x^2)^{k-1} H(x)\,dx + \int_0^r x^{\nu-k+1}(r^2 - x^2)^{k-1}\,dx \int_0^1 H(t) K(x, t)\,dt$$
$$= 2^{k-1}\Gamma(k) r^\nu f(r), \quad 0 < r < 1.$$

The results of §6.3 can be applied to this equation to yield

$$H(x) + x\int_0^1 H(t) K(x, t)\,dt = \frac{2^k \Gamma(k) \sin(1-k)\pi}{\pi} x^{k-\nu} \frac{d}{dx} \int_0^x \frac{r^{\nu+1} f(r)}{(x^2 - r^2)^k}\,dr \tag{6.21}$$

and this is a Fredholm integral equation for the function $H(x)$.

If $G^*(p)$ is small, so also will be $K(x, t)$ and it is reasonable to suppose that the Fredholm integral equation (6.21) can be solved numerically by an iterative process. Once $H(x)$ has been found, the solution $F(p)$ of the dual equations (6.11) is given by formula (6.14). In practical applications the quantities involved are usually real and the solution then applies when $0 < k < 1$, $\nu > k - 1$ and it is worth noticing that it can be given in closed form when $G(p) = p^{1-2k}$ for then $G^*(p) = 0$. A worked example is given below.

Example 2. *Find $F(p)$ from the dual equations*

$$\int_0^\infty F(p) J_1(rp)\,dp = -1 \quad (0 < r < 1), \qquad \int_0^\infty pF(p) J_1(rp)\,dp = 0 \quad (1 < r < \infty).$$

These are the standard dual equations (6.11) with $\nu = 1$, $f(r) = -1$ and $G(p) = 1$. Equation (6.17) shows that $G^*(p) = 0$ if we take $k = \frac{1}{2}$ and, with this value of k, equation (6.20) shows that $K(x, t) = 0$. Hence equation (6.21) reduces to

$$H(x) = \frac{2^{\frac{1}{2}}\Gamma(\frac{1}{2})}{\pi} x^{-\frac{1}{2}} \cdot \frac{d}{dx}\int_0^x \frac{-r^2\,dr}{(x^2-r^2)^{\frac{1}{2}}}$$

$$= -\left(\frac{2}{\pi x}\right)^{\frac{1}{2}} \frac{d}{dx}\int_0^{\pi/2} x^2 \sin^2\theta\,d\theta, \quad \text{putting } r = x\sin\theta,$$

$$= -\left(\frac{2}{\pi x}\right)^{\frac{1}{2}} . 2x . \frac{\pi}{4} = -\left(\frac{\pi x}{2}\right)^{\frac{1}{2}}.$$

Equation (6.14) then gives

$$F(p) = -p^{\frac{1}{2}}\int_0^1 \left(\frac{\pi x}{2}\right)^{\frac{1}{2}} J_{\frac{1}{2}}(px)\,dx = -\int_0^1 \sin px\,dx$$

$$= \left[\frac{\cos px}{p}\right]_0^1 = \frac{\cos p - 1}{p}.$$

6.5 A series solution of the dual integral equations (6.11)

A solution of the dual integral equations (6.11) giving $F(p)$ as a series of Bessel functions is sometimes more convenient than that obtained from the Fredholm integral equation (6.21). This can be found by setting

$$F(p) = p^{-k}\sum_{m=0}^{\infty} a_m J_{\nu+2m+k}(p), \tag{6.22}$$

where k is at present an arbitrary parameter, and proceeding as follows.

Substituting from (6.22) and changing the order of integration and summation, we have

$$\int_0^\infty pF(p)J_\nu(rp)\,dp = \sum_{m=0}^{\infty} a_m \int_0^\infty p^{1-k} J_{\nu+2m+k}(p) J_\nu(rp)\,dp.$$

Provided $\nu > -1$ and $k > 0$, formula (5.30) shows that all the integrals on the right vanish when $r > 1$ [because of the factor $\Gamma(-m)$ in the denominator of the term multiplying the hypergeometric function] and hence the series in (6.22) automatically satisfies the second of the dual equations (6.11).

The coefficients a_m have now to be chosen so that the series in (6.22) satisfies the first of the dual equations (6.11). For this purpose we need the result

$$p^{-k}J_{\nu+2n+k}(p) = \frac{\Gamma(\nu+n+1)}{2^{k-1}\Gamma(\nu+1)\Gamma(n+k)} \times \int_0^1 r^{\nu+1}(1-r^2)^{k-1}\mathscr{F}_n(k+\nu, \nu+1, r^2) J_\nu(pr)\,dr \tag{6.23}$$

where n is a positive integer or zero and

$$\mathscr{F}_n(\alpha, \gamma, x) = {}_2F_1(-n, \alpha+n; \gamma; x) \tag{6.24}$$

is Jacobi's polynomial, the details of the method of derivation of this formula being given in full in Exercises 5, No. 12. Substituting from (6.22) in the first of (6.11), multiplication by

$$r^{\nu+1}(1-r^2)^{k-1}\mathscr{F}_n(k+\nu, \nu+1, r^2),$$

integration with respect to r between 0 and 1, interchange of the order of integrations and use of (6.23) give

$$\sum_{m=0}^{\infty} a_m \int_0^\infty G(p)p^{-2k}J_{\nu+2m+k}(p)J_{\nu+2n+k}(p)\,dp = E(\nu, n, k) \tag{6.25}$$

where

$$E(\nu, n, k) = \frac{\Gamma(\nu+n+1)}{2^{k-1}\Gamma(\nu+1)\Gamma(n+k)}\int_0^1 f(r)r^{\nu+1}(1-r^2)^{k-1}\mathscr{F}_n(k+\nu, \nu+1, r^2)\,dr. \tag{6.26}$$

Equation (6.25) with $n = 0, 1, 2, 3, \ldots$ gives a set of simultaneous equations for the determination of the coefficients a_m. These simultaneous equations can be rewritten in a more convenient form by making use of the formula

$$\int_0^\infty p^{-1}J_{\nu+2m+k}(p)J_{\nu+2n+k}(p)\,dp = \begin{cases} 0, & m \neq n, \\ (2\nu+4n+2k)^{-1}, & m = n, \end{cases} \tag{6.27}$$

this being the form taken by equation (5.33) when μ and ν are replaced respectively by $\nu + 2n + k$, $\nu + 2m + k$ and when at is replaced by p. We find in this way

$$a_n + \sum_{m=0}^{\infty} L_{m,n}a_m = (2\nu+4n+2k)E(\nu, n, k), \tag{6.28}$$

where

$$L_{m,n} = (2\nu+4n+2k)\int_0^\infty \{p^{1-2k}G(p) - 1\}p^{-1}J_{\nu+2m+k}(p)J_{\nu+2n+k}(p)\,dp. \tag{6.29}$$

The iterative solution of the simultaneous equations (6.28) is

$$a_n = E_n - E_n' + E_n'' - \ldots \tag{6.30}$$

where

$$\left.\begin{aligned} E_n &= (2\nu+4n+2k)E(\nu, n, k), \\ E_n' &= \sum_{m=0}^{\infty} L_{m,n}E_n, \quad E_n'' = \sum_{m=0}^{\infty} L_{m,n}E_m', \end{aligned}\right\} \tag{6.31}$$

and so on.

Equations (6.22), (6.30), (6.31), (6.29) and (6.26) provide a theoretical solution of the dual integral equations. For a practical solution it is necessary to be able to choose the parameter k so that the expression $\{p^{1-2k}G(p) - 1\}$, which occurs in the formula (6.29) for $L_{m,n}$, is fairly small. It should be noted that a solution giving the coefficients in closed form can be obtained when $G(p) = p^{2k-1}$ and, since the only restriction on the value of k is that it be positive, this solution covers cases in which $G(p)$ is a power of p outside the range for which the solution given in §6.4 is theoretically valid.

Example 3. *Solve the dual integral equations*

$$\int_0^\infty p^2F(p)J_0(rp)\,dp = f(r) \quad (0 < r < 1), \qquad \int_0^\infty pF(p)J_0(rp)\,dp = 0 \quad (1 < r < \infty)$$

and show that, when $f(r) = 1$,

$$F(p) = \frac{2}{\pi}\left(\frac{\sin p}{p^3} - \frac{\cos p}{p^2}\right).$$

Here $G(p) = p^2$ so we take $2k - 1 = 2$, that is $k = 3/2$. Equation (6.29) then shows that $L_{m,n} = 0$ for all m, n and (6.22), (6.30), (6.31), (6.26) give, with $\nu = 0$, $k = 3/2$,

$$F(p) = p^{-\frac{3}{2}} \sum_{n=0}^{\infty} a_n J_{2n+\frac{3}{2}}(p)$$

where

$$a_n = \frac{(4n + 3)\Gamma(n + 1)}{2^{\frac{1}{2}}(n + 3/2)} \int_0^1 f(r)r(1 - r^2)^{\frac{1}{2}}\mathscr{F}_n(3/2, 1, r^2)\,dr.$$

Since $\mathscr{F}_n(3/2, 1, r^2) = {}_2F_1(-n, 3/2 + n; 1; r^2)$, we have $\mathscr{F}_0(3/2, 1, r^2) = 1$ and, when $f(r) = 1$, the orthogonality theorem for the Jacobi polynomials* shows that $a_n = 0$ when $n \neq 0$ and we have

$$a_0 = \frac{3}{2^{\frac{1}{2}}\Gamma(3/2)} \int_0^1 r(1 - r^2)^{\frac{1}{2}}\,dr = 3\left(\frac{2}{\pi}\right)^{\frac{1}{2}}\left[-\tfrac{1}{3}(1 - r^2)^{\frac{3}{2}}\right]_0^1 = \left(\frac{2}{\pi}\right)^{\frac{1}{2}}.$$

Hence

$$F(p) = \left(\frac{2}{\pi}\right)^{\frac{1}{2}} p^{-\frac{3}{2}}J_{\frac{3}{2}}(p) = \frac{2}{\pi}\left(\frac{\sin p}{p^3} - \frac{\cos p}{p^2}\right).$$

Example 4. *Assuming c to be so large that powers of* $1/c$ *above the third may be neglected, solve the dual equations*

$$\left.\begin{aligned} &\int_0^\infty (1 + e^{-2cp})F(p)J_0(rp)\,dp = \sqrt{(\tfrac{1}{2}\pi)}, && 0 < r < 1, \\ &\int_0^\infty pF(p)J_0(rp)\,dp = 0, && 1 < r < \infty. \end{aligned}\right\}$$

Here $\nu = 0$ and $G(p) = 1 + e^{-2cp} \simeq 1$ when c is large. Hence we take $1 - 2k = 0$ and equation (6.29) gives

$$\begin{aligned} L_{m,n} &= (4n + 1)\int_0^\infty e^{-2cp}p^{-1}J_{2m+\frac{1}{2}}(p)\,J_{2n+\frac{1}{2}}(p)\,dp \\ &= (4n + 1)\sum_{s=0}^{\infty} \frac{(-1)^s 2^{-2m-2n-2s-1}\Gamma(2m + 2n + 2s + 2)}{s!\Gamma(2m + s + 3/2)\Gamma(2n + s + 3/2)\Gamma(2m + 2n + s + 2)} \\ &\qquad \times \int_0^\infty p^{2m+2n+2s}e^{-2cp}\,dp, \end{aligned}$$

* See W. Magnus and F. Oberhettinger (translated by J. Wermer), *Special Functions of Mathematical Physics* (Chelsea Pub. Co., New York, 1949), p. 83.

when use is made of equation (2.20) and the order of integration and summation is changed. Since

$$\int_0^\infty p^{2m+2n+2s}e^{-2cp}\,dp = (2c)^{-2m-2n-2s-1}\Gamma(2m+2n+2s+1),$$

and $c^{-4}, c^{-5}, \ldots$ are negligible, we find

$$L_{0,0} = \frac{1}{\pi c} - \frac{1}{6\pi c^3}, \quad L_{0,1} = \frac{1}{6\pi c^3}, \quad L_{1,0} = \frac{1}{30\pi c^3}$$

and that $L_{m,n}$ is negligible for all other integral values of m and n. From equation (6.26) with $\nu = 0$, $k = \frac{1}{2}$, $f(r) = (\frac{1}{2}\pi)^{\frac{1}{2}}$,

$$E(\nu, n, k) = \frac{\Gamma(n+1)}{2^{-\frac{1}{2}}\Gamma(n+\frac{1}{2})}\int_0^1 (\tfrac{1}{2}\pi)^{\frac{1}{2}} r(1-r^2)^{-\frac{1}{2}}\mathscr{F}_n(\tfrac{1}{2}, 1, r^2)\,dr$$

and, as in the previous example, the value of the integral is zero except when $n = 0$, in which case

$$E(\nu, 0, k) = \int_0^1 r(1-r^2)^{-\frac{1}{2}}\,dr = \Big[-(1-r^2)^{\frac{1}{2}}\Big]_0^1 = 1.$$

Equations (6.31) give, to the order of $1/c$ to be retained,

$$E_0 = 1, \quad E_n = 0 \quad (n > 0),$$

$$E_0' = L_{0,0}E_0 = \frac{1}{\pi c} - \frac{1}{6\pi c^3}, \quad E_1' = L_{0,1}E_0 = \frac{1}{6\pi c^3}, \quad E_n' = 0 \quad (n > 1),$$

$$E_0'' = L_{0,0}E_0' + L_{1,0}E_1' = \frac{1}{\pi^2 c^2}, \quad E_n'' = 0 \quad (n > 0),$$

$$E_0''' = L_{0,0}E_0'' = \frac{1}{\pi^3 c^3}, \quad E_n''' = 0 \quad (n > 0).$$

Hence, from (6.30),

$$a_0 = E_0 - E_0' + E_0'' - E_0''' + \ldots = 1 - \frac{1}{\pi c} + \frac{1}{6\pi c^3} + \frac{1}{\pi^2 c^2} - \frac{1}{\pi^3 c^3},$$

$$a_1 = E_1 - E_1' + E_1'' - E_1''' + \ldots = -\frac{1}{6\pi c^3}, \quad a_n = 0 \quad (n > 1)$$

and, from (6.22),

$$F(p) = p^{-\frac{1}{2}}\{a_0 J_{\frac{1}{2}}(p) + a_1 J_{\frac{5}{2}}(p)\}.$$

6.6 Dual Fourier-Bessel series

The dual integral equations already considered have applications to certain physical problems in a semi-infinite medium. The corresponding problems in which the medium is confined within a circular cylinder or between a pair of parallel planes can be reduced to dual series equations and typical of such equations are the dual Fourier-Bessel series

$$\left.\begin{aligned}\sum_{s=1}^{\infty} c_s p_s^{2k} J_\nu(p_s r) &= f(r), \quad 0 < r < 1,\\ \sum_{s=1}^{\infty} c_s J_\nu(p_s r) &= 0, \qquad 1 < r < a,\end{aligned}\right\} \tag{6.32}$$

where $-1 \leqslant 2k \leqslant 1$, $f(r)$ is specified and p_s is a positive root of $J_\nu(p_s a) = 0$.

Before discussing a method of determining the coefficients c_s in the dual equations (6.32) we require two lemmas and these are given below.

Lemma 1. If m is a positive integer or zero, $\nu > -1$ and the other symbols are as defined above, then

$$\sum_{s=1}^{\infty} \frac{J_{\nu+2m+1+k}(p_s) J_\nu(p_s r)}{p_s^{1+k} J_{\nu+1}{}^2(p_s a)} = 0, \quad 1 < r < a. \tag{6.33}$$

To obtain this result, consider the Fourier-Bessel expansion of the function $\psi(r)$ defined by

$$\psi(r) = \begin{cases} \dfrac{\Gamma(\nu+m+1)}{2^k\Gamma(\nu+1)\Gamma(m+k+1)} r^\nu (1-r^2)^k \mathscr{F}_m(k+1+\nu, \nu+1, r^2), & 0<r<1,\\ 0, & 1<r<a. \end{cases} \tag{6.34}$$

By equation (4.22) this is $\psi(r) = \sum_{s=1}^{\infty} A_s J_\nu(p_s r)$ where

$$\begin{aligned} A_s &= \frac{2}{a^2 J_{\nu+1}{}^2(p_s a)} \int_0^a r\psi(r) J_\nu(p_s r)\, dr\\ &= \frac{2 J_{\nu+2m+k+1}(p_s)}{a^2 J_{\nu+1}{}^2(p_s a) p_s^{1+k}}, \end{aligned}$$

when use is made of equation (6.23) with k replaced by $k+1$, and (6.33) is established.

Lemma 2. If m, n are positive integers or zero, $\nu > -m-n-k-1$ and not a negative integer, and $k > -m-n-1$, then

$$\begin{aligned}\frac{2}{a^2}\sum_{s=1}^{\infty} \frac{J_{\nu+2m+k+1}(p_s) J_{\nu+2n+k+1}(p_s)}{p_s^2 J_{\nu+1}{}^2(p_s a)} &= \frac{\delta_{m,n}}{2\nu+4n+2+2k}\\ &+ (-1)^{m+n} \frac{2}{\pi} \sin k\pi \int_0^\infty \frac{K_\nu(t)}{t I_\nu(t)} I_{\nu+2m+1+k}\left(\frac{t}{a}\right) I_{\nu+2n+1+k}\left(\frac{t}{a}\right) dt \end{aligned} \tag{6.35}$$

where $\delta_{m,n} = 0$ when $m \neq n$ and $\delta_{m,n} = 1$ when $m = n$.

We start by writing

$$G(z) = \frac{J_\nu(az) + iY_\nu(az)}{z J_\nu(az)} \,.\, \Phi(z) \tag{6.36}$$

where

$$\Phi(z) = J_{\nu+2m+k+1}(z)J_{\nu+2n+k+1}(z) \tag{6.37}$$

and consider $\int G(z)\,\mathrm{d}z$ round a contour C. This contour (Fig. 10) consists of:

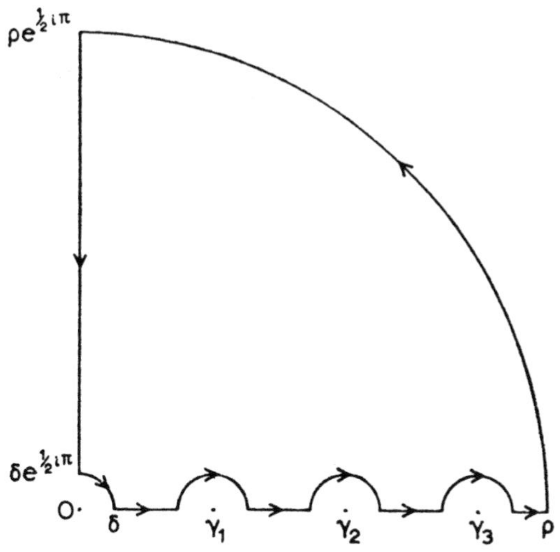

FIG. 10. z-plane

(i) the portions of the positive real axis joining the points δ, $p_1 - \delta_1$; $p_s + \delta_s$, $p_{s+1} - \delta_{s+1}$ $(s = 1, 2, 3, \ldots, q - 1)$; $p_q + \delta_q$, ρ, where the δ's are small and q, ρ are large and such that $p_q < \rho < p_{q+1}$;

(ii) a series of small semi-circles γ_s $(s = 1, 2, 3, \ldots, q)$ above the real axis with centres $z = p_s$ and radii δ_s;

(iii) a large circular quadrant, with centre at the origin and radius ρ, extending from $z = \rho$ to $z = \rho e^{\frac{1}{2}i\pi}$;

(iv) the positive imaginary axis from $z = \rho e^{\frac{1}{2}i\pi}$ to $z = \delta e^{\frac{1}{2}i\pi}$;

(v) a small circular quadrant, with centre at the origin and radius δ, extending from $z = \delta e^{\frac{1}{2}i\pi}$ to $z = \delta$.

This contour avoids all the singularities of $G(z)$ and, if $I_1, I_2, \ldots, I_5$ denote $\int G(z)\,\mathrm{d}z$ taken along the corresponding portions of the contour C, then

$$I_1 + I_2 + I_3 + I_4 + I_5 = 0. \tag{6.38}$$

Now

$$I_1 = \int_{\delta}^{p_1-\delta_1} G(x)\,\mathrm{d}x + \sum_{s=1}^{q-1} \int_{p_s+\delta_s}^{p_{s+1}-\delta_{s+1}} G(x)\,\mathrm{d}x + \int_{p_q+\delta_q}^{\rho} G(x)\,\mathrm{d}x \tag{6.39}$$

and

$$I_2 = \sum_{s=1}^{q} \int_{\gamma_s} G(z)\,\mathrm{d}z. \tag{6.40}$$

With $a > 1$, it can be shown that the integral I_3 along the large quadrant tends to zero as the radius ρ of the quadrant tends to infinity, and

$$I_4 = e^{\frac{1}{2}i\pi}\int_\rho^\delta G(ye^{\frac{1}{2}i\pi})\,dy. \tag{6.41}$$

Finally, with the conditions specified, it can be shown that the integral I_5 along the small quadrant tends to zero as the radius δ of the quadrant tends to zero. Hence, substituting from (6.39), (6.40) and (6.41) in (6.38) and taking the limit as δ tends to zero and q, ρ tend to infinity, we find

$$\int_0^{p_1-\delta_1} G(x)\,dx + \sum_{s=1}^{\infty}\int_{p_s+\delta_s}^{p_{s+1}-\delta_{s+1}} G(x)\,dx + \sum_{s=1}^{\infty}\int_{\gamma_s} G(z)\,dz + e^{\frac{1}{2}i\pi}\int_\infty^0 G(ye^{\frac{1}{2}i\pi})\,dy = 0. \tag{6.42}$$

Since, from (1.59) and (1.51),

$$J_\nu(aye^{\frac{1}{2}i\pi}) + iY_\nu(aye^{\frac{1}{2}i\pi}) = \frac{2}{\pi i}e^{-\frac{1}{2}\nu\pi i}K_\nu(ay),$$

$$J_\nu(aye^{\frac{1}{2}i\pi}) = e^{\frac{1}{2}\nu\pi i}I_\nu(ay),$$

and, since the real part of $G(x)$ is $\Phi(x)/x$, it follows by equating real parts in (6.42), using (6.36), (6.37) and making a few reductions, that

$$R\left\{\sum_{s=1}^{\infty}\int_{\gamma_s} G(z)\,dz\right\} = -\int_0^{p_1-\delta_1} x^{-1}\Phi(x)\,dx - \sum_{s=1}^{\infty}\int_{p_s+\delta_s}^{p_{s+1}-\delta_{s+1}} x^{-1}\Phi(x)\,dx - $$
$$-(-1)^{m+n}\frac{2}{\pi}\sin k\pi\int_0^\infty \frac{K_\nu(ay)}{yI_\nu(ay)} I_{\nu+2m+k+1}(y)I_{\nu+2n+k+1}(y)\,dy. \tag{6.43}$$

If R_s is the residue of $G(z)$ at $z = p_s$, $G(\alpha_s + \delta_s e^{i\theta})\delta_s e^{i\theta}$ tends to R_s uniformly with respect to θ as δ_s tends to zero, and hence

$$\lim_{\delta_s\to 0}\int_{\gamma_s} G(z)\,dz = \int_\pi^0 R_s i\,d\theta = -\pi i R_s. \tag{6.44}$$

Also, since $J_\nu(z)Y_{\nu+1}(z) - J_{\nu+1}(z)Y_\nu(z) = -2/(\pi z)$ and since $J_\nu(p_s a) = 0$,

$$Y_\nu(p_s a) = \frac{2}{\pi p_s a J_{\nu+1}(p_s a)}$$

and, remembering that $J_\nu'(p_s a) = -J_{\nu+1}(p_s a)$, we see that the residue R_s at $z = p_s$ is given by

$$R_s = \frac{iY_\nu(p_s a)}{p_s a J_\nu'(p_s a)}\Phi(p_s) = -\frac{2i\Phi(p_s)}{\pi p_s^2 a^2 J_{\nu+1}^2(p_s a)}. \tag{6.45}$$

Substituting from (6.45) and (6.44) in (6.43), letting δ_s ($s = 1, 2, 3, \ldots$) tend to zero, substituting for Φ and writing $ay = t$ in the infinite integral, we obtain the result (6.35), the first term on the right coming from the term $\int_0^\infty x^{-1}\Phi(x)\,dx$ and application of the result (6.27).

6.7 The determination of the coefficients c_s in the dual series (6.32)

By taking

$$c_s = \frac{1}{p_s^{1+k} J_{\nu+1}{}^2(p_s a)} \sum_{m=0}^{\infty} b_m J_{\nu+2m+1+k}(p_s), \tag{6.46}$$

Lemma 1 shows that the second of equations (6.32) is automatically satisfied. The coefficients b_m have therefore to be chosen so that c_s satisfies the first of equations (6.32). Substituting from (6.46) in the first of (6.32) and changing the order of the summations, this requires that

$$\sum_{m=0}^{\infty} b_m \sum_{s=1}^{\infty} \frac{J_{\nu+2m+1+k}(p_s) J_\nu(p_s r)}{p_s^{1-k} J_{\nu+1}{}^2(p_s a)} = f(r), \quad 0 < r < 1.$$

Multiplying by $r^{\nu+1}(1 - r^2)^k \mathscr{F}_n\,(k + 1 + \nu, \nu + 1, r^2)$, integrating with respect to r between 0, 1, interchange of the order of integration and summation and use of (6.23) then gives

$$\sum_{m=0}^{\infty} b_m \sum_{s=1}^{\infty} \frac{J_{\nu+2m+1+k}(p_s) J_{\nu+2n+1+k}(p_s)}{p_s^2 J_{\nu+1}{}^2(p_s a)} = E(\nu, n, k), \tag{6.47}$$

where now

$$E(\nu, n, k) = \frac{\Gamma(\nu + n + 1)}{2^k \Gamma(\nu + 1)\Gamma(n + k + 1)} \times \int_0^1 f(r) r^{\nu+1}(1 - r^2)^k \mathscr{F}_n(k + 1 + \nu, \nu + 1, r^2)\, dr. \tag{6.48}$$

Equation (6.47) with $n = 0, 1, 2, \ldots$ provides a set of algebraical equations to determine the coefficients b_m and these can be rewritten in a form suitable for an iterative solution by using Lemma 2. Thus writing

$$L_{m,n} = (-1)^{m+n+1}(2\nu + 4n + 2 + 2k)\frac{2}{\pi} \sin k\pi \times \int_0^\infty \frac{K_\nu(t)}{t I_\nu(t)} I_{\nu+2m+1+k}\left(\frac{t}{a}\right) I_{\nu+2n+1+k}\left(\frac{t}{a}\right) dt \tag{6.49}$$

we have

$$b_n - \sum_{m=0}^{\infty} L_{m,n} b_m = \frac{2}{a^2}(2\nu + 4n + 2 + 2k) E(\nu, n, k) \tag{6.50}$$

and the iterative solution of this set of equations is

$$b_n = \sum_{r=0}^{\infty} E_n{}^{(r)} \tag{6.51}$$

where

$$\left.\begin{aligned} E_n^{(0)} &= \frac{2}{a^2}(2\nu + 4n + 2 + 2k)E(\nu, n, k) \\ \text{and} \\ E_n^{(r)} &= \sum_{m=0}^{\infty} L_{m,n} E_m^{(r-1)}. \end{aligned}\right\} \tag{6.52}$$

Equations (6.46), (6.49), (6.51), (6.52) and (6.48) provide a theoretical solution of the dual series (6.32). For a practical solution, the various series must converge and $L_{m,n}$ has to be capable of computation. This is usually possible when a is large and, in this case, the Bessel functions of argument t/a in (6.49) can be expanded in ascending powers of t/a and $L_{m,n}$ can be expressed as series of descending powers of a with the aid of the integrals

$$M_s^{(\nu)} = \int_0^\infty \frac{t^s K_\nu(t)}{I_\nu(t)}\, \mathrm{d}t. \tag{6.53}$$

The values of ν occurring most frequently in practice are $\pm\frac{1}{2}$, 0, 1 and values of the integrals in (6.53) for such values of ν are given in the following table, the entries having been obtained by numerical integration.

$s \backslash \nu$	$-\frac{1}{2}$	0	$\frac{1}{2}$	1
0		1·36768		
1	0·64596		1·29193	
2		0·64689		2·50330
3	1·11570		1·27508	
4		2·06986		3·77139
5	5·80538		5·99265	
6		16·168		23·431
7	61·617		62·102	
8		231·69		302·29
9	112·2		1114·4	
10		5286·6		

Example 5. *If a is so large that a^{-3} and higher powers can be neglected, find the coefficients c_s in the dual series*

$$\sum_{s=1}^{\infty} p_s^{-1} c_s J_0(p_s r) = \tfrac{1}{2}a^2 \quad (0 < r < 1), \quad \sum_{s=1}^{\infty} c_s J_0(p_s r) = 0 \quad (1 < r < a),$$

p_s being the positive zeros of $J_0(pa)$.

Here $k = -\frac{1}{2}$, $\nu = 0$, $f(r) = \frac{1}{2}a^2$ and equation (6.49) gives

$$L_{m,n} = (-1)^{m+n} \frac{(8n+2)}{\pi} \int_0^\infty \frac{K_0(t)}{tI_0(t)} I_{2m+\frac{1}{2}}\left(\frac{t}{a}\right) I_{2n+\frac{1}{2}}\left(\frac{t}{a}\right) dt.$$

By expanding $I_{2m+\frac{1}{2}}(t/a)I_{2n+\frac{1}{2}}(t/a)$ in ascending powers of t/a, we find $L_{m,n}$ is negligible except when $m = n = 0$, in which case

$$\begin{aligned} L_{0,0} &= \frac{2}{\pi}\int_0^\infty \frac{K_0(t)}{tI_0(t)} \cdot \frac{2t}{\pi a}\, dt = \frac{4}{\pi^2 a} M_0^{(0)} \\ &= \frac{5{\cdot}47072}{\pi^2 a}, \end{aligned}$$

using (6.53) and the table given. From equation (6.48)

$$E(0, n, -\tfrac{1}{2}) = \frac{\Gamma(n+1)}{2^{-\frac{1}{2}}\Gamma(n+\frac{1}{2})} \int_0^1 \tfrac{1}{2}a^2 r(1-r^2)^{-\frac{1}{2}} \mathscr{F}_n(\tfrac{1}{2}, 1, r^2)\, dr.$$

Since $\mathscr{F}_0(\frac{1}{2}, 1, r^2) = 1$, this gives

$$E(0, 0, -\tfrac{1}{2}) = \frac{a^2}{(2\pi)^{\frac{1}{2}}} \int_0^1 \frac{r\, dr}{(1-r^2)^{\frac{1}{2}}} = \frac{a^2}{(2\pi)^{\frac{1}{2}}},$$

and the orthogonality relation for the Jacobi polynomials shows that $E(0, n, -\frac{1}{2}) = 0$ when $n > 0$. Equations (6.52) give

$$E_0^{(0)} = \frac{2}{a^2} \cdot \frac{a^2}{(2\pi)^{\frac{1}{2}}} = \left(\frac{2}{\pi}\right)^{\frac{1}{2}}, \quad E_n^{(0)} = 0, \quad n > 0,$$

$$E_0^{(1)} = L_{0,0}E_0^{(0)} = \left(\frac{2}{\pi}\right)^{\frac{1}{2}} \cdot \frac{5{\cdot}47072}{\pi^2 a}, \quad E_n^{(1)} = 0, \quad n > 0,$$

and $E_n^{(r)} = 0$ when $n \geqslant 0$, $r > 1$. Hence, from equation (6.51),

$$b_0 = \left(\frac{2}{\pi}\right)^{\frac{1}{2}}\left(1 + \frac{5{\cdot}47072}{\pi^2 a}\right), \quad b_n = 0, \quad n > 0,$$

and finally, from equation (6.46),

$$\begin{aligned} c_s &= \left(\frac{2}{\pi}\right)^{\frac{1}{2}}\left(1 + \frac{5{\cdot}47072}{\pi^2 a}\right) \frac{J_{\frac{1}{2}}(p_s)}{p_s^{\frac{1}{2}} J_1^2(p_s a)} \\ &= \frac{2}{\pi}\left(1 + \frac{5{\cdot}47072}{\pi^2 a}\right) \frac{\sin p_s}{p_s J_1^2(p_s a)}. \end{aligned}$$

The method just given of determining the coefficients in dual Fourier-Bessel series is rather complicated and only leads to useful results if $L_{m,n}$ as given by equation (6.49) is small. It is, however, possible to obtain closed formulae for the coefficients c_s in the dual series (6.32) in the special cases $\nu = \pm\frac{1}{2}$, $k = \pm\frac{1}{2}$, the Bessel functions then being replaced by sines or cosines. Such dual trigonometrical series are of practical importance but, as a study of them is rather outside the scope of the present book, the reader is referred to the author's paper *Proc. Glasgow Math. Assoc.*, **6** (1964), 136–140.

Exercises 6

1. By writing $F(p) = F_1(p) + F_2(p)$ and taking $F_2(p)$ such that the value of the integral $\int_0^\infty pF_2(p)J_1(rp)\,\mathrm{d}p$ is 0 when $0 < r < 1$ and r^{-1} when $1 < r < \infty$, show that the dual integral equations

$$\int_0^\infty F(p)J_1(rp)\,\mathrm{d}p = 0 \quad (0 < r < 1), \quad \int_0^\infty pF(p)J_1(rp)\,\mathrm{d}p = r^{-1} \quad (1 < r < \infty)$$

are reduced to the dual equations

$$\left.\begin{aligned} &\int_0^\infty F_1(p)J_1(rp)\,\mathrm{d}p = -\tfrac{1}{2}r\,{}_2F_1(\tfrac{1}{2}, \tfrac{1}{2}; 2; r^2), && 0 < r < 1, \\ &\int_0^\infty pF_1(p)J_1(rp)\,\mathrm{d}p = 0, && 1 < r < \infty, \end{aligned}\right\}$$

these latter equations being in canonical form.

2. Find $g(\xi)$ from the integral equation

$$\int_0^x \frac{g(\xi)\,\mathrm{d}\xi}{\sqrt{(x^2 - \xi^2)}} = \tfrac{1}{2}\pi J_0(x)$$

and hence obtain the integral representation given in formula (3.7).

3. Show that the dual integral equations

$$\left.\begin{aligned} &\int_0^\infty F(p)J_0(rp)\,\mathrm{d}p = 1, && 0 < r < 1, \\ &\int_0^\infty pF(p)J_0(rp)\,\mathrm{d}p = 0, && 1 < r < \infty, \end{aligned}\right\}$$

are satisfied by $\pi F(p) = 2p^{-1}\sin p$.

4. Show that the solution of the dual integral equations

$$\left.\begin{aligned}\int_0^\infty F(p)\sin rp\,\mathrm{d}p &= f(r), \quad 0 < r < 1,\\ \int_0^\infty pF(p)\sin rp\,\mathrm{d}p &= 0, \quad 1 < r < \infty,\end{aligned}\right\}$$

is given by

$$F(p) = \frac{2}{\pi}\int_0^1 J_0(px)\left\{\frac{\mathrm{d}}{\mathrm{d}x}\int_0^\infty \frac{rf(r)\mathrm{d}r}{(x^2 - r^2)^{\frac{1}{2}}}\right\}\mathrm{d}x$$

and that, when $f(r) = r$, the solution reduces to $F(p) = p^{-1}J_1(p)$.

5. $F(p)$ satisfies the dual integral equations

$$\left.\begin{aligned}\int_0^\infty \tanh ap\, F(p)J_0(rp)\,\mathrm{d}p &= 1, \quad 0 < r < 1,\\ \int_0^\infty pF(p)J_0(rp)\,\mathrm{d}p &= 0, \quad 1 < r < \infty.\end{aligned}\right\}$$

Show that $(\frac{1}{2}\pi)^{\frac{1}{2}}F(p) = \int_0^1 x^{-\frac{1}{2}}H(x)\cos px\,\mathrm{d}x$ where $H(x)$ is the solution of the Fredholm integral equation

$$H(x) + x\int_0^1 H(t)K(x, t)\,\mathrm{d}t = (2x/\pi)^{\frac{1}{2}}$$

in which

$$\pi(xt)^{\frac{1}{2}}K(x, t) = 2\int_0^\infty (\tanh ap - 1)\cos xp\cos tp\,\mathrm{d}p.$$

6. Use the method of §6.5 to show that the solution of the dual integral equations

$$\int_0^\infty pf(p)\cos rp\,\mathrm{d}p = 1 \quad (0 < r < 1), \qquad \int_0^\infty f(p)\cos rp\,\mathrm{d}p = 0 \quad (1 < r < \infty)$$

is $f(p) = p^{-1}J_1(p)$.

7. Assuming that a is so large that $a^{-2}, a^{-3}, \ldots$ are negligible in comparison with a^{-1}, use the method of §6.5 to show that the solution of the dual integral equations of Exercise 5 above is

$$F(p) = \frac{2}{\pi}\left(1 + \frac{2\log_e 2}{\pi a}\right)\frac{\sin p}{p}.$$

8. By using the relations [derivable from formulae (3.7) and (3.22)]

$$\int_0^x \frac{\cos pr\, dr}{(x^2 - r^2)^{\frac{1}{2}}} = \frac{\pi}{2} J_0(xp) = \int_x^\infty \frac{\sin pr\, dr}{(r^2 - x^2)^{\frac{1}{2}}},$$

show that the dual integral equations

$$\int_0^\infty F(p) \sin rp\, dp = f(r) \quad (0 < r < 1), \quad \int_0^\infty pF(p) \sin rp\, dp = 0 \quad (1 < r < \infty),$$

can be transformed into the integral equation

$$\frac{\pi}{2} \int_0^\infty pF(p) J_0(xp)\, dp = \begin{cases} \displaystyle\int_0^x \frac{f'(r)\, dr}{(x^2 - r^2)^{\frac{1}{2}}}, & 0 < x < 1, \\ 0, & 1 < x < \infty. \end{cases}$$

Deduce that

$$\tfrac{1}{2}\pi F(p) = \int_0^1 x J_0(px)\, dx \int_0^x \frac{f'(r)\, dr}{(x^2 - r^2)^{\frac{1}{2}}}.$$

9. Deduce from equations (5.1), (5.3) that

$$\int_0^x \frac{r J_0(pr)\, dr}{(x^2 - r^2)^{\frac{1}{2}}} = \frac{\sin xp}{p} = x \int_x^\infty \frac{J_1(pr)\, dr}{(r^2 - x^2)^{\frac{1}{2}}}.$$

Use these results to show that the dual equations

$$\int_0^\infty p^2 F(p) J_0(rp)\, dp = f(r) \quad (0 < r < 1), \quad \int_0^\infty pF(p) J_0(rp)\, dp = 0 \quad (1 < r < \infty),$$

can be transformed into the integral equation

$$\int_0^\infty pF(p) \sin xp\, dp = \begin{cases} \displaystyle\int_0^x \frac{rf(r)\, dr}{(x^2 - r^2)^{\frac{1}{2}}}, & 0 < x < 1, \\ 0, & 1 < x < \infty, \end{cases}$$

and deduce that

$$\tfrac{1}{2}\pi p F(p) = \int_0^1 \sin px\, dx \int_0^x \frac{rf(r)\, dr}{(x^2 - r^2)^{\frac{1}{2}}}.$$

10. If p_s is a positive zero of $J_1(pa)$ and a is so large that $a^{-1}, a^{-2}, a^{-3}, \ldots$ are negligible in comparison with unity, show that the coefficients c_s in the dual series

$$\sum_{s=1}^\infty p_s^{-1} c_s J_1(p_s r) = r \quad (0 < r < 1), \quad \sum_{s=1}^\infty c_s J_1(p_s r) = 0 \quad (1 < r < a),$$

are given by

$$\pi p_s^2 a^2 J_2^2(p_s a) c_s = 8(\sin p_s - p_s \cos p_s).$$

CHAPTER 7

THE EQUATIONS OF MATHEMATICAL PHYSICS: SOLUTION BY SEPARATION OF VARIABLES

7.1 Introduction

An important application of Bessel function theory is in the solution of the partial differential equations of mathematical physics. These equations are described in the early part of this chapter and their transformation into polar coordinates is given. Typical solutions are then constructed by separating the variables in the differential equations and the chapter concludes with a set of worked examples in heat conduction, membrane vibrations, hydrodynamics, electrostatics, etc.

7.2 The equations of mathematical physics

Many problems in mathematical physics can be reduced to the solution of the partial differential equation

$$\nabla^2 V = A\frac{\partial^2 V}{\partial t^2} + B\frac{\partial V}{\partial t} + C, \tag{7.1}$$

where V is a physical quantity depending on the three Cartesian space coordinates x, y, z and on the time t, ∇^2 is the differential operator $(\partial^2/\partial x^2 + \partial^2/\partial y^2 + \partial^2/\partial z^2)$ and A, B, C are functions of x, y, z or constants. The following four special cases of equation (7.1) are of particular importance:

(*a*) *Laplace's equation*

Here $A = B = C = 0$ and examples of quantities which can be represented by the function V are

(i) the gravitational potential in a region devoid of attracting matter;
(ii) the electrostatic potential in a uniform dielectric;
(iii) the magnetic potential;
(iv) the velocity potential in the irrotational motion of a homogeneous fluid;
(v) the steady state temperature in a uniform solid.

(*b*) *Poisson's equation*

In this equation $A = B = 0$ and C is a given function of x, y, z. Examples of quantities represented by V are now:

(i) the gravitational potential in a region in which C is proportional to the density of material at a point (x, y, z) in the region;
(ii) the electrostatic potential in a region in which C is proportional to the charge distribution;

(iii) in the two-dimensional (z absent) form of the equation in which C is a constant, V is a measure of the shear stress entailed by twisting a long bar of specified cross-section.

(*c*) *The equation of heat conduction*

When $A = C = 0$ and $B = 1/k$ where k is the diffusivity of a homogeneous isotropic body, equation (7.1) gives the temperature V at a point (x, y, z) of the body. The same equation can, in certain circumstances, be used in diffusion problems, the quantity V then being the concentration of the diffusing substance.

(*d*) *The wave equation*

Equation (7.1) with $B = C = 0$ and $A = 1/c^2$ arises in investigations of waves propagated with velocity c independent of wave length. Typical examples of quantities which can be represented by the function V are:

(i) components of the displacement in vibrating systems;
(ii) the velocity potential of a gas in the theory of sound;
(iii) components of the electric or magnetic vector in the electromagnetic theory of light.

7.3 The transformation of $\nabla^2 V$ into polar coordinates

The solution of equation (7.1), satisfying given boundary conditions, is greatly facilitated if the boundaries can be expressed by the constancy of one of the space coordinates. Thus, for problems involving rectangular parallelepipeds, Cartesian coordinates x, y, z would be chosen, while cylindrical polar coordinates would be used where the boundaries were the surfaces of a right circular cylinder. When the equation is expressed in cylindrical or spherical polar coordinates, Bessel functions are involved in its solution and, as we are here interested in such solutions, we give below the transformation of the equation into these two coordinate systems.

(*a*) *Cylindrical polar coordinates*

The relations between the cartesian coordinates (x, y, z) of a point P and its cylindrical polar coordinates (ρ, ϕ, z) are (see Fig. 11)

$$x = \rho \cos \phi, \quad y = \rho \sin \phi, \quad z = z \tag{7.2}$$

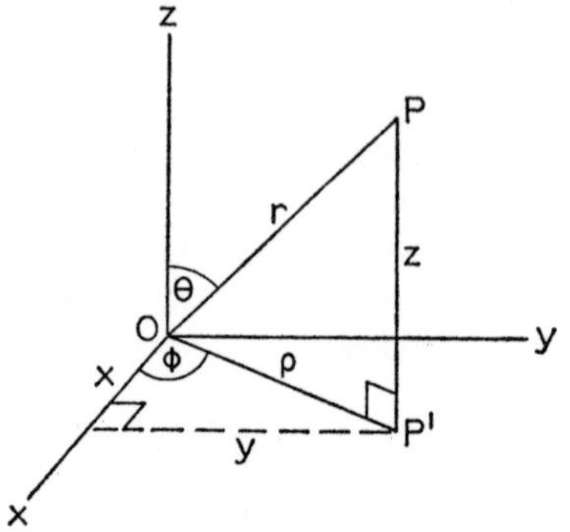

FIG. 11

Hence

$$\frac{\partial V}{\partial \rho} = \frac{\partial V}{\partial x}\frac{\partial x}{\partial \rho} + \frac{\partial V}{\partial y}\frac{\partial y}{\partial \rho} = \cos\phi\frac{\partial V}{\partial x} + \sin\phi\frac{\partial V}{\partial y},$$
$$\frac{\partial V}{\partial \phi} = \frac{\partial V}{\partial x}\frac{\partial x}{\partial \phi} + \frac{\partial V}{\partial y}\frac{\partial y}{\partial \phi} = -\rho\sin\phi\frac{\partial V}{\partial x} + \rho\cos\phi\frac{\partial V}{\partial y}.$$

Solving these equations for $\partial V/\partial x$ and $\partial V/\partial y$,

$$\frac{\partial V}{\partial x} = \cos\phi\frac{\partial V}{\partial \rho} - \frac{\sin\phi}{\rho}\frac{\partial V}{\partial \phi}, \quad \frac{\partial V}{\partial y} = \sin\phi\frac{\partial V}{\partial \rho} + \frac{\cos\phi}{\rho}\frac{\partial V}{\partial \phi}, \tag{7.3}$$

so that, since $\cos\phi \pm i\sin\phi = \exp(\pm i\phi)$,

$$\frac{\partial V}{\partial x} + i\frac{\partial V}{\partial y} = e^{i\phi}\left(\frac{\partial V}{\partial \rho} + \frac{i}{\rho}\frac{\partial V}{\partial \phi}\right), \quad \frac{\partial V}{\partial x} - i\frac{\partial V}{\partial y} = e^{-i\phi}\left(\frac{\partial V}{\partial \rho} - \frac{i}{\rho}\frac{\partial V}{\partial \phi}\right).$$

Consequently,

$$\begin{aligned}\frac{\partial^2 V}{\partial x^2} + \frac{\partial^2 V}{\partial y^2} &= \left(\frac{\partial}{\partial x} + i\frac{\partial}{\partial y}\right)\left(\frac{\partial V}{\partial x} - i\frac{\partial V}{\partial y}\right)\\ &= e^{i\phi}\left(\frac{\partial}{\partial \rho} + \frac{i}{\rho}\frac{\partial}{\partial \phi}\right)\left\{e^{-i\phi}\left(\frac{\partial V}{\partial \rho} - \frac{i}{\rho}\frac{\partial V}{\partial \phi}\right)\right\}\\ &= \frac{\partial^2 V}{\partial \rho^2} + \frac{i}{\rho^2}\frac{\partial V}{\partial \phi} - \frac{i}{\rho}\frac{\partial^2 V}{\partial \rho \partial \phi} + \frac{1}{\rho}\frac{\partial V}{\partial \rho} + \frac{i}{\rho}\frac{\partial^2 V}{\partial \phi \partial \rho} - \frac{i}{\rho^2}\frac{\partial V}{\partial \phi} + \frac{1}{\rho^2}\frac{\partial^2 V}{\partial \phi^2}\\ &= \frac{\partial^2 V}{\partial \rho^2} + \frac{1}{\rho}\frac{\partial V}{\partial \rho} + \frac{1}{\rho^2}\frac{\partial^2 V}{\partial \phi^2},\end{aligned} \tag{7.4}$$

and equation (7.1) becomes

$$\frac{\partial^2 V}{\partial \rho^2} + \frac{1}{\rho}\frac{\partial V}{\partial \rho} + \frac{1}{\rho^2}\frac{\partial^2 V}{\partial \phi^2} + \frac{\partial^2 V}{\partial z^2} = A\frac{\partial^2 V}{\partial t^2} + B\frac{\partial V}{\partial t} + C. \tag{7.5}$$

(*b*) *Spherical polar coordinates*

In the case of spherical polar coordinates (r, θ, ϕ), we have from Fig. 11

$$x = r\sin\theta\cos\phi, \quad y = r\sin\theta\sin\phi, \quad z = r\cos\theta. \tag{7.6}$$

We also have

$$\left.\begin{aligned} z = r\cos\theta, \quad \rho = r\sin\theta,\\ x = \rho\cos\phi, \quad y = \rho\sin\phi,\end{aligned}\right\} \tag{7.7}$$

so that the relations between z, ρ and r, θ are similar to those between x, y and ρ, ϕ. By suitable interchange of symbols we can therefore make use of formulae obtained in (*a*) above.

Thus

$$\nabla^2 V = \frac{\partial^2 V}{\partial \rho^2} + \frac{1}{\rho}\frac{\partial V}{\partial \rho} + \frac{1}{\rho^2}\frac{\partial^2 V}{\partial \phi^2} + \frac{\partial^2 V}{\partial z^2} \tag{7.8}$$

and writing z for x, ρ for y, r for ρ, θ for ϕ, equations (7.3), (7.4) give

$$\frac{\partial V}{\partial \rho} = \sin\theta \frac{\partial V}{\partial r} + \frac{\cos\theta}{r}\frac{\partial V}{\partial \theta},$$

$$\frac{\partial^2 V}{\partial z^2} + \frac{\partial^2 V}{\partial \rho^2} = \frac{\partial^2 V}{\partial r^2} + \frac{1}{r}\frac{\partial V}{\partial r} + \frac{1}{r^2}\frac{\partial^2 V}{\partial \theta^2}.$$

Hence substituting in (7.8) and remembering that $\rho = r\sin\theta$,

$$\nabla^2 V = \frac{\partial^2 V}{\partial r^2} + \frac{1}{r}\frac{\partial V}{\partial r} + \frac{1}{r^2}\frac{\partial^2 V}{\partial \theta^2} + \frac{1}{r\sin\theta}\left(\sin\theta\frac{\partial V}{\partial r} + \frac{\cos\theta}{r}\frac{\partial V}{\partial \theta}\right) + \frac{1}{r^2\sin^2\theta}\frac{\partial^2 V}{\partial \phi^2}$$

and, with a little reduction, equation (7.1) becomes

$$\frac{\partial^2 V}{\partial r^2} + \frac{2}{r}\frac{\partial V}{\partial r} + \frac{1}{r^2}\frac{\partial^2 V}{\partial \theta^2} + \frac{\cot\theta}{r^2}\frac{\partial V}{\partial \theta} + \frac{1}{r^2\sin^2\theta}\frac{\partial^2 V}{\partial \phi^2} = A\frac{\partial^2 V}{\partial t^2} + B\frac{\partial V}{\partial t} + C. \tag{7.9}$$

7.4 Some solutions of equation (7.1) in polar coordinates

In this section we give some particular solutions, obtained by the method of separation of variables, of some of the equations of mathematical physics when these are expressed in polar coordinates.

We start with the wave equation in cylindrical polar coordinates, that is,

$$\frac{\partial^2 V}{\partial \rho^2} + \frac{1}{\rho}\frac{\partial V}{\partial \rho} + \frac{1}{\rho^2}\frac{\partial^2 V}{\partial \phi^2} + \frac{\partial^2 V}{\partial z^2} = \frac{1}{c^2}\frac{\partial^2 V}{\partial t^2}. \tag{7.10}$$

Writing $V = R\Phi ZT$ where R, Φ, Z and T are functions respectively of ρ, ϕ, z and t, substitution in (7.10) and division by V gives

$$\frac{1}{R}\left(\frac{d^2R}{d\rho^2} + \frac{1}{\rho}\frac{dR}{d\rho}\right) + \frac{1}{\rho^2\Phi}\frac{d^2\Phi}{d\phi^2} + \frac{1}{Z}\frac{d^2Z}{dz^2} = \frac{1}{c^2T}\frac{d^2T}{dt^2}.$$

Let

$$\frac{1}{\Phi}\frac{d^2\Phi}{d\phi^2} = -m^2, \quad \frac{1}{Z}\frac{d^2Z}{dz^2} = -n^2, \quad \frac{1}{T}\frac{d^2T}{dt^2} = -c^2p^2, \tag{7.11}$$

where m, n and p are constants, then

$$\frac{1}{R}\left(\frac{d^2R}{d\rho^2} + \frac{1}{\rho}\frac{dR}{d\rho}\right) - \frac{m^2}{\rho^2} = n^2 - p^2 = -\alpha^2 \text{ (say)}$$

giving

$$\frac{d^2R}{d\rho^2} + \frac{1}{\rho}\frac{dR}{d\rho} + \left(\alpha^2 - \frac{m^2}{\rho^2}\right)R = 0. \tag{7.12}$$

The solutions of equations (7.11) are

$$\Phi = A_1 \cos m\phi + B_1 \sin m\phi, \quad Z = A_2 \cos nz + B_2 \sin nz$$

and

$$T = A_3 \cos cpt + B_3 \sin cpt$$

while that of equation (7.12), being Bessel's equation of order m and argument $\alpha\rho$, is

$$R = A_4 J_m(\alpha\rho) + B_4 Y_m(\alpha\rho),$$

the A's and B's being arbitrary constants. Hence a solution of the wave equation in cylindrical polar coordinates is given by an expression of the type*

$$V = \Sigma A J_m(\alpha\rho) \cos m\phi \cos nz \cos cpt \tag{7.13}$$

where $\alpha^2 = p^2 - n^2$. A solution which has axial symmetry and is therefore independent of the coordinate ϕ is given by taking $m = 0$ and is

$$V = \Sigma A J_0(\alpha\rho) \cos nz \cos cpt \tag{7.14}$$

and, if the wave is also independent of z,

$$V = \Sigma A J_0(p\rho) \cos cpt \tag{7.15}$$

for now $n = 0$ and $\alpha = p$.

Solutions of the equation of heat conduction in cylindrical coordinates can be built up in a similar way. A typical result is

$$V = \Sigma A e^{-kp^2t} J_m(\alpha\rho) \cos m\phi \cos nz \tag{7.16}$$

where $\alpha^2 = p^2 - n^2$, with the simplifications

$$V = \Sigma A e^{-kp^2t} J_0(\alpha\rho) \cos nz \tag{7.17}$$

in the case of axial symmetry, and

$$V = \Sigma A e^{-kp^2t} J_0(p\rho) \tag{7.18}$$

when the temperature V is independent of both ϕ and z. Solutions of Laplace's equation can, since V no longer involves the time t be obtained by writing $p = 0$ in either (7.13) or (7.16). It is generally more convenient to use in rather than n and a typical solution is

$$V = \Sigma A J_m(n\rho) \cos m\phi \cosh nz. \tag{7.19}$$

Similar solutions can be obtained when equation (7.1) is expressed in spherical polar coordinates and we again use the wave equation as an example. In this coordinate system the equation is

$$\frac{\partial^2 V}{\partial r^2} + \frac{2}{r}\frac{\partial V}{\partial r} + \frac{1}{r^2}\frac{\partial^2 V}{\partial \theta^2} + \frac{\cot\theta}{r^2}\frac{\partial V}{\partial \theta} + \frac{1}{r^2 \sin^2\theta}\frac{\partial^2 V}{\partial \phi^2} = \frac{1}{c^2}\frac{\partial^2 V}{\partial t^2} \tag{7.20}$$

* In practical applications it is usually necessary for V to retain its value when ϕ is increased by 2π and m must therefore be an integer (or zero) in such cases.

and we now write $V = R\Theta\Phi T$ where R, Θ, Φ and T are respectively functions of r, θ, ϕ and t. This gives

$$\frac{1}{R}\left\{\frac{d^2R}{dr^2} + \frac{2}{r}\frac{dR}{dr}\right\} + \frac{1}{r^2\Theta}\left\{\frac{d^2\Theta}{d\theta^2} + \cot\theta\frac{d\Theta}{d\theta}\right\} + \frac{1}{r^2\sin^2\theta}\frac{1}{\Phi}\frac{d^2\Phi}{d\phi^2} = \frac{1}{c^2T}\frac{d^2T}{dt^2}.$$

Letting

$$\frac{1}{\Phi}\frac{d^2\Phi}{d\phi^2} = -m^2, \quad \frac{1}{c^2T}\frac{d^2T}{dt^2} = -p^2, \tag{7.21}$$

$$\frac{1}{\Theta}\left\{\frac{d^2\Theta}{d\theta^2} + \cot\theta\frac{d\Theta}{d\theta}\right\} = \frac{m^2}{\sin^2\theta} - n(n+1), \tag{7.22}$$

where m, p and n are constants, we find that R has to satisfy the ordinary differential equation

$$\frac{1}{R}\left\{\frac{d^2R}{dr^2} + \frac{2}{r}\frac{dR}{dr}\right\} = \frac{n(n+1)}{r^2} - p^2. \tag{7.23}$$

Solutions of equations (7.21) are of the forms

$$\left.\begin{array}{lll}\Phi = \cos m\phi & \text{or} & \Phi = \sin m\phi, \\ T = \cos cpt & \text{or} & T = \sin cpt,\end{array}\right\} \tag{7.24}$$

and, writing $x = \cos\theta$, equation (7.22) becomes, after a little reduction,

$$\frac{d}{dx}\left\{(1-x^2)\frac{d\Theta}{dx}\right\} + \left\{n(n+1) - \frac{m^2}{1-x^2}\right\}\Theta = 0 \tag{7.25}$$

and a typical solution of this equation is the associated Legendre function denoted by $P_n^m(x)$. Finally, equation (7.23) can be written

$$r^2\frac{d^2R}{dr^2} + 2r\frac{dR}{dr} + \{p^2r^2 + \tfrac{1}{4} - (n+\tfrac{1}{2})^2\}R = 0$$

and the solution of this equation is [see formulae (1.48) and (1.49)]

$$R = r^{-\frac{1}{2}}\{AJ_{n+\frac{1}{2}}(pr) + BY_{n+\frac{1}{2}}(pr)\}. \tag{7.26}$$

A typical solution of the wave equation in spherical polar coordinates is therefore*

$$V = \Sigma Ar^{-\frac{1}{2}}J_{n+\frac{1}{2}}(pr)P_n^m(\cos\theta)\cos m\phi\cos cpt. \tag{7.27}$$

Solutions possessing axial symmetry are those independent of ϕ; these are given by setting $m = 0$ and are

$$V = \Sigma\, Ar^{-\frac{1}{2}}\, J_{n+\frac{1}{2}}\,(pr)\, P_n\,(\cos\theta)\cos cpt \tag{7.28}$$

* For the reason given previously practical applications usually require that m is an integer and, since $P_n^m(\cos\theta)$ is only finite when $\theta = \pi$ if n is an integer, this condition is also usually necessary.

where $P_n(\cos\theta)$ is the Legendre polynomial. Solutions of the equation of heat conduction can be found in the same way and that corresponding to (7.27) is

$$V = \Sigma A e^{-kp^2t} r^{-\frac{1}{2}} J_{n+\frac{1}{2}}(pr) P_n{}^m(\cos\theta)\cos m\phi. \tag{7.29}$$

7.5 Some examples

In the previous section we gave some solutions of the equations of mathematical physics when these equations were expressed in polar coordinates. Particular physical problems require that certain quantities satisfy given boundary and/or initial conditions as well as a partial differential equation. These conditions permit the selection of the appropriate parts of the quite general solutions given in §7.4 and the determination of the constants contained in them. Typical details are illustrated in the worked examples which follow.

Example 1. *The material of a long circular cylinder of radius a is of diffusivity k. The cylinder is initially at constant temperature V_0 and its curved surface is maintained at zero temperature. Find an expression for the temperature V at time t at a point in the cylinder at distance ρ from its axis.*

Here there is symmetry about the z-axis and, as the cylinder is long, the temperature will be independent of z. Hence by (7.18) an appropriate expression for the temperature is

$$V = \Sigma A e^{-kp^2t} J_0(p\rho)$$

where A and p are, as yet, undetermined constants. By taking $p = p_s (s = 1, 2, 3, \ldots)$ where $J_0(p_s a) = 0$, the boundary condition $V = 0$ on the curved surface $\rho = a$ of the cylinder is satisfied for all values of the time t. Hence we can write

$$V = \sum_{s=1}^{\infty} A_s e^{-kp_s^2t} J_0(p_s\rho)$$

where p_s is a positive zero of $J_0(pa)$ and the value of V when $t = 0$ is given by

$$V = \sum_{s=1}^{\infty} A_s J_0(p_s\rho).$$

The coefficients A_s have now to be chosen so that this is equal to the initial temperature V_0 for all values of ρ such that $0 < \rho < a$. This can be done by taking A_s to be the coefficient of $J_0(p_s\rho)$ in the Fourier-Bessel series representing V_0. By equation (4.22), A_s is therefore given by

$$\begin{aligned} A_s &= \frac{2}{a^2 J_1^2(p_s a)} \int_0^a \rho V_0 J_0(p_s\rho)\, \mathrm{d}\rho \\ &= \frac{2V_0}{p_s^2 a^2 J_1^2(p_s a)} \int_0^{p_s a} \lambda J_0(\lambda)\, \mathrm{d}\lambda, \quad \text{putting } \lambda = p_s\rho, \\ &= \frac{2V_0}{p_s a J_1(p_s a)}, \end{aligned}$$

the last step following from equation (2.2). Hence the required expression for the temperature V is

$$V = \frac{2V_0}{a} \sum_{s=1}^{\infty} e^{-kp_s^2 t} \frac{J_0(p_s\rho)}{p_s J_1(p_s a)},$$

where p_s is a positive root of the equation $J_0(pa) = 0$.

Example 2. *A tightly stretched horizontal circular membrane of radius a and uniform surface density σ is fixed round its circumference and a normal impulse N is applied at its centre. Find an expression for the vertical displacement (V) of the membrane from its initial plane at time t and at radial distance ρ.*

The equation for V is the wave equation* and as there is axial symmetry and independence of the z coordinate, equation (7.15) shows that an appropriate solution is

$$V = \Sigma A J_0(p\rho) \sin cpt$$

(sines being used instead of cosines to satisfy the initial condition that $V = 0$ when $t = 0$ for $0 \leqslant \rho < a$). This expression satisfies the boundary condition that $V = 0$ when $\rho = a$ for all t if we take p to be a positive zero of $J_0(pa)$ and we therefore write

$$V = \sum_{s=1}^{\infty} A_s J_0(p_s\rho) \sin cp_s t \tag{7.30}$$

giving

$$\left[\frac{\partial V}{\partial t}\right]_{t=0} = c \sum_{s=1}^{\infty} A_s p_s J_0(p_s\rho). \tag{7.31}$$

When $t = 0$, $\partial V/\partial t = 0$ except over the small circle of radius ϵ on which the impulse acts, so that, applying equations (4.17), (4.22) to equation (7.31)

$$cA_s p_s = \frac{2}{a^2 J_1^2(p_s a)} \int_0^{\epsilon} \rho \left[\frac{\partial V}{\partial t}\right]_{t=0} J_0(p_s\rho)\, d\rho. \tag{7.32}$$

But

$$N = \pi\epsilon^2\sigma \left[\frac{\partial V}{\partial t}\right]_{t=0}$$

so that taking $[\partial V/\partial t]_{t=0}$ as constant and $J_0(p_s\rho)$ as unity over the surface of the small circle, equation (7.32) gives

$$cA_s p_s = \frac{2}{a^2 J_1^2(p_s a)} \cdot \frac{N}{\pi\epsilon^2\sigma} \int_0^{\epsilon} \rho\, d\rho = \frac{N}{\pi\sigma a^2 J_1^2(p_s a)}.$$

* The velocity c in the wave equation can be shown to be given by $c^2 = T/\sigma$ where T is the tension of the membrane.

Hence the required expression for V is

$$V = \frac{N}{\pi\sigma a^2 c}\sum_{s=1}^{\infty}\frac{J_0(p_s\rho)}{p_s J_1^2(p_s a)}\sin cp_s t$$

where $J_0(p_s a) = 0$ for $s = 1, 2, 3, \ldots$

Example 3. *Fluid of viscosity ν is contained between two infinitely long concentric circular cylinders of radii a and b ($a < b$). The inner cylinder is kept at rest and the outer one suddenly starts rotating with uniform angular velocity Ω. Find an expression for the velocity v of the fluid at time t and radial distance ρ, given that v satisfies the differential equation*

$$\frac{\partial^2 v}{\partial\rho^2} + \frac{1}{\rho}\frac{\partial v}{\partial\rho} - \frac{v}{\rho^2} = \frac{1}{\nu}\frac{\partial v}{\partial t}$$

with the conditions $v = \Omega b$ when $\rho = b$, $v = 0$ when $\rho = a$ and $v = 0$ when $t = 0$.

The variables in the given differential equation can be separated by writing $v = RT$ where R, T are respectively functions of ρ and t. Substitution in the equation and division by RT gives

$$\frac{1}{R}\left(\frac{\mathrm{d}^2R}{\mathrm{d}\rho^2} + \frac{1}{\rho}\frac{\mathrm{d}R}{\mathrm{d}\rho} - \frac{R}{\rho^2}\right) = \frac{1}{\nu T}\frac{\mathrm{d}T}{\mathrm{d}t}$$

and, if we let $\mathrm{d}T/\mathrm{d}t = -\nu p^2 T$ where p is a constant, we have

$$\rho^2\frac{\mathrm{d}^2R}{\mathrm{d}\rho^2} + \rho\frac{\mathrm{d}R}{\mathrm{d}\rho} + (p^2\rho^2 - 1)R = 0.$$

The solutions of these ordinary differential equations are respectively

$$T = A_1 e^{-\nu p^2 t}, \quad R = A_2 J_1(p\rho) + A_3 Y_1(p\rho).$$

Hence an appropriate solution of the partial differential equation is

$$v = V + \Sigma\{AJ_1(p\rho) + A' Y_1(p\rho)\}e^{-\nu p^2 t} \tag{7.33}$$

where V is the value of v in the steady state. V satisfies the ordinary differential equation

$$\frac{\mathrm{d}^2V}{\mathrm{d}\rho^2} + \frac{1}{\rho}\frac{\mathrm{d}V}{\mathrm{d}\rho} - \frac{V}{\rho^2} = 0$$

and the conditions $V = \Omega b$ when $\rho = b$, $V = 0$ when $\rho = a$ so that $V = C\rho^{-1} + D\rho$ where the constants C, D are given by

$$Cb^{-1} + Db = \Omega b, \quad Ca^{-1} + Da = 0.$$

These simultaneous equations give $(b^2 - a^2)D = \Omega b^2$, $C = -a^2 D$ and equation (7.33) becomes

$$v = \frac{\Omega b^2}{\rho}\left(\frac{\rho^2 - a^2}{b^2 - a^2}\right) + \Sigma\{AJ_1(p\rho) + A' Y_1(p\rho)\}e^{-\nu p^2 t}.$$

The boundary condition $v = 0$ when $\rho = a$ is satisfied by taking

$$A' = -A\,\frac{J_1(pa)}{Y_1(pa)}$$

and the condition $v = \Omega b$ when $\rho = b$ is fulfilled if p is taken as a root of the equation $B_1(pb) = 0$ where

$$B_1(p\rho) \equiv J_1(p\rho)\,Y_1(pa) - Y_1(p\rho)J_1(pa).$$

Hence we have

$$v = \frac{\Omega b^2}{\rho}\left(\frac{\rho^2 - a^2}{b^2 - a^2}\right) + \sum_{s=1}^{\infty} \frac{A_s}{Y_1(p_s a)}\,B_1(p_s\rho)e^{-\nu p_s^2 t}$$

and the initial condition $v = 0$ when $t = 0$ then requires

$$0 = \frac{\Omega b^2}{\rho}\left(\frac{\rho^2 - a^2}{b^2 - a^2}\right) + \sum_{s=1}^{\infty} \frac{A_s}{Y_1(p_s a)}\,B_1(p_s\rho).$$

Substituting for $(\rho^2 - a^2)/\rho$ from Exercises 4, No. 14 we have

$$0 = \pi\Omega b \sum_{s=1}^{\infty} \frac{J_1(p_s a)J_1(p_s b)}{J_1^2(p_s a) - J_1^2(p_s b)}\,B_1(p_s\rho) + \sum_{s=1}^{\infty} \frac{A_s}{Y_1(p_s a)}\,B_1(p_s\rho)$$

and equating the coefficients of $B_1(p_s\rho)$ for $s = 1, 2, 3, \ldots,$

$$\frac{A_s}{Y_1(p_s a)} = -\frac{\pi\Omega b J_1(p_s a)J_1(p_s b)}{J_1^2(p_s a) - J_1^2(p_s b)}.$$

Hence the required expression for v is

$$v = \frac{\Omega b^2}{\rho}\left(\frac{\rho^2 - a^2}{b^2 - a^2}\right) - \pi\Omega b \sum_{s=1}^{\infty} \frac{J_1(p_s a)J_1(p_s b)}{J_1^2(p_s a) - J_1^2(p_s b)}\,B_1(p_s\rho)e^{-\nu p_s^2 t}$$

p_s being a zero of the expression $B_1(pb) \equiv J_1(pb)\,Y_1(pa) - Y_1(pb)J_1(pa)$.

Example 4. *Find the electrostatic capacity of a condenser consisting of a flat circular plate of unit radius charged to unit potential situated inside a long coaxial earthed circular cylinder of large radius a. (Powers of $1/a$ above the first may be neglected in comparison with unity.)*

The condenser is shown in Fig. 12 and the potential V has to satisfy Laplace's equation in cylindrical coordinates (ρ, z)

$$\frac{\partial^2 V}{\partial \rho^2} + \frac{1}{\rho}\frac{\partial V}{\partial \rho} + \frac{\partial^2 V}{\partial z^2} = 0, \tag{7.34}$$

with the boundary conditions

$$V = 0 \text{ when } \rho = a, \tag{7.35}$$

$$V \to 0 \text{ as } |z| \to \infty, \tag{7.36}$$

$$\left.\begin{aligned} V = 1, &\quad 0 < \rho < 1, \\ \frac{\partial V}{\partial z} = 0, &\quad 1 < \rho < a, \end{aligned}\right\} \text{when } z = 0. \tag{7.37}$$

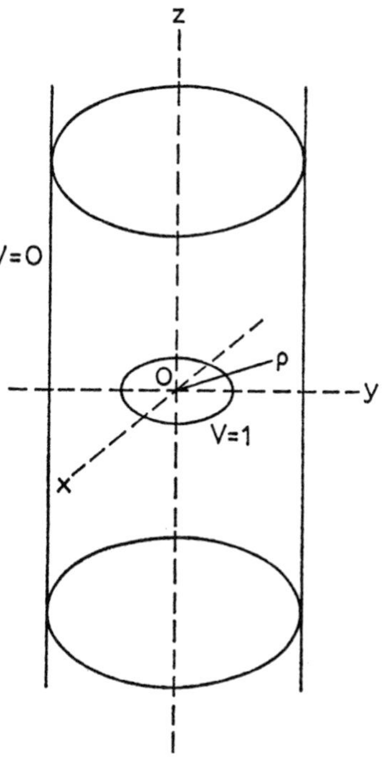

FIG. 12

A suitable solution of the partial differential equation (7.34) which satisfies (7.36) is $V = \Sigma A J_0(p\rho)e^{-p|z|}$ and (7.35) will be satisfied if we take

$$V = \sum_{s=1}^{\infty} A_s J_0(p_s \rho) e^{-p_s|z|} \tag{7.38}$$

where p_s is a positive zero of the function $J_0(pa)$. The "mixed" boundary condition (7.37) requires

$$\sum_{s=1}^{\infty} A_s J_0(p_s\rho) = 1 \ (0 < \rho < 1), \quad \sum_{s=1}^{\infty} p_s A_s J_0(p_s\rho) = 0 \ (1 < \rho < a),$$

and, by writing $A_s = 2c_s/p_s a^2$, these equations become the dual series

$$\sum_{s=1}^{\infty} p_s^{-1} c_s J_0(p_s\rho) = \tfrac{1}{2}a^2 \ (0 < \rho < 1), \quad \sum_{s=1}^{\infty} c_s J_0(p_s\rho) = 0 \ (1 < \rho < a), \tag{7.39}$$

which were discussed in Example 5 of Chapter 6. The surface density of charge on the disc is $(-1/4\pi)(\partial V/\partial z)_{z=0}$ and, taking into account both sides of the disc, the total charge is

$$-\frac{1}{2\pi}\int_0^1 2\pi\rho\left(\frac{\partial V}{\partial z}\right)_{z=0} d\rho = \sum_{s=1}^{\infty} A_s p_s \int_0^1 \rho J_0(p_s\rho)\, d\rho = \sum_{s=1}^{\infty} A_s J_1(p_s)$$

when use is made of (7.38) and (2.2). By Example 5 of Chapter 6 we have, to the order of accuracy required,

$$A_s = \frac{2c_s}{p_s a^2} = \frac{2}{a^2}\left(\frac{2}{\pi}\right)^{\frac{1}{2}}\left(1 + \frac{5{\cdot}47072}{\pi^2 a}\right)\frac{J_{\frac{1}{2}}(p_s)}{p_s^{\frac{3}{2}} J_1^{\,2}(p_s a)}$$

and the capacity C is given by

$$C = \frac{2}{a^2}\left(\frac{2}{\pi}\right)^{\frac{1}{2}}\left(1 + \frac{5{\cdot}47072}{\pi^2 a}\right)\sum_{s=1}^{\infty}\frac{J_{\frac{1}{2}}(p_s)J_1(p_s)}{p_s^{\frac{3}{2}} J_1^{\,2}(p_s a)}. \tag{7.40}$$

By writing $\nu = m = 0$, $k = -\frac{1}{2}$ in the analysis of Lemma 1 of §6.6, we have, since $\mathscr{F}_0(\frac{1}{2}, 1, \rho^2) = 1$,

$$\frac{2}{a^2}\sum_{s=1}^{\infty}\frac{J_{\frac{1}{2}}(p_s)}{p_s^{\frac{1}{2}} J_1^{\,2}(p_s a)} J_0(p_s\rho) = \begin{cases} (2/\pi)^{\frac{1}{2}}(1-\rho^2)^{-\frac{1}{2}}, & 0 < \rho < 1, \\ 0, & 1 < \rho < a. \end{cases}$$

Multiplication by ρ and integration between 0, 1 then gives

$$\frac{2}{a^2}\sum_{s=1}^{\infty}\frac{J_{\frac{1}{2}}(p_s)J_1(p_s)}{p_s^{\frac{3}{2}} J_1^{\,2}(p_s a)} = \left(\frac{2}{\pi}\right)^{\frac{1}{2}},$$

and substitution in (7.40) yields

$$C = \frac{2}{\pi}\left(1 + \frac{5{\cdot}47072}{\pi^2 a}\right).$$

Example 5. *A long metallic solid circular cylinder of specific resistance τ and unit permeability carries an alternating current of period $2\pi/p$. The current density j at a point (x, y, z) of the material satisfies the equation*

$$\nabla^2 j = \frac{K}{c^2}\frac{\partial^2 j}{\partial t^2} + \frac{4\pi}{c^2\tau}\frac{\partial j}{dt}, \tag{7.41}$$

where K is the dielectric constant, c the velocity of light and t the time. Show that $j \simeq A\,(\text{ber}\ \alpha + i\ \text{bei}\ \alpha)e^{ipt}$ where $\alpha = 2(\rho/c)(\pi p/\tau)^{\frac{1}{2}}$, ρ being the radial distance of the point from the axis of the cylinder and A being a constant.

We take the axis of the cylinder to coincide with the x-axis. As the cylinder is long, j is independent of x and

$$\nabla^2 j = \frac{\partial^2 j}{\partial y^2} + \frac{\partial^2 j}{\partial z^2} = \frac{\partial^2 j}{\partial \rho^2} + \frac{1}{\rho}\frac{\partial j}{\partial \rho},$$

where $y = \rho\cos\theta$, $z = \rho\sin\theta$. Since there is axial symmetry we can write $j = \Omega(\rho)e^{ipt}$ and substitution in equation (7.41) gives, after division by e^{ipt},

$$\frac{d^2\Omega}{d\rho^2} + \frac{1}{\rho}\frac{d\Omega}{d\rho} = \left(\frac{4\pi}{c^2\tau}ip - \frac{K}{c^2}p^2\right)\Omega. \tag{7.42}$$

In metallic conductors τ is small and the expression $(K\tau p/4\pi)$ is small unless we are dealing with currents of high frequency. Hence the second term on the right-hand side of equation (7.42) can be neglected in comparison with the first and

$$\frac{d^2\Omega}{d\rho^2} + \frac{1}{\rho}\frac{d\Omega}{d\rho} - \frac{4\pi}{c^2\tau} ip\Omega = 0.$$

Writing $\alpha = 2(\rho/c)(\pi p/\tau)^{\frac{1}{2}}$ this becomes

$$\frac{d^2\Omega}{d\alpha^2} + \frac{1}{\alpha}\frac{d\Omega}{d\alpha} - i\Omega = 0$$

with solution $AI_0(\alpha\sqrt{i})$ as Ω has to be finite on the axis ($\alpha = \rho = 0$). The required result then follows when use is made of the relation (1.75), viz.,

$$I_0(\alpha\sqrt{i}) = ber\ \alpha + i\ bei\ \alpha.$$

Example 6. *When air vibrates freely in a rigid sphere of radius a, the velocity potential V at a point P satisfies the wave equation and the boundary condition* $\partial V/\partial r = 0$ *when* $r = a$, *r being the distance of P from the centre of the sphere. Show that for purely radial vibrations*

$$V = \sum_{s=1}^{\infty} B_s r^{-1} \sin p_s r \cos cp_s t$$

where $p_s(s = 1, 2, 3, \ldots)$ *are the roots of the equation* $\tan pa = pa$ *and the coefficients B are to be determined from the initial state of the air.*

For purely radial vibrations, the expression for V in spherical polar coordinates will be independent of θ and ϕ. An appropriate solution of the wave equation is therefore obtained by setting $m = n = 0$ in formula (7.27) to give

$$\begin{aligned} V &= \Sigma A r^{-\frac{1}{2}} J_{\frac{1}{2}}(pr) \cos cpt \\ &= \Sigma B r^{-1} \sin pr \cos cpt \end{aligned}$$

when we write $B = (2/\pi p)^{\frac{1}{2}} A$ and use the relation (1.38). This gives

$$\frac{\partial V}{\partial r} = \Sigma B(-r^{-2} \sin pr + pr^{-1} \cos pr) \cos cpt$$

and, if $\partial V/\partial r = 0$ when $r = a$, p must be a root of the equation $\tan pa = pa$.

7.6 Solutions of equation (7.1) for unbounded media

In §7.4 we gave some particular solutions of the equations of mathematical physics in the form of infinite series and such solutions are appropriate if the media involved are bounded by cylinders or spheres. When the media are unbounded, similar solutions apply if the series are replaced by infinite integrals and we give below some typical examples.

Example 7. *Find the electrostatic capacity of a flat circular plate of unit radius charged to unit potential.*

This is the problem considered in Example 4 when the surrounding coaxial cylinder is removed. The potential V has now to satisfy Laplace's equation

$$\frac{\partial^2 V}{\partial \rho^2} + \frac{1}{\rho}\frac{\partial V}{\partial \rho} + \frac{\partial^2 V}{\partial z^2} = 0 \tag{7.43}$$

with the boundary conditions

$$V \to 0 \text{ when } \rho \to \infty \tag{7.44}$$

$$V \to 0 \text{ when } |z| \to \infty \tag{7.45}$$

$$\left.\begin{aligned} V = 1, \quad 0 < \rho < 1, \\ \frac{\partial V}{\partial z} = 0, \quad 1 < \rho < \infty, \end{aligned}\right\} \text{ when } z = 0. \tag{7.46}$$

In place of the series (7.38) we now take a solution of Laplace's equation in the form

$$V = \int_0^\infty A(p) J_0(\rho p) e^{-p|z|}\, dp$$

where $A(p)$ is a function of p to be determined. This solution satisfies the conditions (7.44), (7.45) and it satisfies (7.46) if

$$\int_0^\infty A(p) J_0(\rho p)\, dp = 1 \ (0 < \rho < 1), \quad \int_0^\infty p A(p) J_0(\rho p)\, dp = 0 \ (1 < \rho < \infty).$$

These are a particular case of the dual integral equations (6.11) and their solution is easily found to be given by $\pi A(p) = 2p^{-1} \sin p$. As in Example 4, the total charge on the disc is

$$-\frac{1}{2\pi}\int_0^1 2\pi\rho \left(\frac{\partial V}{\partial z}\right)_{z=0} d\rho = \int_0^\infty p A(p)\, dp \int_0^1 \rho J_0(p\rho)\, d\rho = \int_0^\infty A(p) J_1(p)\, dp.$$

The capacity C of the disc is therefore given by

$$C = \frac{2}{\pi}\int_0^\infty \frac{J_1(p) \sin p}{p}\, dp = \left(\frac{2}{\pi}\right)^{\frac{1}{2}} \int_0^\infty \frac{J_1(p) J_{\frac{1}{2}}(p)}{p^{\frac{1}{2}}}\, dp = \frac{2}{\pi},$$

when use is made of formula (5.32).

Example 8. *In the problem of Boussinesq in which a uniform pressure of unit intensity acts over a circle of unit radius in the surface $z = 0$ of a semi-infinite solid and the rest of the surface is stress-free, the normal and shear stresses are given by*

$$\sigma_z = \frac{\partial}{\partial z}\left\{(2 - \sigma)\nabla^2 - \frac{\partial^2}{\partial z^2}\right\} \chi, \quad \tau_{rz} = \frac{\partial}{\partial \rho}\left\{(1 - \sigma)\nabla^2 - \frac{\partial^2}{\partial z^2}\right\} \chi, \tag{7.47}$$

where χ satisfies the biharmonic equation $\nabla^4\chi = 0$ and σ is Poisson's ratio for the material of the solid. Show that the normal stress at the point with cylindrical coordinates (ρ, z) is given by

$$\sigma_z = -\int_0^\infty (1 + zp)e^{-zp}J_1(p)J_0(\rho p)\,dp, \tag{7.48}$$

the centre of the pressed area being the point (0, 0).

A solution of the equation $\nabla^2\chi = 0$ which is finite when $\rho = 0$ and when z tends to infinity is $Ae^{-pz}J_0(p\rho)$ and this function automatically satisfies the equation $\nabla^4\chi = 0$. Also

$$\nabla^2\{Bze^{-pz}J_0(p\rho)\} = \left(\frac{\partial^2}{\partial\rho^2} + \frac{1}{\rho}\frac{\partial}{\partial\rho} + \frac{\partial^2}{\partial z^2}\right)\{Bze^{-pz}J_0(p\rho)\}$$
$$= -2Bpe^{-pz}J_0(p\rho) \tag{7.49}$$

when the differentiations are carried out and use is made of Bessel's equation (1.1). It follows that $\nabla^4\{Bze^{-pz}J_0(p\rho)\} = 0$ and we can take

$$\chi = \int_0^\infty (A + Bz)e^{-zp}J_0(\rho p)\,dp, \tag{7.50}$$

where A and B are functions of p, as a suitable solution of the biharmonic equation. This gives

$$\frac{\partial^2\chi}{\partial z^2} = \int_0^\infty (p^2A - 2pB + p^2zB)e^{-zp}J_0(\rho p)\,dp \tag{7.51}$$

and use of equations (7.47), (7.49), (7.50) and (7.51) gives, after a little reduction,

$$\sigma_z = \int_0^\infty \{(1 - 2\sigma)p^2B + p^3A + p^3zB\}e^{-zp}J_0(\rho p)\,dp, \tag{7.52}$$

$$\tau_{rz} = \frac{\partial}{\partial\rho}\int_0^\infty \{2\sigma pB - p^2A - p^2zB\}e^{-zp}J_0(\rho p)\,dp. \tag{7.53}$$

The shear stress τ_{rz} vanishes on the boundary $z = 0$ if we take $A = 2\sigma B/p$ and the normal stress is then given by

$$\sigma_z = \int_0^\infty (1 + zp)Bp^2e^{-zp}J_0(\rho p)\,dp. \tag{7.54}$$

On $z = 0$ this reduces to $\sigma_z = \int_0^\infty Bp^2J_0(\rho p)\,dp$ and the other boundary condition is therefore satisfied by choosing B so that

$$\int_0^\infty Bp^2J_0(\rho p)\,dp = \begin{cases} -1, & 0 < \rho < 1, \\ 0, & \rho > 1. \end{cases}$$

By Hankel's inversion theorem (4.37), (4.38), we have

$$pB = -\int_0^1 \rho J_0(p\rho)\,d\rho = -p^{-1}J_1(p)$$

and substitution in (7.54) gives the result (7.48).

Exercises 7

1. The surface $z = 0$ of the finite cylinder $0 \leqslant \rho < a$, $0 < z < l$ is kept at unit temperature and the other surfaces at zero temperature. Show that the steady temperature at the point with cylindrical coordinates (ρ, ϕ, z) is

$$\frac{2}{a}\sum_{s=1}^{\infty}\frac{\sinh{(l-z)p_s}}{\sinh{lp_s}}\cdot\frac{J_0(p_s\rho)}{p_sJ_1(p_sa)},$$

where p_s is a positive root of the equation $J_0(pa) = 0$.

2. A semi-infinite circular cylinder occupies the region $0 \leqslant \rho < a$, $z > 0$ where ρ and z are cylindrical polar coordinates. The curved surface $\rho = a$ of the cylinder is kept at zero temperature while the flat end $z = 0$ is maintained at temperature $f(\rho)$. Show that the steady temperature V at the point (ρ, ϕ, z) is given by

$$V = \frac{2}{a^2}\sum_{s=1}^{\infty}\frac{J_0(p_s\rho)}{J_1^2(p_sa)}\,e^{-p_sz}\int_0^a \rho f(\rho)J_0(p_s\rho)\,d\rho,$$

where p_s is a positive zero of $J_0(pa)$.

3. Show that a solution of the wave equation

$$\frac{\partial^2 V}{\partial \rho^2} + \frac{1}{\rho}\frac{\partial V}{\partial \rho} + \frac{1}{\rho^2}\frac{\partial^2 V}{\partial \phi^2} = \frac{1}{c^2}\frac{\partial^2 V}{\partial t^2}$$

which satisfies the boundary condition $\partial V/\partial \rho = 0$ when $\rho = a$ and the initial condition $V = -\rho\cos\phi$ when $t = 0$ is

$$V = \frac{2\cos\phi}{a}\sum_{s=1}^{\infty}\frac{J_1(p_s\rho)}{p_s^2J_1''(p_sa)}\cos cp_st,$$

where p_s is a positive zero of $J_1'(pa)$.

4. The two surfaces of a long cylindrical tube of internal and external radii a, b respectively are maintained at zero temperature. The diffusivity of the material of the tube is k and its initial temperature is unity. Show that the temperature V at time t and radial distance ρ is given by

$$V = \pi\sum_{s=1}^{\infty}\frac{J_0(p_sb)B_0(p_s\rho)}{J_0(p_sa)+J_0(p_sb)}\,e^{-kp_s^2t},$$

where $B_0(p\rho) = J_0(p\rho)Y_0(pa) - Y_0(p\rho)J_0(pa)$ and p_s is a root of the equation $B_0(pb) = 0$.

5. All the surfaces $\rho = a$, $\phi = 0$, $\phi = \alpha$ of an infinite wedge of diffusivity k are kept at zero temperature and its initial temperature is $f(\rho, \phi)$. Show that the temperature V at time t at the point with cylindrical coordinates (ρ, ϕ, z) is given by

$$V = \sum_{r=1}^{\infty}\sum_{s=1}^{\infty} A_{r,s}\,e^{-kp_s^2t}\sin\frac{r\pi\phi}{\alpha}\,J_{r\pi/\alpha}(p_s\rho)$$

where p_s are the positive roots of the equation $J_{r\pi/\alpha}(pa) = 0$ and

$$A_{r,s} = \frac{4}{a^2\alpha\{J_{r\pi/\alpha}'(p_s a)\}^2}\int_0^a\int_0^\alpha \rho f(\rho, \phi) J_{r\pi/\alpha}(p_s\rho) \sin\frac{r\pi\phi}{\alpha}\, d\rho\, d\phi.$$

6. A long circular cylinder of radius a containing liquid of viscosity ν is initially at rest. It is then made to rotate with uniform angular velocity Ω about its axis. Show that the velocity of the liquid at radial distance ρ and time t is

$$\Omega\rho + 2\Omega \sum_{s=1}^{\infty} \frac{J_1(p_s\rho)}{p_s J_1'(p_s a)} e^{-\nu p_s^2 t}$$

where p_s are the positive zeros of the function $J_1(pa)$.

7. A problem involving the oscillations of a heavy chain requires the solution of the partial differential equation

$$\frac{\partial^2 y}{\partial z^2} + \frac{1}{z}\frac{\partial y}{\partial z} = \frac{\partial^2 y}{\partial t^2}$$

subject to the conditions $y = 0$ when $x = l$, $t > 0$ and

$$y = 1 - x/l, \quad \frac{\partial y}{\partial t} = 0 \text{ when } t = 0,\ 0 < x < l,$$

where $x = \frac{1}{4}gz^2$. Show that

$$y = 8 \sum_{s=1}^{\infty} \frac{J_0(p_s x^{\frac{1}{2}}/l^{\frac{1}{2}})}{p_s^3 J_1(p_s)} \cos\left(\frac{g^{\frac{1}{2}}}{2l^{\frac{1}{2}}} p_s t\right)$$

where p_s are the positive roots of the equation $J_0(p) = 0$.

8. A function V of ρ and t satisfies the differential equation

$$\frac{\partial V}{\partial t} = \frac{\partial^2 V}{\partial \rho^2} + \frac{1}{\rho}\frac{\partial V}{\partial \rho}$$

subject to the conditions:

(i) V tends to zero as t tends to infinity;
(ii) V is finite as ρ tends to zero;
(iii) $\partial V/\partial \rho = -V$ when $\rho = 1$, $t > 0$;
(iv) $V = f(\rho)$ when $t = 0$, $0 < \rho < 1$.

Show that

$$V = \sum_{s=1}^{\infty} A_s e^{-p_s^2 t} J_0(p_s\rho)$$

where

$$\tfrac{1}{2}\{J_0^2(p_s) + J_1^2(p_s)\}A_s = \int_0^1 \rho f(\rho) J_0(p_s\rho)\, d\rho$$

and p_s is a root of the equation $J_0(p) = pJ_1(p)$.

9. The function ϕ satisfies the differential equation

$$\frac{\partial^2\phi}{\partial\rho^2}+\frac{1}{\rho}\frac{\partial\phi}{\partial\rho}-\frac{\phi}{\rho^2}+\frac{\partial^2\phi}{\partial z^2}=0,\quad 0\leqslant\rho<1,\quad -h<z<h,$$

and the boundary conditions

$$\phi=0 \text{ when } \rho=1,\quad \phi=\rho \text{ when } z=h,\quad \phi=0 \text{ when } z=-h.$$

Show that

$$\phi=2\sum_{s=1}^{\infty}\frac{1}{p_sJ_2(p_s)}\cdot\frac{\sinh(h+z)p_s}{\sinh 2hp_s}J_1(p_s\rho)$$

where $J_1(p_s)=0$.

10. The magnetic potential Ω for a circular disc of radius a and strength ω, magnetized parallel to its axis, satisfies Laplace's equation, is equal to $2\pi\omega$ on the disc itself and vanishes at exterior points in the plane of the disc. Show that at the point with cylindrical coordinates (ρ, z), $z>0$,

$$\Omega=2\pi a\omega\int_0^\infty e^{-pz}J_0(\rho p)J_1(ap)\,dp.$$

11. In the static case of the Reissner-Sagoci problem concerning the distribution of stress in a semi-infinite medium due to an axially-symmetrical torsional displacement of its surface, the two non-vanishing stress components are given by

$$\tau_{z\theta}=\mu\frac{\partial u}{\partial z},\quad \tau_{\rho\theta}=\frac{\partial u}{\partial\rho}-\frac{u}{\rho},$$

where μ is an elastic constant of the medium and u satisfies the differential equation

$$\frac{\partial^2u}{\partial\rho^2}+\frac{1}{\rho}\frac{\partial u}{\partial\rho}-\frac{u}{\rho^2}+\frac{\partial^2u}{\partial z^2}=0,\quad 0\leqslant\rho<\infty,\quad 0\leqslant z<\infty.$$

If the conditions on the surface $z=0$ of the medium are $u=\rho$ inside the circle $\rho<1$ and $\tau_{z\theta}=0$ outside this circle, show that

$$u=\int_0^\infty A(p)e^{-zp}J_1(\rho p)\,dp$$

where $A(p)$ satisfies the dual integral equations

$$\int_0^\infty A(p)J_1(\rho p)\,dp=\rho\ (0<\rho<1),\quad \int_0^\infty pA(p)J_1(\rho p)\,dp=0\ (1<\rho<\infty).$$

12. Complete the solution of Exercise 11 by showing that

$$A(p)=\frac{4}{\pi}\left(\frac{\sin p-p\cos p}{p^2}\right)$$

and deduce that when $z=0$ and $0<\rho<1$,

$$\tau_{z\theta}=-\frac{4\mu}{\pi}\left(\frac{1}{\rho^2}-1\right)^{-\frac{1}{2}}.$$

CHAPTER 8

THE EQUATIONS OF MATHEMATICAL PHYSICS: SOLUTION BY INTEGRAL TRANSFORMS

8.1 Introduction

It has already been mentioned in §4.9 that integral transforms have recently been applied to the solution of the partial differential equations of mathematical physics. Their use does not solve equations which are incapable of solution by the classical method of separation of variables explained in the last chapter but it has the distinct advantage of reducing the analysis almost to a "drill" and the considerable experience and judgment required in working some of the examples of Chapter 7 (in which the correct form of solution had to be assumed at the outset) is therefore avoided.

The present chapter gives the formulae used and describes the procedure required in the application of transforms to some physical problems whose solutions involve Bessel functions.

8.2 The Laplace transform

The Laplace transform $F(p)$ of a function $f(t)$ is defined by

$$F(p) = \int_0^\infty e^{-pt} f(t)\, dt \tag{8.1}$$

and it is a simple matter to determine the Laplace transforms of given functions of t. For example, if $f(t) = 1$,

$$F(p) = \int_0^\infty e^{-pt}\, dt = \left[-\frac{e^{-pt}}{p}\right]_0^\infty = \frac{1}{p},$$

it being assumed that $R(p) > 0$ in order that the integral may exist. Again, if $f(t) = t^n$ where $R(n) > -1$,

$$F(p) = \int_0^\infty e^{-pt} t^n\, dt = \frac{\Gamma(n+1)}{p^{n+1}},$$

when use is made of the definition of the gamma function.

Next, consider the Laplace transform of $e^{at}f(t)$ where a is a constant. This is given by

$$\int_0^\infty e^{-pt} e^{at} f(t)\, dt = \int_0^\infty e^{-(p-a)t} f(t)\, dt, \quad R(p-a) > 0,$$

and we conclude that if $F(p)$ is the Laplace transform of $f(t)$, then the transform of $e^{at}f(t)$ is $F(p-a)$. Taking $f(t)$ to be unity and t^n in turn, we therefore see that the transforms of e^{at} and $e^{at}t^n$ are respectively

$$\frac{1}{p-a} \quad \text{and} \quad \frac{\Gamma(n+1)}{(p-a)^{n+1}}.$$

Writing ib in place of a in the first of these results, we have

$$f(t) = e^{ibt}, \qquad F(p) = \frac{1}{p - ib} = \frac{p + ib}{p^2 + b^2}.$$

Since $e^{ibt} = \cos bt + i \sin bt$, it follows by equating real and imaginary parts that

$$f(t) = \cos bt, \qquad F(p) = \frac{p}{p^2 + b^2},$$

$$f(t) = \sin bt, \qquad F(p) = \frac{b}{p^2 + b^2}.$$

The transforms of $e^{at} \cos bt$ and $e^{at} \sin bt$ are then given by writing $(p - a)$ in place of p.

An inversion formula for the Laplace transform, giving $f(t)$ when $F(p)$ is known, can be obtained from Fourier's integral formula

$$\pi f(t) = \int_0^\infty d\alpha \int_{-\infty}^\infty f(t') \cos \alpha(t - t') \, dt'.$$

The repeated integral in this formula can be replaced by

$$\tfrac{1}{2} \int_{-\infty}^\infty d\alpha \int_{-\infty}^\infty f(t') \cos \alpha(t - t') \, dt'$$

and since

$$\int_{-\infty}^\infty d\alpha \int_{-\infty}^\infty f(t') \sin \alpha(t - t') \, dt' = 0,$$

the formula can be written in the form

$$2\pi f(t) = \int_{-\infty}^\infty e^{it\alpha} \, d\alpha \int_{-\infty}^\infty e^{-i\alpha t'} f(t') \, dt'. \tag{8.2}$$

Writing $p = \gamma + i\alpha$ and using (8.1)

$$\int_{\gamma - i\omega}^{\gamma + i\omega} e^{tp} F(p) \, dp = \int_{\gamma - i\omega}^{\gamma + i\omega} e^{tp} \, dp \int_0^\infty e^{-pt'} f(t') \, dt'$$

$$= ie^{\gamma t} \int_{-\omega}^{\omega} e^{it\alpha} \, d\alpha \int_0^\infty e^{-i\alpha t'} \{e^{-\gamma t'} f(t')\} \, dt'.$$

But the limit as ω tends to infinity of this double integral is, by (8.2), equal to $2\pi e^{-\gamma t} f(t)$ for $t > 0$ and to zero for $t < 0$ so that, when $t > 0$,

$$2\pi i f(t) = \int_{\gamma - i\infty}^{\gamma + i\infty} e^{tp} F(p) \, dp. \tag{8.3}$$

This is the required inversion formula for the Laplace transform and a more detailed discussion than that given here shows that γ must be greater than the real parts of all the singularities of $F(p)$.

Example 1. *Find the function of t whose Laplace transform is* $(p + 1)^{-1}$.
Here formula (8.3) gives

$$2\pi i f(t) = \int_{\gamma - i\infty}^{\gamma + i\infty} e^{tp}(p + 1)^{-1}\,\mathrm{d}p$$

and the line of integration must lie to the right of the singularity at $p = -1$. The integral can be evaluated by completing the contour with the arc of a circle, centre the origin, lying to the left of the line of integration. It is easy to show that the integral along this arc tends to zero as the radius of the arc tends to infinity and Cauchy's theorem then shows that the line integral is equal to $2\pi i$ times the residue at the pole $p = -1$. This gives $f(t) = e^{-t}$.

In what follows, the Laplace transforms of the derivatives of $f(t)$ will be required and these can be obtained by integration by parts. Thus

$$\int_0^\infty e^{-pt}\frac{\mathrm{d}f}{\mathrm{d}t}\,\mathrm{d}t = \Big[e^{-pt}f(t)\Big]_0^\infty + p\int_0^\infty e^{-pt}f(t)\,\mathrm{d}t = -f(0) + pF(p), \quad (8.4)$$

where $f(0)$ denotes the value of $f(t)$ when $t = 0$ and we have assumed, as is usually the case in physical problems, that $\lim_{t\to\infty}\{e^{-pt}f(t)\} = 0$. Again

$$\int_0^\infty e^{-pt}\frac{\mathrm{d}^2f}{\mathrm{d}t^2}\,\mathrm{d}t = \left[e^{-pt}\frac{\mathrm{d}f}{\mathrm{d}t}\right]_0^\infty + p\int_0^\infty e^{-pt}\frac{\mathrm{d}f}{\mathrm{d}t}\,\mathrm{d}t$$

$$= -f'(0) + p\{-f(0) + pF(p)\} = -f'(0) - pf(0) + p^2F(p), \quad (8.5)$$

where $f'(0)$ denotes the value of $\mathrm{d}f/\mathrm{d}t$ when $t = 0$. In obtaining (8.5) we have used equation (8.4) and assumed further that $e^{-pt}(\mathrm{d}f/\mathrm{d}t)$ tends to zero as t tends to infinity. It can be shown similarly that, provided $e^{-pt}(\mathrm{d}^{s-1}f/\mathrm{d}t^{s-1})$ tends to zero as t tends to infinity for $s = 1, 2, 3, \ldots, n$,

$$\int_0^\infty e^{-pt}\frac{\mathrm{d}^nf}{\mathrm{d}t^n}\,\mathrm{d}t = -f^{(n-1)}(0) - pf^{(n-2)}(0) - \ldots - p^{n-1}f(0) + p^nF(p). \quad (8.6)$$

These results enable the Laplace transform of the derivatives of a function to be expressed in terms of the Laplace transform of the function, its initial value and the initial values of its lower derivatives.

8.3 Hankel transforms

The Hankel transform of order ν of a function has been defined in §4.9, and with slight changes in notation, this is

$$F_{\mathrm{H}}(p) = \int_0^\infty \rho f(\rho) J_\nu(p\rho)\,\mathrm{d}\rho, \quad (8.7)$$

with the inversion formula

$$f(\rho) = \int_0^\infty p F_{\mathrm{H}}(p) J_\nu(\rho p)\, \mathrm{d}p \tag{8.8}$$

to give $f(\rho)$ when $F_{\mathrm{H}}(p)$ is known. In applying this transform to the solution of differential equations, we require a result which corresponds to formula (8.5) and this is obtained as follows.

$$\int_0^\infty \rho \left(\frac{\partial^2 f}{\partial \rho^2} + \frac{1}{\rho}\frac{\partial f}{\partial \rho}\right) J_\nu(p\rho)\, \mathrm{d}\rho = \int_0^\infty \frac{\partial}{\partial \rho}\left(\rho \frac{\partial f}{\partial \rho}\right) J_\nu(p\rho)\, \mathrm{d}\rho$$
$$= \left[\rho \frac{\partial f}{\partial \rho} J_\nu(p\rho)\right]_0^\infty - p\int_0^\infty \rho \frac{\partial f}{\partial \rho} J_\nu{}'(p\rho)\, \mathrm{d}\rho. \tag{8.9}$$

In physical applications the first term on the right usually vanishes and a second integration by parts gives

$$\int_0^\infty \rho \left(\frac{\partial^2 f}{\partial \rho^2} + \frac{1}{\rho}\frac{\partial f}{\partial \rho}\right) J_\nu(p\rho)\, \mathrm{d}\rho = -p\left[\rho f J_\nu{}'(p\rho)\right]_0^\infty$$
$$+ p\int_0^\infty f\{p\rho J_\nu{}''(p\rho) + J_\nu{}'(p\rho)\}\, \mathrm{d}\rho.$$

The first term on the right is again usually zero and noting that

$$p\rho J_\nu{}''(p\rho) + J_\nu{}'(p\rho) = \left(\frac{\nu^2}{p\rho} - p\rho\right) J_\nu(p\rho),$$

by equation (1.1), we obtain after a slight rearrangement,

$$\int_0^\infty \rho \left(\frac{\partial^2 f}{\partial \rho^2} + \frac{1}{\rho}\frac{\partial f}{\partial \rho} - \frac{\nu^2}{\rho^2} f\right) J_\nu(p\rho)\, \mathrm{d}\rho = -p^2 \int_0^\infty \rho f J_\nu(p\rho)\, \mathrm{d}\rho = -p^2 F_{\mathrm{H}}(p) \tag{8.10}$$

and this formula is useful in what follows.

The finite Hankel transform of order ν is defined by equation (4.45) as

$$F_{\mathrm{H}}(p) = \int_0^a \rho f(\rho) J_\nu(p\rho)\, \mathrm{d}\rho \tag{8.11}$$

and, if p is taken as a positive root p_s of the equation $J_\nu(pa) = 0$, the inversion formula is

$$f(\rho) = \frac{2}{a^2}\sum_{s=1}^\infty \frac{F_{\mathrm{H}}(p_s)}{J_{\nu+1}^2(p_s a)} J_\nu(p_s \rho). \tag{8.12}$$

To obtain the formula corresponding to (8.10), we have

$$\int_0^a \rho \left(\frac{\partial^2 f}{\partial \rho^2} + \frac{1}{\rho}\frac{\partial f}{\partial \rho}\right) J_\nu(p_s\rho)\, \mathrm{d}\rho = \int_0^a \frac{\partial}{\partial \rho}\left(\rho \frac{\partial f}{\partial \rho}\right) J_\nu(p_s\rho)\, \mathrm{d}\rho$$
$$= \left[\rho \frac{\partial f}{\partial \rho} J_\nu(p_s\rho)\right]_0^a - p_s\int_0^a \rho \frac{\partial f}{\partial \rho} J_\nu{}'(p_s\rho)\, \mathrm{d}\rho$$

and the first term on the right vanishes when $\rho = a$ since $J_\nu(p_s a) = 0$. A second integration by parts now gives

$$\int_0^a \rho \left(\frac{\partial^2 f}{\partial \rho^2} + \frac{1}{\rho}\frac{\partial f}{\partial \rho}\right) J_\nu(p_s\rho)\, d\rho = -p_s \Big[\rho f J_\nu{}'(p_s\rho)\Big]_0^a + p_s \int_0^a f\{p_s\rho J_\nu{}''(p_s\rho) + J_\nu{}'(p_s\rho)\}\, d\rho.$$

The first term on the right is $-p_s a f(a) J_\nu{}'(p_s a)$ and the second term can be reduced as in the derivation of equation (8.10) to give finally

$$\int_0^a \rho \left(\frac{\partial^2 f}{\partial \rho^2} + \frac{1}{\rho}\frac{\partial f}{\partial \rho} - \frac{\nu^2}{\rho^2} f\right) J_\nu(p_s\rho)\, d\rho = -p_s a f(a) J_\nu{}'(p_s a) - p_s^2 F_{\mathrm{H}}(p_s). \quad (8.13)$$

8.4 The solution of differential equations by integral transforms

The transform of a given differential equation is formed by multiplying the equation by the kernel of the selected transform and integrating between appropriate limits. The effect of this operation is to reduce a partial differential equation in n independent variables to one in $(n - 1)$ variables or, in other words, to exclude a selected independent variable from the equation. The repeated use of transforms can therefore ultimately reduce a partial to an ordinary differential equation—it can, in fact, reduce it to an algebraical equation but this is seldom worth while as it is usually fairly simple to write down the solution of the ordinary differential equation obtained when all but one of the independent variables have been excluded. Once the solution of the ordinary differential equation has been found, the solution of the original partial equation is then given by the inversion formula appropriate to the transforms used.

Some guidance on the selection of the transform to be used in given circumstances may be helpful. Firstly, the Laplace transform is very useful in excluding the time variable t from a partial differential equation and can be used when terms like $\partial V/\partial t$ or $\partial^2 V/\partial t^2$ are present. Again, a group of terms like

$$\frac{\partial^2 V}{\partial \rho^2} + \frac{1}{\rho}\frac{\partial V}{\partial \rho} - \frac{\nu^2}{\rho^2} V$$

can be dealt with by using a Hankel transform of order ν. The transform defined in equation (8.7) would be used when the range of the coordinate ρ in the problem under discussion was from 0 to ∞ and a finite transform, such as that given by (8.11), would be employed when the range of ρ was finite. The sine and cosine transforms given by formulae (4.40), (4.42) are the special cases $\nu = \pm\frac{1}{2}$ of the Hankel transform of order ν and these transforms will deal with a term like $\partial^2 V/\partial x^2$ in a partial differential equation in which the range of the independent variable is from 0 to ∞.

8.5 Some worked examples

The operations described in §8.4 are illustrated below by some worked examples and it should be noticed that the "drill" followed in the solutions is the same whatever the kernel or range of the transform used. The problems discussed are ones whose solutions involve Bessel functions and Laplace or Hankel transforms (including the special cases of the sine and cosine transforms) are used in obtaining these solutions. Other transforms, such as those of Mellin and Legendre, are useful in dealing with problems in other coordinate systems but these are outside the scope of the present book.

Example 2. *Heat is supplied at a constant rate Q per unit area per unit time over a circular area of radius a in the plane $z = 0$ to an infinite solid of thermal conductivity K, the rest of this plane being unheated. Find an expression for the steady temperature at a point distant ρ from the axis of the circular area and distant z from its plane.*

If V is the required steady temperature, we have to solve Laplace's equation in cylindrical coordinates

$$\frac{\partial^2 V}{\partial \rho^2} + \frac{1}{\rho}\frac{\partial V}{\partial \rho} + \frac{\partial^2 V}{\partial z^2} = 0 \tag{8.14}$$

subject to the boundary conditions

$$V \to 0 \text{ as } z \to \pm\infty, \quad V \to 0 \text{ as } \rho \to \infty, \tag{8.15}$$

$$\left.\begin{aligned} -K\frac{\partial V}{\partial z} &= \tfrac{1}{2}Q, \quad \rho < a, \\ &\;0, \quad\;\; \rho > a, \end{aligned}\right\} \text{ when } z = 0. \tag{8.16}$$

Writing $\bar{V} = \int_0^\infty \rho V J_0(p\rho)\,\mathrm{d}\rho$ so that $\bar{V}$ is the Hankel transform of order zero of V, equations (8.14), (8.15), (8.16) give after multiplication by $\rho J_0(p\rho)$, integration with respect to ρ between 0, ∞ and use of (8.10)

$$-p^2\bar{V} + \frac{\mathrm{d}^2\bar{V}}{\mathrm{d}z^2} = 0, \tag{8.17}$$

$$\bar{V} \to 0 \text{ as } z \to \pm\infty, \tag{8.18}$$

$$-K\frac{\mathrm{d}\bar{V}}{\mathrm{d}z} = \int_0^a \tfrac{1}{2}Q\rho J_0(p\rho)\,\mathrm{d}\rho = \frac{Qa}{2p}J_1(ap) \text{ when } z = 0. \tag{8.19}$$

It should be noticed that the derivation of this ordinary differential equation and its boundary conditions assumes that the interchange of certain operations such as

$$\int_0^\infty \rho\frac{\mathrm{d}^2 V}{\mathrm{d}z^2}J_0(p\rho)\,\mathrm{d}\rho = \frac{\mathrm{d}^2}{\mathrm{d}z^2}\int_0^\infty \rho V J_0(p\rho)\,\mathrm{d}\rho$$

is permissible. Such assumptions are usually justified in physical problems and will be made in this and the following examples. The solution of (8.17) which satisfies (8.18) is

$$\bar{V} = Ae^{-p|z|}$$

and, to satisfy (8.19), the constant A must take the value

$$\frac{Qa}{2Kp^2}J_1(ap).$$

Inversion by formula (8.8) then gives

$$V = \frac{Qa}{2K}\int_0^\infty \frac{e^{-|z|p}}{p} J_1(ap)J_0(\rho p)\,\mathrm{d}p$$

as the required expression for the temperature V.

Example 3. *An infinite region of unit diffusivity is bounded internally by an infinitely long cylinder of unit radius and this boundary is maintained at unit temperature. The initial temperature of the region is zero. Find an expression for the temperature V at time t at a point in the region at radial distance ρ from the axis of the cylindrical boundary.*

Here V has to satisfy the partial differential equation

$$\frac{\partial^2 V}{\partial \rho^2} + \frac{1}{\rho}\frac{\partial V}{\partial \rho} = \frac{\partial V}{\partial t} \tag{8.20}$$

with the boundary and initial conditions

$$V = 1 \text{ when } \rho = 1, \tag{8.21}$$

$$V = 0 \text{ when } t = 0, \tag{8.22}$$

Writing $\bar{V} = \int_0^\infty e^{-pt}V\,\mathrm{d}t$ so that $\bar{V}$ is the Laplace transform of the temperature V, multiplication of (8.20), (8.21) by e^{-pt}, integration with respect to t between $0, \infty$ and use of (8.4), (8.22) gives

$$\frac{\mathrm{d}^2\bar{V}}{\mathrm{d}\rho^2} + \frac{1}{\rho}\frac{\mathrm{d}\bar{V}}{\mathrm{d}\rho} = p\bar{V}, \tag{8.23}$$

$$\bar{V} = \int_0^\infty e^{-pt}\,\mathrm{d}t = \frac{1}{p} \text{ when } \rho = 1. \tag{8.24}$$

The general solution of the ordinary differential equation (8.23) is (using §1.14)

$$\bar{V} = AI_0(\rho\sqrt{p}) + BK_0(\rho\sqrt{p})$$

and, since $I_0(\rho\sqrt{p}) \to \infty$ as $\rho \to \infty$, we must take $A = 0$ if the temperature is to be everywhere finite. To satisfy the boundary condition (8.24) B must take the value $1/\{pK_0(\sqrt{p})\}$ and the inversion formula (8.3) then gives

$$V = \frac{1}{2\pi i}\int_{\gamma-i\infty}^{\gamma+i\infty} \frac{e^{tp}K_0(\rho\sqrt{p})}{pK_0(\sqrt{p})}\,\mathrm{d}p. \tag{8.25}$$

The integrand in (8.25) has a branch point at the origin and the integral (which is along the line $A'A$ of Fig. 13) can be replaced by integrals along the circular arcs $A'F$, CA, the lines FE, DC and the small circle surrounding the origin O.

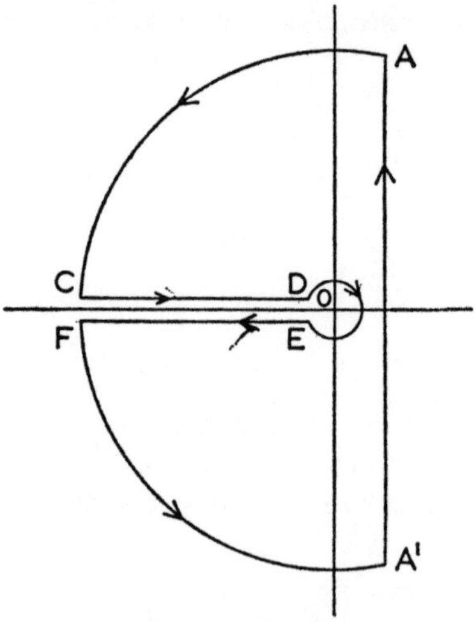

FIG. 13. p-plane

The integrals along the arcs tend to zero as their radii tend to infinity and that round the small circle takes the value $2\pi i$ as the radius of the circle tends to zero. On FE put $p = u^2e^{-i\pi}$ so that, using equation (1.59) which gives

$$K_0(\rho\sqrt{p}) = K_0(\rho u e^{-i\pi/2}) = \tfrac{1}{2}\pi i\{J_0(\rho u) + iY_0(\rho u)\},$$

the integral becomes

$$\int_\infty^0 e^{-tu^2}\frac{J_0(\rho u) + iY_0(\rho u)}{J_0(u) + iY_0(u)}\cdot\frac{2\,du}{u}.$$

The integral along DC is minus the conjugate of this and we find finally

$$V = 1 + \frac{2}{\pi}\int_0^\infty e^{-tu^2}\left\{\frac{J_0(\rho u)Y_0(u) - Y_0(\rho u)J_0(u)}{J_0^2(u) + Y_0^2(u)}\right\}\frac{du}{u}.$$

Example 4. *A circular membrane of unit radius is stretched by a tension T and is at rest in its position of equilibrium. If a uniform pressure* $\sin t$ *is applied at time* $t = 0$ *to its surface, find an expression for the subsequent displacement V of the membrane.*

If σ is the surface density of the membrane and we write $c^2 = T/\sigma$, we have to solve

$$\frac{\partial^2 V}{\partial\rho^2} + \frac{1}{\rho}\frac{\partial V}{\partial\rho} - \frac{1}{c^2}\frac{\partial^2 V}{\partial t^2} = -\frac{\sin t}{T} \tag{8.26}$$

with

$$V = 0 \text{ when } \rho = 1, \tag{8.27}$$

and

$$V = \frac{\partial V}{\partial t} = 0 \text{ when } t = 0. \tag{8.28}$$

Taking $\bar{V}$ as the Laplace transform of V, these equations transform into

$$\frac{d^2\bar{V}}{d\rho^2} + \frac{1}{\rho}\frac{d\bar{V}}{d\rho} - \frac{p^2}{c^2}\bar{V} = -\frac{1}{T(p^2+1)} \tag{8.29}$$

with $\bar{V} = 0$ when $\rho = 1$. The solution of this equation which is finite when $\rho = 0$ is

$$\bar{V} = \frac{c^2}{Tp^2(p^2+1)} + AI_0\left(\frac{p\rho}{c}\right)$$

and, when the constant A is determined to satisfy the boundary condition we find

$$\bar{V} = \frac{c^2}{Tp^2(p^2+1)}\left\{1 - \frac{I_0(p\rho/c)}{I_0(p/c)}\right\}. \tag{8.30}$$

The first term in this expression can be written $(c^2/T)\{p^{-2} - (p^2+1)^{-1}\}$ and, by §8.2, its inverse is $(c^2/T)(t^{-1} - \sin t)$. By equation (8.3) the inverse of the second term in (8.30) is

$$-\frac{c^2}{2\pi iT}\int_{\gamma-i\infty}^{\gamma+i\infty} \frac{e^{tp}I_0(p\rho/c)}{p^2(p^2+1)I_0(p/c)}\,dp \tag{8.31}$$

and the integrand is a single-valued function of p inside the contour shown in Fig. 14. The integral round the circular arc tends to zero as the radius of the

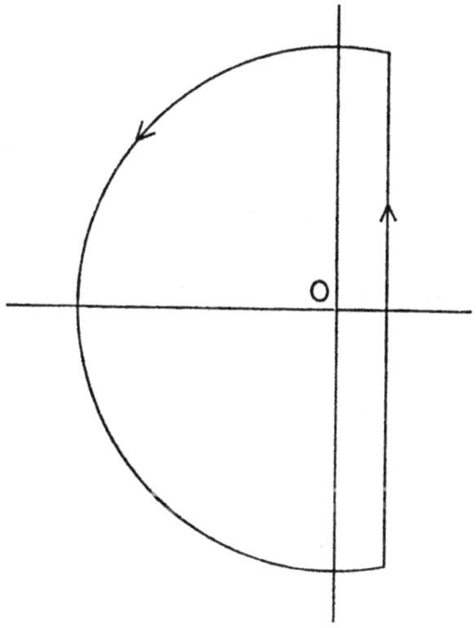

FIG. 14. p-plane

arc tends to infinity, so that Cauchy's theorem shows that the integral in (8.31) can be replaced by $2\pi i$ times the sum of the residue at the poles. There is a double pole at $p = 0$ with residue t and simple poles at $p = \pm i$ with residues

$$\frac{e^{\pm it}}{\mp 2i}\frac{J_0(\rho/c)}{J_0(1/c)}.$$

There are also simple poles at $\pm ic\alpha_s$ where $\pm\alpha_s (s = 1, 2, 3 \ldots)$ are the roots of $J_0(\alpha) = 0$ and the residues there are

$$\frac{e^{\pm ic\alpha_s t} J_0(\rho\alpha_s)}{\pm ic\alpha_s^2(1 - c^2\alpha_s^2) J_0'(\alpha_s)}.$$

Collecting all these terms, we have finally

$$V = \frac{c^2}{T}\sin t\left\{\frac{J_0(\rho/c)}{J_0(1/c)} - 1\right\} - \frac{2c}{T}\sum_{s=1}^{\infty}\frac{\sin c\alpha_s t}{\alpha_s^2(1 - c^2\alpha_s^2)}\frac{J_0(\rho\alpha_s)}{J_0'(\alpha_s)}.$$

Example 5. *In a problem involving the flow of perfect fluid through a circular aperture of unit radius in a plane rigid screen, the velocity potential ϕ satisfies Laplace's equation in cylindrical coordinates (ρ, z) and the boundary condition $\phi = 1$ $(0 < \rho < 1)$, $\partial\phi/\partial z = 0$ $(\rho > 1)$ on the plane $z = 0$. Show that*

$$\phi = \frac{2}{\pi}\int_0^\infty \frac{\sin p}{p} e^{-p|z|} J_0(\rho p)\, dp.$$

Laplace's equation is

$$\frac{\partial^2\phi}{\partial\rho^2} + \frac{1}{\rho}\frac{\partial\phi}{\partial\rho} + \frac{\partial^2\phi}{\partial z^2} = 0$$

and taking $\bar{\phi} = \int_0^\infty \rho\phi J_0(p\rho)\, d\rho$, the Hankel transform of this equation is

$$\frac{d^2\bar{\phi}}{dz^2} - p^2\bar{\phi} = 0.$$

The solution of this ordinary differential equation which tends to zero as $|z|$ tends to infinity is

$$\bar{\phi} = A(p)e^{-p|z|}$$

where $A(p)$ is a function of p and when this is inverted we have

$$\phi = \int_0^\infty pA(p)e^{-p|z|} J_0(\rho p)\, dp. \tag{8.32}$$

The boundary condition shows that $A(p)$ satisfies the dual integral equations

$$\left.\begin{aligned} &\int_0^\infty pA(p)J_0(\rho p)\, dp = 1, \quad 0 < \rho < 1,\\ &\int_0^\infty p^2A(p)J_0(\rho p)\, dp = 0, \quad \rho > 1,\end{aligned}\right\}$$

and, by Exercises 6, No. 3, the solution of these equations is

$$\pi pA(p) = \frac{2\sin p}{p}.$$

The required result then follows by substituting for $pA(p)$ in equation (8.32).

Example 6. *Find the temperature V in a long cylinder of radius a and diffusivity k with initial temperature zero, when for time $t > 0$ the surface is kept at unit temperature over a band of width $2c$ in the middle of the cylinder and at zero outside this band.*

We have to find V from the equation

$$\frac{\partial^2 V}{\partial \rho^2} + \frac{1}{\rho}\frac{\partial V}{\partial \rho} + \frac{\partial^2 V}{\partial z^2} = \frac{1}{k}\frac{\partial V}{\partial t}, \tag{8.33}$$

with the boundary condition

$$V = 1\ (|z| < c), \quad V = 0\ (|z| > c) \text{ when } \rho = a, \tag{8.34}$$

and the initial condition $V = 0$ when $t = 0$. This then is a problem with three independent variables ρ, z, t and two transforms applied successively will reduce it to an ordinary differential equation in a single independent variable. We start with the cosine transform given by

$$\bar{V}_c = \int_0^\infty V \cos pz\, dz \tag{8.35}$$

and, since from symmetry $\partial V/\partial z = 0$ when $z = 0$, two integrations by parts show that

$$\int_0^\infty \frac{\partial^2 V}{\partial z^2} \cos pz\, dz = -p^2 \bar{V}_c. \tag{8.36}$$

Multiplication of equations (8.33), (8.34) and the initial condition by $\cos pz$, integration with respect to z between 0, ∞ and use of equations (8.35), (8.36) then gives

$$\frac{\partial^2 \bar{V}_c}{\partial \rho^2} + \frac{1}{\rho}\frac{\partial \bar{V}_c}{\partial \rho} - p^2 \bar{V}_c = \frac{1}{k}\frac{\partial \bar{V}_c}{\partial t} \tag{8.37}$$

with the boundary condition

$$\bar{V}_c = \int_0^c \cos pz\, dz = \frac{\sin pc}{p} \text{ when } \rho = a \tag{8.38}$$

and the initial condition $\bar{V}_c = 0$ when $t = 0$. The solution of this boundary-value problem in the two independent variables ρ and t can be obtained by the application of the Laplace transform. We write

$$\bar{V}_L = \int_0^\infty e^{-p't}\, \bar{V}_c\, dt \tag{8.39}$$

and the problem is reduced to the solution of the ordinary differential equation

$$\frac{d^2 \bar{V}_L}{d\rho^2} + \frac{1}{\rho}\frac{d\bar{V}_L}{d\rho} - p^2 \bar{V}_L = \frac{p'}{k}\bar{V}_L \tag{8.40}$$

with the boundary condition

$$\bar{V}_L = \int_0^\infty e^{-p't} \frac{\sin pc}{p} \, dt = \frac{\sin pc}{pp'} \text{ when } \rho = a. \tag{8.41}$$

The solution of this, finite when $\rho = 0$, is

$$\bar{V}_L = \frac{\sin pc}{pp'} \frac{I_0\{\sqrt{(p^2 + p'/k)}\rho\}}{I_0\{\sqrt{(p^2 + p'/k)}a\}}$$

and the inversion formula for the Laplace transform gives

$$\bar{V}_c = \frac{1}{2\pi i} \frac{\sin pc}{p} \int_{\gamma - i\infty}^{\gamma + i\infty} e^{p't} \frac{I_0\{\sqrt{(p^2 + p'/k)}\rho\}}{I_0\{\sqrt{(p^2 + p'/k)}a\}} \frac{dp'}{p'}. \tag{8.42}$$

Using the contour and procedure adopted in Example 4 above, the line integral can be replaced by $2\pi i$ times the sum of the residues at the poles within the contour. These poles are at $p' = 0$ and $p' = -k(\alpha_s^2 + p^2)$ where α_s is a root of the equation $J_0(\alpha a) = 0$. The pole at $p' = 0$ has residue $I_0(\rho p)/I_0(ap)$ while the other poles give residues

$$\frac{\exp\{-k(\alpha_s^2 + p^2)t\} I_0(i\alpha_s \rho)}{\left[p' \frac{d}{dp'} I_0\{\sqrt{(p^2 + p'/k)}a\}\right]_{p' = -k(\alpha_s^2 + p^2)}}.$$

The denominator in this expression is

$$\frac{1}{2k}\left[ap'\left(p^2 + \frac{p'}{k}\right)^{-\frac{1}{2}} I_0'\{\sqrt{(p^2 + p'/k)}a\}\right]_{p' = -k(\alpha_s^2 + p^2)}$$

$$= -\frac{a}{2\alpha_s}(\alpha_s^2 + p^2) J_1(\alpha_s a),$$

so that

$$\bar{V}_c = \frac{\sin pc}{p}\left[\frac{I_0(\rho p)}{I_0(ap)} - \frac{2}{a}\sum_{s=1}^\infty \frac{\alpha_s}{\alpha_s^2 + p^2} \frac{J_0(\alpha_s \rho)}{J_1(\alpha_s a)} \exp\{-k(\alpha_s^2 + p^2)t\}\right].$$

Inversion to V is now carried out by formula (4.43) for the cosine transform, viz.

$$V = \frac{2}{\pi}\int_0^\infty \bar{V}_c \cos zp \, dp,$$

and we find finally

$$V = \frac{2}{\pi}\int_0^\infty \frac{I_0(\rho p)}{I_0(ap)} \frac{\sin cp \cos zp}{p} \, dp$$

$$- \frac{4}{\pi a}\sum_{s=1}^\infty e^{-k\alpha_s^2 t} \frac{\alpha_s J_0(\alpha_s \rho)}{J_1(\alpha_s a)} \int_0^\infty e^{-ktp^2} \frac{\sin cp \cos zp}{\alpha_s^2 + p^2} \frac{dp}{p}.$$

Exercises 8

1. Use the inversion formula to show that $p/(p^2 + b^2)$ is the Laplace transform of $\cos bt$.

2. Deduce from the integral

$$\int_0^\infty \exp\{-\alpha^2x^2 - \beta^2x^{-2}\}\,dx = \left(\frac{\sqrt{\pi}}{2\alpha}\right)\exp(-2\alpha\beta)$$

where α, β are positive, that $p^{-\frac{1}{2}}\exp(-ap^{\frac{1}{2}})$ is the Laplace transform of $(\pi t)^{-\frac{1}{2}}\exp(-a^2/4t)$, $a > 0$.

3. The Fourier sine and cosine transforms of a function $f(x)$ are defined respectively by

$$F_s(p) = \int_0^\infty f(x)\sin px\,dx, \quad F_c(p) = \int_0^\infty f(x)\cos px\,dx.$$

If $f(x)$ and its first derivative tend to zero as x tends to infinity, show that the sine and cosine transforms of $\partial^2 f/\partial x^2$ are given respectively by

$$pf(0) - p^2F_s(p), \quad -f'(0) - p^2F_c(p).$$

4. If p is a root of the equation $pJ_0'(pa) + hJ_0(pa) = 0$, show that

$$\int_0^a \rho\left(\frac{\partial^2 f}{\partial\rho^2} + \frac{1}{\rho}\frac{\partial f}{\partial\rho}\right)J_0(p\rho)\,d\rho = aJ_0(pa)\left[\frac{\partial f}{\partial\rho} + hf\right]_{\rho=a} - p^2\int_0^a \rho f J_0(p\rho)\,d\rho.$$

5. Show that the Laplace transform of the temperature V, at time t and radial distance ρ from the axis, of an infinitely long circular cylinder of unit radius of material of unit diffusivity whose surface is kept at unit temperature and whose initial temperature is zero is

$$\frac{1}{p}\frac{I_0(\rho\sqrt{p})}{I_0(\sqrt{p})}.$$

Use the inversion theorem for the Laplace transform to show that

$$V = 1 - 2\sum_{s=1}^\infty e^{-p_s^2 t}\frac{J_0(p_s\rho)}{p_sJ_1(p_s)}$$

where p_s is a positive root of the equation $J_0(p) = 0$.

6. Solve Exercise 5 above by the use of a finite Hankel transform.

7. The material of a long cylinder of unit radius is of diffusivity k and its initial temperature is V_0. If its temperature at time t and radial distance ρ from the axis is V and radiation takes place into a medium at zero temperature, the boundary condition at the surface $\rho = 1$ of the cylinder is

$$\frac{\partial V}{\partial\rho} + hV = 0$$

where h is a constant. Use a finite Hankel transform and the result given in Exercise 4 above to show that

$$V = 2V_0\sum e^{-kp^2t}\frac{pJ_1(p)}{h^2 + p^2}\cdot\frac{J_0(\rho p)}{J_0^2(p)}$$

where the summation is over the positive roots of the equation

$$pJ_0'(p) + hJ_0(p) = 0.$$

8. A circular membrane of unit radius and uniform surface density σ is fixed round its edge and stretched by a tension T. It is subject to a uniform constant pressure P acting over its whole surface for time $t > 0$. Show that the displacement V at radial distance ρ is given by

$$V = \frac{2P}{T}\sum_{s=1}^{\infty}(1 - \cos cp_s t)\frac{J_0(\rho p_s)}{p_s^3 J_1(p_s)}$$

where p_s is a root of the equation $J_0(p) = 0$ and $c^2 = T/\sigma$.

9. Use the Laplace transform to show that the solution of the equation

$$\frac{\partial^2\phi}{\partial\rho^2} + \frac{1}{\rho}\frac{\partial\phi}{\partial\rho} - \frac{\phi}{\rho^2} = \frac{1}{c^2}\frac{\partial^2\phi}{\partial t^2}, \quad t > 0, \quad 0 < \rho < 1,$$

with the initial condition $\phi = -\rho$ when $t = 0$ and the boundary condition $\partial\phi/\partial\rho = 0$ when $\rho = 1$ is

$$\phi = 2\sum_{s=1}^{\infty}\frac{J_1(\rho\alpha_s)}{\alpha_s^2 J_1''(\alpha_s)}\cos\alpha_s ct$$

where α_s are the positive roots of the equation $J_1'(\alpha) = 0$.

10. Use cylindrical polar coordinates (ρ, z) and a sine transform to show that the steady temperature in the semi-infinite tube bounded by the plane $z = 0$ and the cylindrical surfaces $\rho = a, \rho = b$ $(a > b)$, when the surfaces $z = 0$, $\rho = a$ are maintained at zero and the surface $\rho = b$ is kept at temperature $f(z)$ is

$$\frac{2}{\pi}\int_0^{\infty}\int_0^{\infty} F(a, b, \rho, p)\, f(u) \sin zp \sin up \, \mathrm{d}p \, \mathrm{d}u$$

where

$$F(a, b, \rho, p) = \frac{I_0(\rho p)K_0(ap) - I_0(ap)\, K_0(\rho p)}{I_0(bp)\, K_0(ap) - I_0(ap)\, K_0(bp)}.$$

11. For the transform defined by

$$F(p) = \int_a^b \rho f(\rho) B_0(p\rho)\, \mathrm{d}\rho$$

where $B_0(p\rho) = J_0(p\rho)\, Y_0(pa) - Y_0(p\rho)J_0(pa)$ and p is a root of the equation $B_0(pb) = 0$, show that

(i) the transform of unity is

$$\frac{2}{\pi p^2}\left\{\frac{J_0(pa)}{J_0(pb)} - 1\right\};$$

(ii) $$\int_a^b \frac{\partial}{\partial\rho}\left(\rho\frac{\partial f}{\partial\rho}\right) B_0(p\rho)\, \mathrm{d}\rho = \frac{2}{\pi}\left\{f(b)\frac{J_0(pa)}{J_0(pb)} - f(a)\right\} - p^2 F(p).$$

12. The two surfaces of a long cylindrical tube of internal and external radii a, b respectively are kept at zero temperature. The diffusivity of the material

of the tube is k and its initial temperature is unity. Use the transform defined in Exercise 11 above to show that the temperature at time t is given by

$$\pi \sum_{s=1}^{\infty} \frac{J_0(bp_s)B_0(\rho p_s)}{J_0(ap_s) + J_0(bp_s)} e^{-ktp_s^2}$$

the summation being over the roots of $B_0(bp) = 0$ and ρ being the radial distance of the point considered from the axis of the tube.

APPENDIX

THE GAMMA FUNCTION

A.1 Introduction

Certain formulae involving the gamma function have been used in this book in building up the theory of Bessel functions. These formulae are easily derived from the definition of the gamma function and, to save continual reference to other works, a short formal treatment is given in this appendix.

A.2 Definitions of the gamma function

The gamma function $\Gamma(z)$ can be defined by any one of the following expressions:

$$\Gamma(z) = \int_0^\infty e^{-t}\, t^{z-1}\,\mathrm{d}t, \quad R(z) > 0, \tag{A.1}$$

$$\Gamma(z) = \lim_{n\to\infty}\left\{\frac{n!n^z}{z(z+1)(z+2)\ldots(z+n)}\right\}, \tag{A.2}$$

$$1/\Gamma(z) = ze^{\gamma z}\prod_{n=1}^{\infty}\left\{\left(1+\frac{z}{n}\right)e^{-z/n}\right\} \tag{A.3}$$

where

$$\gamma = \lim_{n\to\infty}\left(1+\frac{1}{2}+\frac{1}{3}+\ldots+\frac{1}{n}-\log_e n\right) = 0{\cdot}5772\ldots \tag{A.4}$$

is Euler's constant and the equivalence of these three expressions is easily established. Thus, for a positive integer n and $R(z) > 0$, repeated integration by parts gives

$$\int_0^n\left(1-\frac{t}{n}\right)^n t^{z-1}\,\mathrm{d}t = \frac{n!n^z}{z(z+1)(z+2)\ldots(z+n)}$$

so that the formal equivalence of (A.1) and (A.2) follows by taking the limit as n tends to infinity. Also, starting from (A.2),

$$\begin{aligned}1/\Gamma(z) &= \lim_{n\to\infty}\{z(1+z)(1+z/2)\ldots(1+z/n)\exp(-z\log_e n)\}\\ &= \lim_{n\to\infty}\Big[\{z(1+z)e^{-z}(1+z/2)e^{-z/2}\ldots(1+z/n)e^{-z/n}\}\\ &\qquad\times\exp\left\{z\left(1+\frac{1}{2}+\ldots+\frac{1}{n}-\log_e n\right)\right\}\Big]\\ &= ze^{\gamma z}\prod_{n=1}^{\infty}\left\{\left(1+\frac{z}{n}\right)e^{-z/n}\right\}.\end{aligned}$$

This is formula (A.3) and it is worth noticing that it shows that $\Gamma(z)$ is infinite when z is zero or a negative integer.

A.3 Functional equations satisfied by $\Gamma(z)$

From equation (A.1), integration by parts gives

$$\Gamma(z) = \left[\frac{e^{-t}t^z}{z}\right]_0^\infty + \int_0^\infty \frac{e^{-t}t^z}{z}\,dt = \frac{1}{z}\int_0^\infty e^{-t}t^z\,dt = \frac{\Gamma(z+1)}{z}$$

so that

$$\Gamma(z+1) = z\Gamma(z). \tag{A.5}$$

Since

$$\Gamma(1) = \int_0^\infty e^{-t}\,dt = 1, \tag{A.6}$$

we have, if n is a positive integer,

$$\begin{aligned}\Gamma(n+1) &= n\Gamma(n) = n(n-1)(\Gamma(n-1) = \dots \\ &= n(n-1)(n-2)\dots 2\,.\,1\,.\,\Gamma(1) = n!\end{aligned} \tag{A.7}$$

Another important functional relationship can be derived from equation (A.3) which gives

$$\Gamma(z)\Gamma(-z) = -\frac{1}{z^2}\prod_{n=1}^{\infty}\left(1-\frac{z^2}{n^2}\right)^{-1}.$$

Since

$$\sin \pi z = \pi z \prod_{n=1}^{\infty}\left(1-\frac{z^2}{n^2}\right),$$

we have

$$\Gamma(z)\Gamma(-z) = -\frac{\pi}{z\sin \pi z},$$

and, using (A.5) in the form $\Gamma(1-z) = -z\Gamma(-z)$, this can be written

$$\Gamma(z)\Gamma(1-z) = \frac{\pi}{\sin \pi z}. \tag{A.8}$$

By writing $\frac{1}{2}+z$ in place of z, this formula becomes

$$\Gamma(\tfrac{1}{2}+z)\Gamma(\tfrac{1}{2}-z) = \frac{\pi}{\cos \pi z} \tag{A.9}$$

and, setting $z = 0$, we find

$$\Gamma(\tfrac{1}{2}) = \sqrt{\pi}, \tag{A.10}$$

since formula (A.1) shows that $\Gamma(\frac{1}{2})$ is positive.

A.4 Some definite integrals expressible in gamma functions

We start by letting

$$I_1 = 2\int_0^a e^{-x^2} x^{2z-1}\,dx, \quad I_2 = 2\int_0^a e^{-y^2} y^{2z'-1}\,dy$$

so that

$$I_1 I_2 = 4\int_0^a \int_0^a e^{-(x^2+y^2)} x^{2z-1} y^{2z'-1}\,dx\,dy$$

$$= 4\iint e^{-r^2} r^{2z+2z'-1} \cos^{2z-1}\theta \sin^{2z'-1}\theta\,dr\,d\theta$$

where $x = r\cos\theta$, $y = r\sin\theta$ and the double integral is taken over the square bounded by the lines $x = 0$, $x = a$, $y = 0$, $y = a$. Since the integrand is positive, the value of the double integral lies between its values taken over the first quadrants of the circles $x^2 + y^2 = a^2$ and $x^2 + y^2 = 2a^2$, that is between

$$4\int_0^{\pi/2} \cos^{2z-1}\theta \sin^{2z'-1}\theta\,d\theta \int_0^a e^{-r^2} r^{2z+2z'-1}\,dr$$

and

$$4\int_0^{\pi/2} \cos^{2z-1}\theta \sin^{2z'-1}\theta\,d\theta \int_0^{a\sqrt{2}} e^{-r^2} r^{2z+2z'-1}\,dr.$$

Taking the limit as a tends to infinity, we therefore have

$$\int_0^\infty e^{-x^2} x^{2z-1}\,dx \times \int_0^\infty e^{-y^2} y^{2z'-1}\,dy$$

$$= \int_0^{\pi/2} \cos^{2z-1}\theta \sin^{2z'-1}\theta\,d\theta \times \int_0^\infty e^{-r^2} r^{2z+2z'-1}\,dr.$$

By setting x^2, y^2 and r^2 equal to t, the infinite integrals in this formula become, if the real parts of z, z' exceed $\frac{1}{2}$, $\frac{1}{2}\Gamma(z)$, $\frac{1}{2}\Gamma(z')$ and $\frac{1}{2}\Gamma(z+z')$ and we obtain the important result,

$$\int_0^{\pi/2} \cos^{2z-1}\theta \sin^{2z'-1}\theta\,d\theta = \frac{\Gamma(z)\Gamma(z')}{2\Gamma(z+z')}. \qquad \text{(A.11)}$$

Writing $\sin^2\theta = t$, this becomes

$$\int_0^1 (1-t)^{z-1} t^{z'-1}\,dt = \frac{\Gamma(z)\Gamma(z')}{\Gamma(z+z')}, \qquad \text{(A.12)}$$

and this form of the result is often useful. These formulae, although derived here for a more restricted range, are in fact valid when the real parts of z and z' are positive. For details of the way in which this relaxation can be obtained the reader is referred to E. T. Whittaker and G. N. Watson, *Modern Analysis* (Cambridge, 1946), §12.41.

Writing $z' = z$ in (A.11), we have

$$\frac{\Gamma(z)\Gamma(z)}{2\Gamma(2z)} = \int_0^{\pi/2} \sin^{2z-1}\theta \cos^{2z-1}\theta \, d\theta$$

$$= 2^{1-2z}\int_0^{\pi/2} \sin^{2z-1} 2\theta \, d\theta$$

$$= 2^{-2z}\int_0^{\pi} \sin^{2z-1} u \, du, \quad \text{putting } 2\theta = u,$$

$$= 2^{1-2z}\int_0^{\pi/2} \sin^{2z-1} u \, du$$

$$= 2^{1-2z}\frac{\Gamma(z)\Gamma(\frac{1}{2})}{2\Gamma(z+\frac{1}{2})},$$

formula (A.11) having been again used in carrying out the last step. A few reductions then lead to

$$\Gamma(2z) = \frac{2^{2z-1}}{\sqrt{\pi}}\Gamma(z)\Gamma(z+\tfrac{1}{2}) \tag{A.13}$$

and this is generally known as the duplication formula for the gamma function.

We now consider the integral $\int t^{z-1}e^{-t}\,dt$, where $0 < R(z) < 1$, taken round a contour (Fig. 15) consisting of (i) the positive real axis from $t = \delta$ to $t = \rho$,

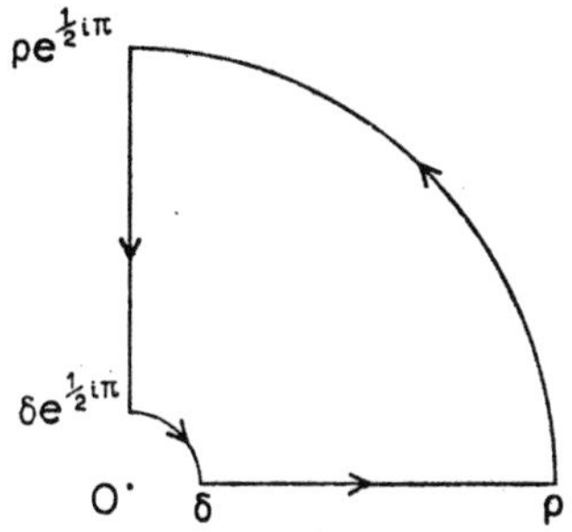

FIG. 15. t-plane

(ii) a large circular quadrant with centre the origin and radius ρ, extending from $t = \rho$ to $t = \rho e^{\frac{1}{2}i\pi}$, (iii) the positive imaginary axis from $t = \rho e^{\frac{1}{2}i\pi}$ to $t = \delta e^{\frac{1}{2}i\pi}$ and (iv) a small circular quadrant with centre the origin and radius δ extending from $t = \delta e^{\frac{1}{2}i\pi}$ to $t = \delta$. This contour avoids all singularities of the integrand and it can be shown that the integrals along the quadrants tend to zero as their radii ρ and δ tend respectively to infinity and zero. Hence

$$\int_0^{\infty} t^{z-1}e^{-t}\,dt + \int_{\infty}^{0} (te^{\frac{1}{2}i\pi})^{z-1}e^{-te^{\frac{1}{2}i\pi}}e^{\frac{1}{2}i\pi}\,dt = 0$$

giving

$$e^{\frac{1}{2}iz\pi}\int_0^{\infty} t^{z-1}e^{-it}\,dt = \int_0^{\infty} t^{z-1}e^{-t}\,dt = \Gamma(z)$$

when use is made of equation (A.1). It follows that

$$\int_0^\infty t^{z-1} \cos t \, dt = \Gamma(z) \cos \tfrac{1}{2}z\pi. \tag{A.14}$$

A contour integral representation of $1/\Gamma(z)$ can be obtained by considering the integral $\int e^t t^{-z} \, dt$ taken round the contour described in §3.4 and shown in Fig. 6. This contour can be deformed into the lower edge of the cut from $-\infty$ to $-\rho$, the circle $t = \rho e^{i\theta}$ $(-\pi \leqslant \theta < \pi)$ and the upper edge of the cut from $-\rho$ to $-\infty$ (see Fig. 16). Hence, putting $t = ve^{-\pi i}$ and $ve^{\pi i}$

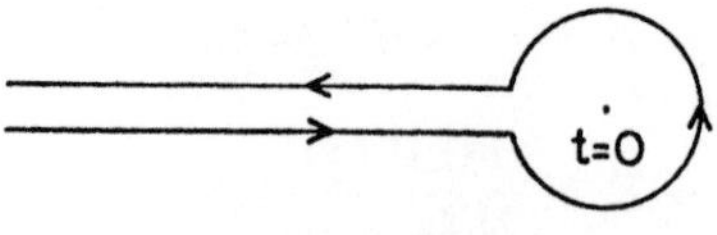

FIG. 16. t-plane

$$\int_{-\infty}^{(0+)} e^t t^{-z} \, dt = \int_\infty^\rho e^{-v} v^{-z} e^{-i\pi z} \, dv + \int_\rho^\infty e^{-v} v^{-z} e^{i\pi z} \, dv + I$$

where I is the integral round the circle $|t| = \rho$ and it can be shown that, provided $R(z) < 1$, I tends to zero as ρ tends to zero. We therefore have

$$\int_{-\infty}^{(0+)} e^t t^{-z} \, dt = 2i \sin \pi z \int_0^\infty e^{-v} v^{-z} \, dv$$

and, using equations (A.1), (A.8), this gives

$$\begin{aligned}\int_{-\infty}^{(0+)} e^t t^{-z} \, dt &= 2i \sin \pi z \,.\, \Gamma(1-z) \\ &= (2\pi i)/\Gamma(z). \end{aligned} \tag{A.15}$$

A.5 The derivative of the gamma function

A useful formula for the derivative of the gamma function can be found from formula (A.2) which gives

$$\frac{\Gamma'(z)}{\Gamma(z)} = \frac{d}{dz}\{\log_e \Gamma(z)\} = \lim_{n\to\infty}\left\{\log_e n - \frac{1}{z} - \frac{1}{z+1} - \cdots - \frac{1}{z+n}\right\}.$$

Hence

$$\frac{\Gamma'(z+1)}{\Gamma(z+1)} = \frac{1}{z} + \frac{\Gamma'(z)}{\Gamma(z)}, \quad \frac{\Gamma'(1)}{\Gamma(1)} = -\gamma, \tag{A.16}$$

formula (A.4) being used to obtain the last result. If z is a positive integer n, this yields in succession

$$\begin{aligned}\frac{\Gamma'(n+1)}{\Gamma(n+1)} &= \frac{1}{n} + \frac{\Gamma'(n)}{\Gamma(n)} = \frac{1}{n} + \frac{1}{n-1} + \frac{\Gamma'(n-1)}{\Gamma(n-1)} = \cdots \\ &= \frac{1}{n} + \frac{1}{n-1} + \cdots + \frac{1}{2} + \frac{1}{1} + \frac{\Gamma'(1)}{\Gamma(1)} \\ &= -\gamma + 1 + \frac{1}{2} + \frac{1}{3} + \cdots + \frac{1}{n}. \end{aligned} \tag{A.17}$$

BIBLIOGRAPHICAL NOTE

Treatises on Bessel functions in the English language include the following—

1. G. N. Watson, *Theory of Bessel Functions* (Cambridge, 1944).
   There is now a paperback edition, published in 1966—this is identical with the 1944 edition.
2. A. Erdélyi (ed.), *Higher Transcendental Functions* (McGraw-Hill, 1953), Vol. 2.
3. A. Gray, G. B. Mathews and T. M. MacRobert, *A Treatise on Bessel Functions* (Macmillan, 1922).
4. N. W. McLachlan, *Bessel Functions for Engineers* (Oxford, 1955).
5. Y. L. Luke, *Integrals of Bessel Functions* (McGraw-Hill, 1962).
6. F. Bowman, *An Introduction to Bessel Functions* (Longmans Green, 1937; Dover Publications, 1958).
7. F. E. Relton, *Applied Bessel Functions* (Blackie, 1946).

Reference (1) is the classic work on the subject; it contains a very full list of original papers written before 1922. For papers appearing during the period 1922–1952, reference (2) should be consulted. The theory of dual integral and dual series equations, which is the subject matter of Chapter 6 of the present book, has been considerably developed in the last fifteen years and a list of published papers on the subject can be found in C. J. Tranter, *Integral Transforms in Mathematical Physics*, Third Edition (Methuen, 1966). The reader is also referred to I. N. Sneddon, *Mixed Boundary Value Problems in Potential Theory* (North Holland Pub. Co., 1966).

INDEX

Date Due
